D1572110

The Letters of a
Victorian Madwoman

Women's Diaries and Letters
of the Nineteenth-Century South

Carol Bleser, *Series Editor*

The Letters of a
Victorian Madwoman

edited by **John S. Hughes**

University of South Carolina Press

All photographs courtesy of the Heritage Commission of Tuscaloosa County, Alabama.

Copyright © 1993 University of South Carolina

Published in Columbia, South Carolina, by the University of South Carolina Press

Manufactured in the United States of America

Library of Congress Cataloging-in-Publication Data

The Letters of a Victorian madwoman / edited by John S. Hughes.
    p.   cm.
    Includes bibliographical references and index.
    ISBN 0–87249–840–9 (hard : acid-free paper)
    1. Sheffield, Andrew M., d. 1920—Correspondence. 2. Psychiatric hospital patients—Alabama—Tuscaloosa—Correspondence. 3. Bryce Hospital (Tuscaloosa, Ala.)—History.   I. Hughes, John S., 1954–

RC464.S5A4   1993
362.2'1'092—dc20   92–27442

*For the men and women, past and present,
who have lived and worked at
Bryce Hospital.*

The sickness of the individual is not readily differentiated from the sickness of society.
René Dubos, 1959

Contents

Series Editor's Introduction

The Letters of a Victorian Madwoman is the seventh volume in an ongoing series of women's diaries and letters of the nineteenth-century South. This series published by the University of South Carolina Press includes a number of never-before-published diaries, some collections of unpublished correspondence, and a few reprints of published diaries—a potpourri of nineteenth-century women's writings.

The Women's Diaries and Letters of the Nineteenth-Century South Series enables women to speak for themselves providing readers with a rarely opened window into Southern society before, during, and after the American Civil War. The significance of these letters and journals lies not only in the personal revelations and the writing talents of these women authors but also in the range and versatility of their contents. Taken together these publications will tell us much about the heyday and the fall of the Cotton Kingdom, the mature years of the "peculiar institution," the war years, and the adjustment of the South to a new social order following the defeat of the Confederacy. Through these writings the reader will also be presented with firsthand accounts of everyday life and social events, courtships and marriages, family life and travels, religion and education, and the life-and-death matters which made up the ordinary and extraordinary world of the nineteenth-century South.

The Letters of a Victorian Madwoman documents the thirty-year institutionalization of Andrew M. Sheffield, whose brother and father committed her to Bryce Hospital in Tuscaloosa, Alabama, in 1890. Accused of a crime, suspected of sexual impropriety, and addicted to chloral hydrate, Sheffield came to the asylum unwillingly. Nearly ninety of the letters she wrote while in the hospital are included here. Early letters follow her vigorous efforts (through pleas to various governors) to win her release and transfer to the women's penitentiary. Unable to obtain her release, Sheffield lived in an increasingly narrow world as the years passed, and her later letters focus more on the details of Victorian asylum life in the deep South.

At the time of her committal, Andrew Sheffield was forty-one years old and had long been suspected of insanity. By her own account, she had abused a variety of drugs off and on for a decade and was involved in a destructive relationship with her doctor that culminated in his request that she commit arson. Sheffield was awaiting trial for her unsuccessful attempt at this crime when her family arranged to have her committed. Sheffield herself attributed her behavior not to insanity but to a "disappointment in love" in 1880, which had caused her extreme distress and, she felt, had led to her drug addiction. Repeatedly in her letters Sheffield asks to be tried and imprisoned as a sane woman. This was never to happen, and Andrew Sheffield died and was buried at Bryce Hospital in 1920.

Unlike many accounts by mental patients, these letters were never intended for publication. They are uncensored; at least a few were smuggled out of the asylum by nurses friendly to Sheffield. As such, they provide a unique resource for students of the history of the treatment of mental illness, especially in the South. John Hughes's extensive introduction is particularly thorough in this regard. Sheffield's letters are excellent sources that meet at the intersection of Southern, medical, social, and women's history.

Carol Bleser

Acknowledgments

This book is an accumulation of debts. Without the gracious and unceasing help of the men and women who work at Bryce Hospital this project would never have reached completion. Kathy Fetters, the mental health librarian in the staff library at the hospital, has been a dependable source of assistance for many years. Her interest in preserving the rich history of the institution has made my work immeasurably easier. Annie Gay Norris, who was director of medical records when I did my archival research, also deserves mention. For months on end she allowed me to occupy space in her busy and crowded office while I transcribed, checking and rechecking the words and peculiarities of Andrew Sheffield's letters. I am also indebted to Charles Fetner, the executive director, who allowed me to use the Hospital's oldest records.

The History Department at the University of Alabama made this project possible. As the Bankhead Fellow in American History there I received valuable release time from teaching that enabled me to begin this project. My chairman and friend, Bill Barnard, pointed me toward the hospital (for professional reasons I assume) and encouraged me to explore its rich archives. I have also relied heavily on the good offices of the Alabama Department of Archives and History in Montgomery. The entire staff was unfailingly helpful. Keena Kendall in particular gave help beyond what I could reasonably have expected.

Others have helped at later stages of the project. Carol Bleser's support has been indispensable. Megan Seaholm read and helpfully commented on an earlier version of the Introduction. Other friends—Howard Miller, Dave Bowman, and Bob Moats—have helped me keep perspective if not my sanity. A special thanks also must go to my wife, Harriet Hall, and our sons, Noah and Michael. They have given the kind of support that Andrew Sheffield must surely have wanted from her family a century ago.

A Note on the Editing

Apart from the use of ample explanatory notes, I have attempted to keep editorial intrusions to a minimum. I have particularly tried to keep bracketed material out of the text of the correspondents' letters. This practice does, however, put the reader under a slight burden. For, although Sheffield is a good writer, she is also eccentric. For example, she seldom uses paragraphs, perhaps because she viewed stationary as a precious commodity that ought to be used to its fullest. And when she does indicate a break in thought she often neglects to indent opening lines of paragraphs. She also tends to ignore punctuation, periods in particular. Her capitalization and use of apostrophes are also idiosyncratic, and sometimes vary even within the same letter. In grammar, as in life, Sheffield could defy predictability. Her style changes, often abruptly.

Sheffield also spells words to suit herself. "Women," for example, is almost always "weomen," "business" becomes "buisness." She often leaves out part of a double consonant (as in "realy" or "naturaly"). At other times she adds additional letters ("propper" for "proper," or "moove" for "move"). She also uses "e" and "i" as largely interchangeable (as in "revinge").

In rare instances, she spells words as she heard them. She always writes "tongue clash" instead of "tongue lash," for example. In this and in other respects, the idiosyncrasies of her prose, I think, tell us something about her. They are part of the historical record. So, wherever possible, I have left them unchanged.

Sheffield's Correspondents

Buck, Mary Louise—Supervisor of Nurses on the women's side of Bryce Hospital from the early 1890s until about 1913.

Comer, Braxton Bragg—Governor of Alabama, 1907–1911.

Creagh, Minnie E.—Supervisor of Nurses on women's side of Bryce Hospital beginning about 1913.

Jelks, William D.—Governor of Alabama, 1901–1907.

John, Samuel Will—Trustee of Bryce Hospital, 1899–1922.

Johnston, Joseph F.—Governor of Alabama, 1896–1900.

Jones, Thomas G.—Governor of Alabama, 1890–1894.

Lanford, Dr. John A.—Assistant physician at Mt. Vernon Hospital for blacks in 1905 and 1906; assistant physician at Bryce, 1907–1911; senior assistant physician on the women's side, 1910–1911.

Little, Dr. Jonathon—Assistant physician, 1869–1875; Treasurer during much of Sheffield's stay; in private practice in Tuscaloosa.

Oates, William C.—Governor of Alabama, 1894–1896.

Partlow, Dr. R. C.—Assistant physician, 1912–1944; brother of Dr. W. D. Partlow.

Partlow, Dr. William D.—Assistant physician, 1901–1908; Assistant Superintendent, 1908–1919; Superintendent, 1919–1949.

Rau, Dr. George R.—Assistant physician, 1899–1901; in private practice in Tuscaloosa thereafter.

Searcy, Dr. James T.—Resident Trustee, 1887–1892; Superintendent, 1892–1919.

Staugh, Emma—A former nurse who corresponded with Sheffield in 1908.

Street, Oliver Day—Sheffield's nephew (son of T. A. Street) and guardian following T. A. Street's death in 1904.

Street, Thomas Atkins—Sheffield's half brother (from her mother's first marriage) and guardian following the death of her father in 1892.

The Letters of a
Victorian Madwoman

Introduction

Andrew Moore Sheffield was a woman apart from her peers. Having borne a man's name for all her forty-one years, she never married, never managed to conform to standards of ladylike behavior, and never succeeded in pleasing the men of her prominent family. In July 1890, while she sat in a jail cell in Guntersville, Alabama, her brother, the local probate judge, and her father, a former slaveholder and signer of the state's ordinance of secession, decided that her long suspected madness required her immediate commitment to the state mental hospital in Tuscaloosa.

Her deviant behavior had at last required action. She was addicted to chloral hydrate, an opiate commonly used to induce sleep, and had become involved in an abusive and sexual relationship with the doctor who supplied her the drug. Most immediately, she had attempted to burn down the house of a neighbor who was feuding with the doctor. So, embarrassed and concerned, the men of her family decided that she must be forcibly confined. Facing the grim and nearly certain prospect of Andrew's prison term for arson, her brother and father grasped at the less stigmatizing alternative of her hospitalization for madness. Before ever standing trial, Andrew Sheffield thus boarded a train with her nephew and Marshall County's sheriff, and traveled to Tuscaloosa, where they committed her to the Bryce Hospital.[1]

Andrew Sheffield wrote the nearly ninety letters in this collection while she was a patient in Bryce Hospital, Alabama's only state mental institution for whites.[2] In 1920, having outlived the men who committed

---

1. Case history in file of patient #3910, Medical Records Office, Bryce Hospital, Tuscaloosa, Alabama. Before 1892, when the institution's first superintendent, Dr. Peter Bryce, died, the institution was called the Alabama Insane Hospital.
2. The letters of both Sheffield and her correspondents in this collection come from two sources. The first is her patient file at Bryce Hospital, which is located in the Medical

1

her, she died as a ward of the state and was buried on the Hospital's grounds. These letters, which are probably only a tiny fraction of the total number she wrote during those thirty years, provide a valuable resource to historians, psychiatrists, sociologists, and others interested in mental institutions. Students of gender will also find the peculiar life history of this troublesome woman to be a rich source of information. And unlike most glimpses of asylum life, nearly all of which are provided by ex-patients, Sheffield's depiction is uncensored and unintended for public consumption. She wrote these letters for herself and her correspondents—and nobody else.

For the last half century or so, scholars have increasingly taken seriously the history of such mental institutions as held Sheffield. Even as far back as 1937, Albert Deutsch's *The Mentally Ill in America* focused scholarly attention on the treatment of the insane. Deutsch's work, which remains a valuable starting point in the history of asylums, proceeded from uncritically Whiggish assumptions. While he angrily denounced the current state of such institutions, he never doubted that a more enlightened public policy or increased funding could restore mental hospitals to the noble houses of cure envisioned by their founders in the nineteenth century.[3] Not until the 1960s did less transparently Progressive and more rigorously scholarly works appear. Gerald N. Grob and Norman Dain, the senior statesmen of American insanity studies, both published important studies that probed beyond the published reports on which Deutsch relied. Before others, they began to explore the rich manuscript collections of asylums and their superintendents.[4] Grob's study of Massachusetts's

---

Records Office of that facility. Like most other patient records, these have been well cared for over the years and are now bound in a large cloth folder. They have been moved from time to time and no longer remain in any particular order. Most of the letters are undated, and I have attempted to date them for this collection by textual analysis (mention of doctors, nurses, fellow patients, specific dated events, the number of years in the hospital or on a particular ward, for example). The second source of her letters in the collection is the Alabama Department of Archives and History in Montgomery. Sheffield regularly corresponded with various governors of the state, and, as a result, some of her letters are found in the State Hospitals Collection housed there.

3. *The Mentally Ill in America: A History of Their Care and Treatment from Colonial Times* (Garden City, N. Y.: Doubleday, 1937). Deutsch also published a second and revised edition of this book (New York: Columbia University Press, 1949).

4. Gerald N. Grob, *The State and the Mentally Ill: A History of the Worcester State Hospital in Massachusetts, 1830–1920* (Chapel Hill: University of North Carolina Press, 1966); *Mental Institutions in America: Social Policy to 1875* (New York: Free Press, 1973); and Norman Dain, *Disordered Minds: The First Century of Eastern State Hospital in Williamsburg, Virginia 1766–1866* (Williamsburg: Colonial Williamsburg Foun-

Worcester State Hospital and Dain's history of Virginia's Eastern Lunatic Asylum in Williamsburg were characterized by detailed scholarship and careful conclusions, and still remain models of the institutional study of mental illness.

But like Deutsch, both Grob and Dain largely accepted the humanitarianism of their reformer protagonists. Given the limited nature of the available sources about patients' perceptions, their histories largely reflected the perspectives of the asylum physicians and their lay supporters (and detractors). Helpful as these studies were, they remained to a large extent history "from the top down." In that limited sense they shared the emphasis of Progressives such as Deutsch. More recently Dain has deviated somewhat from this emphasis in a valuable biography of Clifford Beers, a contemporary of Sheffield's and perhaps America's most famous former mental patient.[5] But even this biography of Beers reflects the tone of a top-down study. Despite sympathies for those who were held in mental institutions, Beers became a Progressive reformer who led the National Committee for Mental Hygiene, an organization which aimed partly at making asylums more humane, but which was primarily geared toward preventing mental illness. As a result, he spent much more time with (and won a great deal of support from) doctors specializing in insanity than he did with patients.

The Progressive tradition in this historiography was soon challenged. David J. Rothman's Beveridge Award-winning *The Discovery of the Asylum* appeared in 1971 and differed with the received tradition in several important ways.[6] First, Rothman was influenced by French philosopher Michel Foucault's *Madness and Civilization*. Foucault's broad-ranging study, subtitled *A History of Insanity in the Age of Reason,* argued that institutionalization served primarily the interests of those seeking to enforce social conformity. Madness in this view became deviance, not disease. Foucault invited sympathy for the patient in ways that went beyond the medical definition of insanity. His view was less wedded to the medical experts' construction of their enterprise.[7] Second, Rothman's

---

dation, 1971). Even before Grob, Dain published his important early work, Concepts of Insanity in the United States, 1789–1865 (New Brunswick, N. J.: Rutgers University Press, 1964).

5. *Clifford W. Beers: Advocate for the Insane* (Pittsburgh: University of Pittsburgh Press, 1980).

6. *The Discovery of the Asylum: Social Order and Disorder in the New Republic* (Boston: Little, Brown, 1971). Rothman's book studies prisons, almshouses, and orphanages, in addition to mental institutions.

7. *Madness and Civilization* (New York: Random House, 1965).

ideological assumptions relied far more than his Progressive forebears' on sociological theories that self-consciously challenged the status quo. This sociological perspective differed from what might be called the medical or psychiatric model and, like Foucault, focused more on patients than doctors. Ever since Rothman's study, the sociological concept of "social control" has figured prominently in the historiography of insanity.[8] Physicians who managed asylums have come increasingly to be seen as controllers rather than reformers. According to this view, the medical elite's "reforms" sustained rather than challenged the status quo. Patients like Andrew Sheffield, it was argued, profited less than those who were seeking to enhance social order.

During the academic debates that followed *The Discovery of the Asylum,* Rothman revealed how close a student of the sociologists he was. Their theoretical work, he explained, supplied historians with an analytic concept (social control) that enabled them "to break out of the old morality play that Progressive historians were prone to present." Influenced by sociologists of the 1950s and 1960s (Richard Cloward and Francis Piven in particular), Rothman observed that these scholars were politically less interested than their Progressive-era sociologists in cooperation or the maintenance of the status quo. As products of the Great Depression and social upheavals such as that begun by *Brown v. Board of Education,* they looked more to the sources of conflict, coercion, and manipulation.[9]

This reaction to Progressive assumptions reached into other academic disciplines by the 1960s. Even among the alleged controllers, psychiatrists such as Thomas Szasz and R. D. Laing launched criticisms of their own profession. Szasz, for example, began a long, frequently polemical career with his influential *The Myth of Mental Illness.* Szasz argued that madness was not a disease in the sense of most medical ailments. Before Foucault, he argued that madness was a construct of society, a label that served the interests of those in power.[10] The fullest articulation of "labeling theory" has appeared more recently in the writings of sociologist Thomas Scheff. His *Being Mentally Ill: A Sociological Theory,* published in 1966, strengthened the social-control school by providing a carefully reasoned

---

8. "Social Control: The Uses and Abuses of the Concept in the History of Incarceration," *Rice University Studies* 67 (Winter 1981): 9–20.
9. "Social Control," 11–15; quotation, 15.
10. *The Myth of Mental Illness: Foundations of a Theory of Personal Conduct,* rev. ed. (New York: Harper & Row, 1974). Some of the many other books by Szasz are *The Manufacture of Madness: A Comparative Study of the Inquisition and the Mental Health Movement* (New York: Harper & Row, 1970), and *Law, Liberty and Psychiatry: An Inquiry into the Social Uses of Mental Health Practices* (New York: Colliers, 1968). For R. D. Laing, see *The Politics of Experience* (New York: Pantheon, 1967).

theoretical framework for interpreting madness as deviance rather than disease.[11]

In a curious way, however, Rothman's theoretically informed work mirrored Deutsch's more Progressive analysis in ways that theory did not detect. Methodologically, both relied largely on published sources—in many respects, the very same sources. The key difference lay in the meanings and motivations assigned to the medical authorities who wrote those documents. Older historians tended to take seriously the reformers' claims to humanitarianism aimed at the conquest of disease, while revisionists inferred darker and often unconscious motivations behind the labeler-reformers' public professions. As a result, something of a false dichotomy emerged in studies of mental hospitals. Rothman and other historians of "deviance" lined up on one side, while Grob and others eschewed theoretical and thesis-driven arguments of the behavioral sciences. The former tended to view asylums as failures, whereas the latter allowed for greater complexity in assessing final judgments.[12]

Were asylums designed for humanitarian reasons or out of more class-oriented desires to control those outside the mainstream of American life? In either event, did they "succeed"? Judging from the history of the Bryce Hospital, which held Andrew Sheffield, the answers must be qualified on all counts. Service to humanity, broadly defined, was clearly a conscious motive of the institution's nineteenth-century founders. Alabama's legislature was expressly responding to an impassioned appeal from the crusader Dorothea Dix when it established the Hospital in 1852 (though construction was not completed until 1861).[13] But so too were the reformers concerned with controlling a class they believed to be enlarging rapidly. To the asylum superintendents and trustees, the needs of humanity and the imperative to control were in no way exclusive. To them, distinctions between deviance and disease (which they termed "depravity" and "insanity") seemed blurred at best. And while the doctors' asylums never

---

11. *Being Mentally Ill: A Sociological Theory* (Chicago: Aldine, 1966). See also Scheff, ed., *Labelling Madness* (Englewood Cliffs, N. J.: Prentice-Hall, 1975). Sociology has not stood still since Scheff first wrote. Recent studies of social control have attempted to move beyond by the purely medical model of madness and the almost purely sociological interpretation. See, for example, Allan V. Horwitz, *The Social Control of Mental Illness* (New York: Academic, 1982).
12. Gerald Grob, "Rediscovering Asylums: The Unhistorical History of the Mental Hospital," *Hastings Center Report* 7 (August 1977): 33–41. Grob correctly points out here that Deutsch also saw the asylums as failures and that his Whiggish interpretation was as ahistorical as Rothman's.
13. Robert O. Mellown, "The Construction of the Alabama Insane Hospital, 1852–1861," *Alabama Review* 38 (April 1985): 83–104. Dix had traveled to Alabama in 1847 and 1849.

seriously reduced the proportion of the insane, they did succeed in bringing madness partially under medical control, and they did relieve countless families of the burden of managing the aged, the deranged, the
eccentric, and the dangerous. In such dense and complex conceptual ter-
rain, debates over benevolence or control, success or failure, dissolve into
matters of perspective.

Modern debates often turn on the function of methodology. Historians focusing on *intellectual history,* in this case on the reformers' visions
of ideal treatments for the insane, get a disproportionately large dose of
controlling language. Rothman's study, for example, focused far more on
ideals than on the everyday realities of asylum life. Historians who are
more grounded in *social history,* who are more familiar with the unpublished and archival sources, tend to see matters as more muddled and
less readily conceptualized. As a result, their histories tend to be less
thesis-driven.

Andrew Sheffield's correspondence throws some light on this modern
debate. Her letters, which are essentially documents in social history,
demonstrate that while she did receive the public's charity, she did so
against her wishes and at the expense of her free choice. Proponents of
social-control theory might argue that, given her incredible inability to
conform, she came under the dominion of others who were sanctioned by
her society to restrain or at least to hide her inappropriate behavior. Superintendent James T. Searcy's letters, written mostly to Alabama's governors (and included in the following collection along with letters from
family members), suggest in part a sense of the official ideals. Because Dr.
Searcy's remarks are frequently defensive in tone, his letters seem guarded
and less frank than Sheffield's. It is possible therefore to reconstruct a sort
of case study that offers the perspectives both of the controllers (the doctors and the family) and the controlled (Sheffield).

The rich detail that Sheffield's case provides also suggests how im-
precise the more highly abstract argument over the nature of social control
can be. On one level, the proponents of social control are surely right.
Sheffield did lose the freedom to make important life choices, and the considerable frustration and embarrassment that she had caused her family
was finally controlled or hidden in the Hospital. But it was not any controlling or hegemonic elite, such as doctors or legal authorities, who
gained the most by her commitment. It was her family.[14] Moreover, Sheffield's letters suggest that, once she was in the asylum, Superintendent

---

14. In "Rediscovering Asylums," 37, Grob makes this point in a criticism of Rothman's
    social-control thesis.

Searcy never succeeded in controlling or seriously altering her character. His control was more narrowly limited to restraints on her range of movement and her contact with the outside world. If these letters are any indication, Sheffield's often belligerent and assertive persona actually dictated much about the quality of life on the wards. It was never entirely clear who was controlling whom.

More recent studies of individual asylums have both moved beyond and bridged these dichotomous conceptualizations. Nancy Tomes's 1984 study, *A Generous Confidence: Thomas Story Kirkbride and the Art of Asylum-Keeping, 1840–1883*, avoids the pitfalls of the Progressive-revisionist confrontation of the 1970s.[15] This excellent history of a leading superintendent and his model Pennsylvania Hospital successfully combines the methodology of intellectual and social history. Kirkbride, who was a Quaker, was his generation's chief authority on asylum architecture and management. Indeed, Bryce Hospital (then called the Alabama Insane Hospital) was carefully designed in the 1850s with Kirkbride's ideals in mind. In the 1880 edition of his influential book *On the Construction, Organization, and General Arrangements of Hospitals for the Insane*, he discussed the Alabama asylum's architecture in detail.[16]

In addition to this emphasis on precise architecture, Kirkbride's generation of antebellum asylum superintendents pursued a hopeful therapy called "moral treatment," which relied on a careful ordering of the asylum's environment. Anne Digby's excellent study of York Retreat in England, *Madness, Morality, and Medicine* (1985), provides a good starting point for understanding the English and Quaker origins of this therapy that characterized the practice of Kirkbride's American colleagues.[17] Insanity specialists believed that by controlling their patients' surroundings and routine, they could reduce excitements and irritations. The diseased brain could rest, begin to recover, and even be cured. The brain's manifestation, the mind, could then be restored to reason. In other words, the world of the asylum worked best when it rearranged the world outside. Doctors at Bryce Hospital, for example, encouraged what they considered to be the best qualities of the larger society—sobriety, cooperation, and order, for

---

15. *A Generous Confidence* (Cambridge: Cambridge University Press, 1984).
16. *On the Construction*, 2d ed. (Philadelphia: Lippincott, 1880), 129–34.
17. *Madness, Morality and Medicine: A Study of the York Retreat, 1796–1914* (Cambridge: Cambridge University Press, 1985). Also see Charles L. Cherry, *A Quiet Haven: Quakers, Moral Treatment, and Asylum Reform* (Rutherford, N. J.: Fairleigh Dickinson University Press, 1989).

example—but they tried as well to eliminate the dangers of temptations, competition, and society's fast pace. Moral treatment required the firm, but gentle authority of doctors and nurses, and absolutely forbade physical correction.[18]

Sheffield's letters suggest how these ideals, which had their widest currency among Kirkbride's Northern colleagues during the antebellum period, were translated to another region in an extremely large institution at a later period. Sheffield's vivid depictions of life on this public hospital's wards show the distance that Kirkbride's ideals had traveled since his death. Indeed, her letters provide a view of the twilight of the moral therapy which had its dawn a century earlier at York Retreat. By the time of Sheffield's death in 1920, Bryce Hospital held over sixteen hundred patients.[19] Kirkbride and the English Quakers had warned repeatedly against such vast institutions.[20] Bryce Hospital was also a biracial institution that, while it was segregated racially, usually mixed patients from different social classes. Kirkbride's Pennsylvania Hospital was smaller and took into account the patients' social class in its ward arrangements. Finally, during Sheffield's stay, the Hospital underwent a transition from the self-conscious gentleness of Kirkbride's therapeutic era to a less optimistic acceptance of crowding and the primary demands of custodial care. Moral treatment in those years totally disappeared from the institutional vocabulary.

Ellen Dwyer's study of New York asylums in the nineteenth century, *Homes for the Mad*, is comparable to Tomes's book. It too pushes beyond dichotomous historiographical debates to combine intellectual and social history. Even more than *A Generous Confidence*, however, Dwyer's study bears the texture of social history. Dwyer discusses in greater detail the role of families in the lives of patients who had left their families' homes to enter asylums which the superintendents defined metaphorically as domesticated spheres. She also reconstructs the asylum routine of these giant

---

18. For a few examples of the ideal of moral treatment in this hospital, see Bryce, "Annual Report," 1864, manuscript in State Hospitals Collection, Alabama Dept. of Archives and History, Montgomery (hereafter cited as ADAH): *Annual Report*, 1870 (Montgomery: John G. Stokes State Printers, 1870), 11, 28, 33–34; and *Annual Report*, 1875 (Montgomery: W. W. Screws, State Printers, 1875), 13.

19. For data on 1890, see Thomas M. Owen, *Alabama Official and Statistical Register, 1907* (Montgomery: Brown Printing, 1907), 135; for 1920, see *Annual Report of the Alabama Insane Hospitals* (Tuscaloosa: Weatherford Printing, [1920]), 10.

20. See, for example, Kirkbride, *On the Construction, Organization and General Arrangements of Hospitals for the Insane*, 49ff.

"homes" quite well.[21] More than any other study, *Homes for the Mad* emphasizes the ambiguous but key role of nurses in the institutional life of the insane, and thereby adds a crucial third perspective to that of doctors and patients.

Sheffield's letters show that Dwyer's emphasis is well placed. Sheffield's constant complaints over institutional power struggles indicate how central were the nurses to vast institutions and to the patients housed there. Doctors came onto the wards usually once a day at prescribed times. Nurses, on the other hand, lived most of their day among the patients and left the Hospital grounds only on Sunday afternoons.[22] Despite the ideal expectations of superintendents and trustees, Sheffield's letters show that much power actually lay in the attendants' hands. The ethic of following doctors' orders, it seems, had not yet fully evolved among the nursing staff at Bryce Hospital. Here again, Sheffield's social history confirms trends of recent scholarship and belies the narrower intellectual history.

With the exception of Dain's study of the Virginia asylum from the colonial through antebellum periods, few published studies have focused on Southern institutions. Recently, Samuel Thielman and Peter McCandless have offered helpful studies of South Carolina as well as Virginia, but like Dain, they have focused largely on the period before the Civil War.[23] No one has examined the region's asylums for the period of the late

---

21. Elaine Showalter uses the phrase "the domestication of insanity" to describe nineteenth-century English institutions. Unlike Dwyer, she is not referring to an explicit use of domestic metaphors, but rather to the consequences of moral management. See "Victorian Women and Insanity," *Victorian Studies* 23 (Winter 1980): 157–81. I have explored this same issue with regard to the Alabama Insane Hospital in "The Madness of Separate Spheres: Insanity and Masculinity in Victorian Alabama," in Mark C. Carnes and Clyde Griffen, eds., *Meanings for Manhood: Constructions of Masculinity in Victorian America* (Chicago: University of Chicago Press, 1990), 67–78.

22. *By-Laws, Rules, and Regulations of the Alabama Insane Hospital, at Tuscaloosa, Alabama* (Tuscaloosa: Montgomery I. Burton, 1890), 60.

23. Thielman, "Madness and Medicine: Medical Therapeutics for Insanity in Antebellum America, with Special Reference to the Eastern Lunatic Asylum of Virginia and the South Carolina Lunatic Asylum" (Ph.D. diss., Duke University, 1986); "Madness and Medicine: Trends in American Medical Therapeutics for Insanity, 1820–1860," *Bulletin of the History of Medicine* 61 (1987): 35; "Southern Madness: The Shape of Mental Health Care in the Old South," in Ronald L. Numbers and Todd L. Savitt, eds., *Science and Medicine in the Old South* (Baton Rouge: Louisiana State University Press, 1989); McCandless, " 'A House of Cure': The Antebellum South Carolina Lunatic Asylum," *Bulletin of the History of Medicine* 64 (Summer 1990): 220–42; and "Liberty and Lunacy: The Victorians and Wrongful Confinement," *Journal of Social History* 11 (Spring 1978): 366–86. Also see Clark R. Cahow, "The History of the North Carolina Mental Hospitals, 1848–1960" (Ph.D. diss., Duke University, 1967).

nineteenth and early twentieth centuries. Sheffield's letters therefore provide a valuable resource for the study of the care of the insane in the South. Generally speaking, Southern states came to support public charities such as mental hospitals later than Northern states (Dain's Eastern State Hospital in Virginia was an exception) and provided less dependable funding once they were established. Bryce Hospital during Sheffield's years should not be viewed as an institution after which others were modeled, such as York Retreat, the Pennsylvania Hospital, or the New York asylums studied by Dwyer. It was instead a more representative rank-and-file institution, albeit one with a different racial and ethnic composition than would be found in the North.

In addition to these who have focused on madness and mental institutions, a few historians have studied insanity from the perspective of the patient. A helpful starting place for exploring this tradition is Dale Peterson's *A Mad People's History of Madness,* an edited collection of the memoirs of American and English mental patients during the last five hundred years. Peterson also provides perhaps the best bibliography of published accounts by ex-patients.[24] Sheffield's voice provides a valuable added perspective. Unlike those individuals presented by Peterson, she never became an ex-patient.

Among Peterson's subjects was the crusading Clifford Beers, whose biographer is Norman Dain. Beers's *A Mind That Found Itself* is perhaps the most famous and widely read of all ex-patients' autobiographies written in America.[25] Beers, as we have seen, was a public lobbyist who used his quite readable book to fuel the mental hygiene movement of the Progressive era. Dain's 1980 biography, which was funded by the American Foundation for Mental Hygiene and the Maurice Falk Medical Fund, understandably rejects most of the ideology of Foucault, Rothman, or the sociological labelers in discussing this seminal figure. While open to the possibility that mental illness may in part be deviance, Dain remains essentially supportive of Beers's and the Progressives' medical-disease model.

More recently, Roy Porter's *A Social History of Madness: The World Through the Eyes of the Insane* has contributed to this genre. Porter, an Englishman whose study ranges across centuries and national borders, sets out "to examine not the unconscious of the mad but their consciousness." "Instead of principally reading between the lines," his object is to look at

---

24. *A Mad People's History of Madness* (Pittsburgh: University of Pittsburgh Press, 1982).
25. *A Mind That Found Itself* (Garden City, N. Y.: Doubleday, 1923).

the mad (Beers among them) historically without the blinders of any particular theory, whether medical, psychiatric, or sociological. He wants to know "what it was like to be mad or to be thought to be mad."[26] Despite this effort to appear neutral in theoretical debates, Porter's patient-centered analysis has won a warmer reception from the revisionists who have been influenced by the behavioral sciences than it has from others. Like Peterson and Dain, Porter's work rests largely on the published work of ex-patients.

A much closer parallel to Sheffield's case is the familiar story of Elizabeth Packard. Unlike Beers, her public crusade never served the ends of the mental health authorities. And like Sheffield, she was an assertive and nonconformist woman whose ambiguous madness was arguably a product of social labeling. She was committed in Illinois by her clergyman-husband in 1860, she claimed, because of her rejection of orthodox Calvinism, her acceptance of spiritualism, and her sympathy for phrenology. In other words, her commitment seemed to serve the ends of conformity and control. Trustees of the Illinois hospital released her as both difficult and incurable. After her release in 1863, she returned to her husband's home in Manteno, Illinois, where he kept her a virtual prisoner. Alarmed friends who had never considered her deranged appealed to a Kankakee County judge to have her husband present her in court on a writ of habeas corpus. He complied, and at a hearing on the issue of her sanity, a jury ruled her sane and the judge ordered her husband to release her. Thereafter the Packards lived apart. Elizabeth lobbied many state legislatures, wrote extensively about the abuses of institutionalization, and made a comfortable living. As a result of her crusading, late nineteenth-century asylum doctors came to see her as a sort of anti-Christ to Dorothea Dix's earlier image of savior.[27]

26. *A Social History of Madness: The World Through the Eyes of the Insane* (New York: Weidenfeld & Nicholson, 1987), 1.
27. The best single account of Packard's case is Barbara Sapinsley, *The Private War of Mrs. Packard* (New York: Paragon House, 1991). Sapinsley's account is not strictly scholarly (it provides no notes, for example), but is quite solid and dependable in its treatment. Sapinsley draws on much of the best primary as well as secondary material. The best scholarly secondary account of Packard is Myra S. Himelhoch and Arthur H. Shaffer, "Elizabeth Packard: Nineteenth-Century Crusader for the Rights of Mental Patients," *Journal of American Studies* 13 (December 1979): 343–76. Himelhoch and Shaffer provide a solid overview, but Sapinsley's account explains better the rich complexity of Packard's personality. Just a few of Packard's many books are *Marital Power Exemplified in Mrs. Packard's Trial, and Self-Defence from the Charge of Insanity: or, Three Years Imprisonment for Religious Belief, by the Arbitrary Will of a Husband, with an Appeal to the Government to So Change the Laws as to Afford Legal Protection*

Virtually all historians since Deutsch have included at least a passing
mention of Packard's famous case in their histories of nineteenth-century
asylums. Her highly visible persona helped to stereotype for Americans
the typical involuntary patient of the late nineteenth century. If explored in
detail, however, Packard's case reveals the ambiguous space between anger and madness, between eccentricity and insanity. To contemporary
medical authorities, she seemed certainly insane; to modern observers, the
evidence for labeling and controlling has likewise seemed compelling.

In one sense, Andrew Sheffield was the Elizabeth Packard who never
got out. Indeed there were striking differences. Sheffield had committed a
crime, was addicted to drugs, and was widely suspected of sexual mis-
conduct. But both women showed remarkable independence from the men
in their lives. Both were assertive and articulate, and because of their undeniable intellectual vigor, doctors diagnosed them as "morally insane,"
a label which was highly charged and controversial in the 1860s and 1890s
when it was applied to them. Such morally deranged persons showed no
delusions and no impairment of reasoning. Only their moral sense or, more
correctly, their ability (or desire) to live in accordance with accepted morality seemed insane.[28]

As the comparison with Packard suggests, Sheffield's case provides
evidence not only for insanity studies but for gender studies as well. Anne
Firor Scott, a leading historian of Southern women, has argued that during
the nineteenth century "[t]he social role of women was unusually confin-

to Married Women (Hartford, Conn.: Case, Lockwood, 1866); Modern Persecution, or
Insane Asylums Unveiled, as Demonstrated by the Report of the Investigating Commit-
tee of the Legislature of Illinois, 12th ed. (Hartford, Conn.: Case, Lockwood & Brain-
ard, 1891); and The Mystic Key: or, The Asylum Secret Unlocked (Harford, Conn.:
Case, Lockwood & Brainard, 1886). For a sense of the insanity specialists' negative
view of Packard, see [Isaac Ray], "Legislation for the Insane" (Philadelphia) Medical
Times 4 (March 14, 1874): 378. Ray was one of the founders of the Association of
Medical Superintendents of American Institutions for the Insane (today called the
American Psychiatric Association).

28. See Sapinsley, The Private War of Mrs. Packard, 96–97; Himelhoch and Shaffer,
"Elizabeth Packard," 365; Searcy to Gov. William C. Oates, January 1, 1896. Another
case of ex-patients parallels Sheffield's and Packard's: that of two sisters, both unmarried, who were committed in 1888 in Wisconsin. Like Packard and Sheffield, they
tested the limits of acceptability. Both were supporters of the movement for organized
labor. See Barbara and Rose Trautman, Wisconsin's Shame. Insane Asylums or the
American Bastile! The Narrative of the Kidnapping of the Misses Trautman. Of Sauk
City, Wis., on a Sunday Afternoon and Running Them into an Insane Asylum (Chicago:
Guiding Star, 1892).

ing . . . and the sanctions used to enforce obedience peculiarly effective. One result was that southern women became in time a distinct type among American women."[29] Andrew Sheffield would likely have agreed. Unmarried, intelligent, socially prominent, and in middle age, she found that life in rural northern Alabama offered her few opportunities and many restrictions. Her history was not simply that of mad person. It was, above all, the history of a mad *woman*.

Histories of American women have tended to focus on the North during the antebellum period. Nancy Cott and Barbara Berg, for example, have provided excellent studies of Northern women's changing roles and link those changes (in particular, the growing importance of women's relationships with other women) to the wider social and economic transformation that characterized Jacksonian America. Suzanne Lebsock's fine study of the women of Petersburg, Virginia, provides an important Southern counterpart to these findings about Northern women. She too found a growing sense of independence among white and free black women in the antebellum period.[30]

A shortcoming in the literature has been too few studies reaching outside the North and the early nineteenth century. "Historically speaking," Anne Scott wrote in 1983, "southern women in the century since 1880 scarcely exist."[31] A recent book has helped to reduce this deficiency. Jean E. Friedman's *The Enclosed Garden* (1985) examines women in the predominantly rural nineteenth-century South and compares women there to those in the Northern and more urban settings described by other historians. Friedman also carries her analysis to the beginning of the twentieth century. Intrigued by the lack of a group consciousness rooted in gender among Southern women, she concluded that "[c]ommunity and not

29. *The Southern Lady: From Pedestal to Politics, 1830–1930* (Chicago: University of Chicago Press, 1970), x–xi.
30. Nancy Cott, *The Bonds of Womanhood: "Women's Sphere" in New England, 1780–1835* (New Haven: Yale University Press, 1977); Barbara J. Berg, *The Remembered Gate: Origins of American Feminism: The Woman and the City, 1800–1860* (New York: Oxford University Press, 1978); and Suzanne Lebsock, *The Free Women of Petersburg: Status and Culture in a Southern Town, 1784–1860* (New York: Norton, 1984). See also Elizabeth Fox-Genovese, *Within the Plantation House: Black and White Women in the Old South* (Chapel Hill: University of North Carolina Press, 1988).
31. "Historians Construct the Southern Woman," in Joanne V. Hawks and Sheila L. Skemp, eds., *Sex, Race, and the Role of Women in the South* (Jackson: University of Mississippi Press, 1983), 108. Perhaps the best survey of the literature is Scott and Jacquelyn Dowd Hall, "Women in the South," in John B. Boles and Evelyn T. Nolen, eds., *Interpreting Southern History: Historiographical Essays in Honor of Sanford W. Higginbotham* (Baton Rouge: Louisiana State University Press, 1987), 454–509.

gender bound southern womanhood.'' For Friedman, kin networks and
evangelical religion provided cohesiveness to group consciousness far
more than gender. Later than Northern women who had earlier experienced the effects of modernization, therefore, women in the rural South
came to see themselves as "a distinct class" only late in the century.[32]

More recently, Carol Bleser's collection *In Joy and in Sorrow:
Women, Family, and Marriage in the Victorian South, 1830–1900* has provided an excellent starting point for the exploration of gender and family
in the South. In a more textured account than Friedman's single study, this
collection stresses the primacy of family over sex consciousness (though
with less emphasis on the importance of evangelical Protestantism). In
particular, the essays by Bleser and Frederick Heath, Bertram Wyatt-
Brown, and Virginia Burr provide rich case studies of women, the importance of kinship, and the quality of relationships in elite white families.
Drew Gilpin Faust concludes discerningly in her "Epilogue" to the volume that "[t]he theme of male failure is central to *In Joy and in
Sorrow.* . . ."[33]

This insight brings us back to Andrew Sheffield. As her letters pow-
erfully show, Sheffield lived with a vague sense of masculine failure. This
sense remained unconscious and masked by a fierce pride in her father, for
not only had he and his generation begun and lost the Civil War, but he had
lost his fortune as well. By the end of his life, Col. James L. Sheffield,
who had been a prominent planter, organizer of the 48th Alabama Infantry,
and perennial officeholder, held only a clerkship in the office of the State
Superintendent of Education. As Friedman and many of the essays in
Bleser's collection suggest, Andrew Sheffield's conscious sense of belonging lay with her male-dominated family, not with other women. But as
Faust suggests, this consciousness may have been tinctured with a measure
of disappointment and perhaps even shame. Sheffield's letters show that
she had great trouble sustaining any kind of cordial relationships with men
for very long.

Beyond the biographical fragments found in these letters, few details
of Sheffield's upbringing are known. Her father, who would later experience declining fortunes, was something of a self-made man of the Jacksonian west who numbered among the leaders of Marshall County,
Alabama, until well after Reconstruction. Born in poverty in Huntsville,
Alabama, in neighboring Madison County, James Sheffield moved to

32. *The Enclosed Garden: Women and Community in the Evangelical South, 1830–1900*
(Chapel Hill: University of North Carolina Press, 1985), xii–xiii.
33. *In Joy and in Sorrow* (New York: Oxford University Press, 1991).

Marshall in 1837, where he clerked in a store, saved his salary, and invested well. By the outbreak of the Civil War, he owned a plantation and thirty-four slaves, rather a large holding for this mountainous region of northern Alabama.[34] An active Unionist, he was elected by his neighbors to the secession convention in Montgomery, where, according to Andrew, he was the last to accept the ordinance of secession.[35]

Once having committed himself to disunion, however, Sheffield worked energetically for the Confederacy's success. He enlisted at once as a lieutenant, attained a captaincy, and in 1862 returned as a colonel to Marshall County, where he raised and equipped the 48th Alabama Infantry. Several reports corroborate Andrew's memory that her father had spent (and later lost) nearly $60,000 of his own money in the process.[36] He saw action at Gettysburg and later at Chicamauga, where he suffered a concussion from an exploding artillery shell, causing him to leave active service.

James Sheffield's non-military career reflected similar civic energy. Beginning in the 1840s as sheriff, he served in the Alabama House during the 1850s before his election to the secession convention in 1861. During and after the war, he represented Marshall County at state constitutional conventions. Following Reconstruction, he suffered the financial reverses from which he would never entirely recover. Perhaps as a result of his economic decline, he became a leader of the Greenback Party in Alabama and ran unsuccessfully for governor on that ticket (with Republican support) in 1882. Back in his traditional political-party home, the Democratic Party, he served a term in the Alabama Senate in the late 1880s. Thereafter, with out a significant holding or an occupation in Marshall County, he stayed in Montgomery to take the clerkship he held until his death in 1892.[37]

Andrew Sheffield's letters reveal an intense pride in her father. Occasionally she threw his valued memory up to her doctors as a shining

---

34. According to the 1860 manuscript census rolls for Marshall County, Sheffield, who was then forty years old, described himself as a "retired farmer." His real estate was valued at $6000, and the personal property, which included slaves, had a value of $45,000. The slave schedules of the same year showed thirty-four slaves, a large holding for Marshall County, which was located outside Alabama's Black Belt.

35. Thomas M. Owen, *History of Alabama and Dictionary of Alabama Biography* (Chicago: S. J. Clarke, 1921), 4:1540. Northern Alabama was considerably more Unionist than the more central and southern portions of the state, the Black Belt region, where rich lands made cotton production and slavery more lucrative.

36. See *History of Alabama;* Katherine M. Duncan and Larry J. Smith, *The History of Marshall County, Alabama* (Albertville, Ala.: Thompson Printing, 1969), 50–51; and Sheffield to Partlow and Lanford, March 14, 1909.

37. Duncan and Smith, *The History of Marshall County,* 50–51.

example of honor and accomplishment. By comparison, the Hospital's doctors always seemed mean and small. She told Dr. John Lanford, her ward physician with whom she was constantly feuding, that her father was "as near a good man, as any man, even the best, his motto was 'Do right', and he did do right, did not 'preach one thing and practice another[.]' His charity knew no bounds, was charatable [*sic*] almost to a fault. Was conscientious, just, and honest. . . . [W]as '*poor raised*' and '*self made*' (Unlike most self made men he never did get to where he imagined he had 'harnessed and buckled' the world[.]'"[38] This near adoration of her father contrasted with Sheffield's almost total ignoring of her relationships with other women, especially her mother, Mary Ann Atkins Street Sheffield. The widow of an Alabama Presbyterian minister and descended from a prominent Kentucky family, she had a heritage that contrasted sharply with Andrew's father's social origins. Andrew Sheffield's mother also brought to the Sheffield marriage a son, Thomas Atkins Street, who to some extent would take precedence over the six children she later bore James Sheffield. He became a prosperous civic leader, while none of Sheffield's children (except perhaps Andrew) achieved distinction. Street would also engineer her commitment to the asylum in the difficult summer of 1890.[39]

In all of her letters, Andrew Sheffield mentions her mother but once, and then only when she tries to present an exhaustive catalogue of her family tree. By contrast, as noted above, she refers to her father often and with emotion. She points occasionally with pride to her half-brother, T. A. Street, but her letters make clear that their relationship was formal and distant. (She usually refers to him as "Judge Street.") He was ten years older than she and lived, not with her, but on the farm of their maternal

---

38. Sheffield to Partlow and Lanford, March 14, 1909; emphasis in original.

39. Owen, *History of Alabama and Dictionary of Alabama Biography*, 4:1540. Thomas Atkins, James L. Sheffield's father-in-law, had settled in Marshall County, perhaps having followed his daughter there. According to the manuscript census for 1860, he was probably a prominent man. He owned twenty-one slaves and operated a farm. Thomas Atkins Street, Andrew's half-brother, lived with his grandfather and namesake in 1860 and not with his stepfather and mother. He was then twenty-one years old. The *Guntersville Democrat* (January 10, 1888, p. 3) noted, "Judge T. A. Street is probably the most popular man in the county. He is personally acquainted with nearly everybody within the borders of old Marshall." This was particularly high praise, given that Street was a Republican whom the paper consistently opposed. By contrast, none of James L. Sheffield's children won notice in the paper's columns, with the exception of one son, and even then, the reason was not to praise: "James B. Sheffield, son of Col. J. L. Sheffield, is back from a visit of several years in Colorado. Now we believe Jim will be content to remain in Marshall" (*Guntersville Democrat*, April 10, 1884, p. 3).

grandfather in Marshall County.[40] After Col. Sheffield's death in 1892, Street (and later his son) became the Hospital's contact with Andrew's family. In fact, as Marshall County's probate judge during much of the decade following her confinement, he sometimes corresponded with the Hospital in his official capacity. In none of his surviving official letters, however, does he inquire about the welfare of his half-sister.

In summary, what little is known of Andrew Sheffield's family suggests her identification with her father. This daughter with a son's name took greater pride in her father's "*self made*" status than in her mother's inherited respectability. Perhaps she saw herself as an imperfect mirror of her father. One newspaper account, for example, described him as "hotheaded and quick to fight."[41] And with good reason. A few days following her arrest on the charge of arson, Col. Sheffield shot and killed the man who had supplied her with chloral hydrate, accomplished her sexual "ruin," and brought dishonor to his family. As dozens of the letters in this collection show, Andrew was similarly quick to anger and often physically abusive. More than once, she "knocked" a fellow patient or a nurse who had crossed her. Both father and daughter seemed poised in a defensive stance toward the world, suggesting that neither ever felt particularly secure. There is a quality of pathos in this attitude. Both had fallen in their rather different ways and, as a result, lived out their final years far from home in circumstances that neither would have chosen.

T. A. Street once told Superintendent Searcy that the family had considered his half-sister insane from childhood.[42] By her own account, Sheffield's family and neighbors believed her to be crazy during at least a decade or more before her commitment. She located the causes of her distress, which she always denied was insanity, in a "disappointment in love" and her addiction to chloral hydrate.[43] Her letters also imply that she had used both morphine and alcohol. She complained on occasion that nurses on her wards used these drugs and were unable to perform their duties as a result. "No one, can sit and lie round me under the influence of morphine and me not know it," she told Dr. Lanford. "I know all about what

---

40. According to the manuscript census rolls for Marshall County for 1850, 1860, and 1870, Street never resided in the home of his stepfather.
41. From an unidentified source who was "well acquainted with Sheffield," *Birmingham Daily News*, June 21, 1890, p. 1.
42. Street to Searcy, August 21, 1893.
43. Sheffield to Gov. William C. Oates, December 30, 1895.

morphine will do for one."[44] On another occasion, she admitted to Dr. Searcy with regret that "I love whiskey—the taste, and effects. . . ."[45]

According to her own account, it was at the age of thirty, sometime in 1880, that she suffered her "disappointment in love, which was the first disap[p]ointment, the first cross of my life." "[B]eing naturaly of a very high temperament," she explains in a long letter to Gov. William C. Oates in 1895, " . . . I was not able to hold up under it—and was raving and frantic—*not with insanity*—but from grief and trouble, heartbroken. . . ." As a result, she began "the bad habit of taking opiates" and became a chloral drinker for four years.[46] According to the manuscript census for 1880, the same year as her "disappointment," Dr. William May (known to his friends as "Buck"), who would later supply her with chloral hydrate, boarded with her and her parents.[47] It is possible, in fact, that May had caused her heartbreak. He may also have been the one who first gave her chloral hydrate to help her sleep. In any event, he enjoyed a familiar relationship with her at that critical, perhaps even life-defining, moment.

Sometime in the mid-1880s, she broke the chloral habit. In 1888, however, her health failed. By that time, her father had left Marshall County to work in Montgomery, and she lived alone in Warrenton. Her nearest doctor was her old acquaintance and the former member of her father's household, Dr. May. He was then about fifty, and Andrew was thirty-eight years old and a spinster. In her letter to Gov. Oates (who had known her father well) she clung to her family's prominence and remembered May as "a man devoid of gentlemanly principals [*sic*]," and added that "while I felt it degratory to my high standing to have him attend me, necessity forced it." Necessity, however, may have been only a convenient rationale, for she likely knew precisely what he would prescribe. His treatment was, she said, "much to my joy *chloral* . . . the *much loved stuff*." "During his visits," Sheffield recalled, "he furnished me with chloral by the quantity."[48] So, on this foundation of sickness and addiction, a new stage in their long relationship began.

---

44. Sheffield to Lanford, September 16, 1909.
45. Sheffield to Searcy, early 1910.
46. Sheffield to Gov. Oates, December 30, 1895; emphasis in original.
47. Manuscript Census Rolls, Marshall County, 1880. May was listed as being forty years old, ten years Andrew's senior. It is not known how long he lived in the Sheffield home or when he left. Manuscript census rolls for 1890 are unavailable. Most such records were lost in a fire. As a result, household configurations for 1890, the year of her commitment, cannot be ascertained.
48. Sheffield to Gov. Oates, December 30, 1895. Sheffield's lowly view of May was not universal. Newspapers identified him as a "prominent man" in Marshall County (*Bir-*

And judging from Sheffield's recollection, a sad and perhaps even cruel association it was. Sheffield resorted to euphemism when she explained that May had "accomplished" her "ruin." In all likelihood, she meant that she and the doctor had a sexual relationship outside of marriage. In any event, such was the widely assumed nature of their association. The day before her father shot May, and while Andrew sat in the Guntersville jail, the *Guntersville Democrat* reported that a friend had "exhibited to Col. Sheffield letters showing illicit connections between them."[49] Records at the Hospital which were supplied by her family and the courts in Marshall County also described May as her "paramour."[50]

In addition most likely to being sexual, the relationship was almost certainly abusive. May often came to Sheffield's house unannounced and intoxicated, threatening to expose to her family their relationship and her resumption of the chloral habit, "all this while keeping me well supplied with the chloral bottle . . . to see that it was kept filled at his own expense." Sheffield later claimed to have abandoned her house for long periods and to have sat behind "closed and locked doors to avoid him."[51]

As a tragic culmination of this manipulative relationship, Sheffield claimed that May forced her to attempt to burn down the house of a neighbor, a man with whom the doctor was feuding. According to the story she told Gov. Oates, May prepared the kindling and loosened the man's fence so that she could finish the deed. Fortunately for the neighbor, however, Sheffield was caught and placed in jail before serious damage to the property occurred. It was shortly thereafter that her father returned home from Montgomery and, following a brief verbal confrontation with May, shot and killed him. "Calumny lay at the bottom of the tragedy," reported the Montgomery *Advertiser*, "and the universal sentiment is that the killing was justifiable."[52] One Birmingham paper even reported that his act had been ruled "justifiable homicide."[53]

---

mingham Daily News, June 21, 1890, p. 7, for example). At his funeral, reportedly a "large concourse of people were present" (*Guntersville Democrat*, June 28, 1890, p. 3).

49. *Birmingham Daily News*, June 27, 1890, p. 3.
50. Sheffield to Oates, December 30, 1895; *Case History Book #6*, p. 185.
51. Sheffield to Oates, December 30, 1895.
52. Montgomery *Advertiser*, June 21, 1890, p. 1. The error was made by the *Birmingham Daily News*, July 1, 1890, p. 4.
53. *Birmingham Daily News*, July 1, 1890, p. 4.

No such ruling actually occurred, however. The circuit court judge released Sheffield on $2000 bail after a three-day hearing.[54] Andrew evidently attended this proceeding and reported in one of her letters that she behaved so disruptively that she embarrassed herself and her family.[55] Col. Sheffield did not stand trial until November, after Andrew had been safely transported out of the county in July 1890 and placed in the Hospital. He was acquitted. She later advanced the theory that her half-brother arranged her commitment to the Hospital specifically to keep her away from her father's trial and generally to help salvage the family's wounded reputation.[56]

Her theory was plausible. Long before her arrest on arson charges, Andrew Sheffield almost certainly presented a troubling and even deviant image to her family and community. A typical woman of her age in the deep South would already have been married for nearly half her life and borne five or more children. Many women entering their forties were in fact nearly grandmothers. They were women whose personal identities and public personae were deeply entwined with the lives of their husbands and children. In other words, Sheffield's social deviance in the summer of 1890 was by no means recent or even surprising. Probably throughout her adulthood, she had troubled her family and neighbors by her abnormal, perhaps even unwomanly image. Thus, given the dramatic and undeniable problems created by her arrest, her father and brother likely did not have to deliberate long as they searched for a remedy that would both help Andrew and diminish the damage to their own reputation.

Andrew's letters suggest that even she believed her reputation, too, was in need of repair. She was, after all, an admitted drug abuser. When she recounted her personal history for Gov. Oates, she even argued that her dependence on chloral had nearly killed her. After four years of addiction, "I was no more than a walking skeleton, except that I was breathing," she told him.[57] Clearly she agreed with her family and others that

54. *Guntersville Democrat*, July 3, 1890, p. 3.
55. Sheffield to Searcy, ca. 1906. In this letter, Sheffield describes a "preliminary hearing." Just what this was remains unclear; it may have been an "arraignment" on her charge of arson but was probably her father's preliminary hearing for murder. She claimed to have sat quietly when unpleasant but true things about her were entered into evidence, but whenever a witness told a lie, she created a commotion and would not be stilled. "I paid no attention to [the judge's] raps," she remembers. See also *Guntersville Democrat*, July 3, 1890, p. 3.
56. Sheffield to Searcy, ca. 1906. See also *Guntersville Democrat*, July 17, 1890, p. 3, and November 20, 1890, p. 3.
57. Sheffield to Oates, December 30, 1895. That such a prolonged use of chloral hydrate could cause severe weight loss is corroborated by a contemporary medical description of the habit. Dr. T. D. Crothers explained in reference to "chloralism" that "After a

her personal habits of the 1880s were unacceptable. Unlike experimenters with drugs a century later, Andrew Sheffield never viewed or labeled her behavior as rebellion against conformity. She always paid homage to the social orthodoxy of which her family was such an important part. She never argued that she was right and they were wrong.

Interestingly, however, in none of her self-descriptions did she apply any variant of the label "drug abuser." Instead, the most common way in which she characterized herself was as a "prostitute." The Hospital's earliest surviving case note for her also employed that label.[58] Yet it is almost certain that she was *not* a prostitute, at least not in the twentieth-century sense as a woman who seeks and receives money for sex. Instead, the label—which she as well as others applied (and here we get a sense of the complex realities that history offers up for the modern labeling theorists)—signified that she had had an extramarital sexual relationship with someone she did not love, indeed someone who was using her—and someone she may well have been using in return. There was also in Sheffield and May's relationship what lawyers would call a consideration, that is, the chloral hydrate presumably given in return for sexual gratification.

In a letter to Superintendent Searcy in 1908, Sheffield states flatly that "I'm a prostitute" and adds grandiosely that "I am the deepest dyed, the most prominent criminal in the South."[59] Interestingly, though, these seeming admissions carry the tone of one who was throwing another's words back into his face. By 1908, Sheffield had been under Searcy's care for about fifteen years. The two had never gotten along well. As letters from the end of 1907 show, Sheffield had angrily accused the Superintendent of punishing her by placing her on the Hospital's "back wards," those parts of the institution where the least sensible patients were kept along with the "prostitutes and criminals." In other words, this seemingly bold admission of prostitution to Dr. Searcy eighteen years after her commitment is plausibly no more than an angry reminder that he had emphatically labeled her so by placing her on wards that she believed were reserved for such deviants. Perhaps she was sarcastically, even defiantly, mirroring what she believed to be his own description of her.

Many letters in the collection suggest that sarcasm had colored Sheffield's conversation with the Superintendent for some time. In September 1897, for example, she hoped that Searcy would allow her a personal

---

time the effect of its use appears in disordered digestion, the irregular heart's action, and the increase of nervousness and muscular unsteadiness." See Crothers, *The Drug Habits and Their Treatment: A Clinical Summary of Some of the General Facts Recorded in Practice* (Chicago: G. P. Engelhard, 1902), 86.

58. *Case History Book #6*, p. 185.
59. Sheffield to Searcy, ca. 1908.

in terview with Gov. Joseph F. Johnston, the governor with whom she would have the most sustained correspondence. He visited the Hospital occasionally—when he attended the University's commencement exercises at the Tuscaloosa campus or the annual meetings of the Hospital's trustees, for example. In a note to Searcy asking for permission to speak with Johnston, Sheffield explains, "You need not fear to trust him alone [with me.] I will not ask him for *Tobacco* or *money,* neither will I ask him to have *intercourse* with me, so you need not have him *guarded.*"[60] A literal interpretation of her words might suggest that she had in fact asked other men to have sex with her. A more plausible reading, however, is that this difficult and defiant woman was mocking her keeper.

It is possible that in every letter where she refers to herself as a prostitute, she is mimicking the judgment of others. Her statement that "I'm a prostitute" is her only direct admission of such activity. All her others are inferential and, like this reference, can plausibly be construed as mocking. A letter to Searcy in 1908 is typical. She classifies herself as of the "indigent, prostitute and criminal" class of patients.[61] Obviously she is referring to labels commonly used inside the institution, ones that Searcy knew only too well, and not to labels of her own design. "Indigent," for instance, was the official label given to the vast majority of patients who were wards of the state. The Hospital also cared for a few "private" patients whose families paid for their maintenance. This description therefore probably has nothing to do with her sexual conduct nearly two decades before, apart from acknowledging her social disgrace.

In ten of her ninety-one surviving letters, Sheffield refers to herself in some manner as a "prostitute." Interestingly, all but one of these date from the end of 1907 or later.[62] In other words, only once in the first seventeen years of her confinement did she employ that term. The next eight references, however, occurred in letters she wrote during the next two years or so. One later reference occurs in 1915. So not until many years into her life as a patient did the highly charged term "prostitute" become a commonplace in her discourse, and it remained such for only a relatively limited time.

---

60. Sheffield to Searcy, early September 1897; emphasis in the original.
61. Sheffield to Searcy, ca. October 1908.
62. Sheffield's letter to Gov. Oates, December 30, 1895, was the first to include a reference to prostitution. Sheffield's other such letters are to Lanford, ca. November 1907; to Lanford, late 1907; to Searcy, ca. 1908; to Gov. Braxton B. Comer, June 10, 1908; to Searcy, ca. October 1908; to Col. Samuel Will John, late October 1908; to Lanford, September 16, 1909; to Searcy, early January 1910; and to Dr. D. M. Collier, January 4, 1915.

Why the particular timing and pace of such language? The answer, as already suggested, comes not solely, or even primarily, from her experiences with May or anyone else prior to her commitment. The explanation stems apparently from the internal history of the Hospital. First, the references correspond to her assignment to the back wards, which were removed from the Hospital's main channels of life and communication. Residents of the back wards had less freedom, often associated with the most violent inmates, and were deprived of the valued company of the more rational patients. Sheffield sometimes called them the "violent wards." Though Searcy denied it, Sheffield considered this move an attempt to control her, to force her to "come under" to him, as she expressed it.[63]

Perhaps more important than the shift to the back wards was the Alabama state legislature's detailed investigation of the Hospital conducted in August and September 1907. Several former patients and employees had publicly charged the institution with abusive treatment of the patients. As a result, a select investigating committee of five senators and representatives took testimony in Montgomery, Birmingham, and Tuscaloosa (both at the Hospital and at the county courthouse). For over two weeks, the investigation, which included examination of 125 witnesses, received front-page coverage in the Alabama press. Chief among those witnesses giving testimony was a former nurse named Freda Crump, who alleged that patients who resided on the back wards of the women's side of the Hospital had been physically mistreated by their attendants.[64]

Legal counsel for the Hospital countered these charges with the assertion that Crump was a well-known prostitute and that her testimony was therefore unreliable. When the committee took testimony in Birmingham (where Crump had gone to live after leaving the Hospital), two

---

63. See Sheffield to Lanford, May 28, 1909, for her use of the phrase "come under."
64. Montgomery *Advertiser,* August 21, 1907, p. 9; August 22, p. 8, cols. 1–2; August 23, p. 1; August 24, p. 1; August 26, p. 1; August 27, p. 1; August 29, p. 1; August 30, p. 1; August 31, p. 1; September 2, p. 1; September 3, p. 1; September 4, p. 1; September 5, p. 2; September 6, p. 1; September 7, p. 1; and September 8, 1907, p. 1. The Tuscaloosa *Times Gazette* also covered the events for this period, but most of its articles rely on the reporting of the *Advertiser,* which was widely considered to be the principal newspaper in the state. The *Birmingham Age-Herald* gave the investigation front-page coverage while the *Daily News* usually kept it on the back pages. The committee's final report was *Reports on the Legislative Investigation of the Alabama Insane Hospitals in 1907* (Tuscaloosa: Hospital Print, 1907). This was a pamphlet published at the institution that faithfully reported the investigation's findings but that also added newspaper quotations which allegedly exonerated the institution. Copies of this pamphlet exist in the Staff Library at Bryce Hospital and in the State Hospitals Collection in ADAH.

witnesses testified, in opinions based entirely on speculation, that Crump
was indeed a prostitute. The first witness, a "real estate man," testified
that he had seen Crump frequently in the company of known prostitutes,
whom he called "street walkers." The second, an electrician named Edward Patillo, stated that he and a friend had taken Crump and a friend of
hers out on a date. Patillo claimed direct knowledge that Crump's friend,
with whom he had personally stayed all night, was a prostitute. His male
companion, he said, told him the next day that he had spent the night with
Crump. Patillo's friend could not be found to corroborate the testimony,
but the story left the clear impression of Crump's life as a street walker. No
evidence to the contrary was ever brought forward.[65]

The tactic was as effective as it was clear. By labeling Crump, rightly
or wrongly, as a prostitute, the Hospital's lawyers discredited her charges
of patient abuse.[66] They did this at some price, however. They suggested
that one of the Hospital's former attendants soon became a street walker
after leaving the institution's employ. This in turn suggested something
rather less than purity in the institution's nursing corps. Sheffield later
claimed that, as a result of this negative publicity, many good nurses quit
the Hospital for fear of their reputations: "many of the better sort of
weomen [sic] nurses," Sheffield reported, "have decided to leave, on account of their not wishing to be any longer identified with the
Institution. . . ."[67] For a time at least, it may have become stigmatizing
for a woman to work in the Tuscaloosa institution.

For Sheffield, the entire investigation and especially the dismissal of
Crump's testimony had a powerful impact. She never gave any damaging
testimony before the committee, however, and even claimed that she considered testifying in favor of the institution. While she was certain that
many abuses had in fact occurred, she was equally convinced that many of
the allegations were lies. What rankled Sheffield was the dismissal of
Crump's evidence and the Hospital's strategy to discredit her testimony.
Assistant Superintendent W. D. Partlow especially angered Sheffield in
this regard. She wrote to one of the institution's trustees, Col. Samuel
Will John of Birmingham, that "Dr Partlow had been heard to say, in

---

65. No record of Crump's testimony has survived. For the evidence offered by her detractors, however, see the testimony of T. H. Mosely and Edward Patillo, afternoon session, August 29, 1907, Birmingham, "Official Report" (a typescript of testimony),
Alabama Hospitals Collection, ADAH. Testimony of only twenty-three of the nearly
125 witnesses has survived. All of these witnesses gave their testimony in Birmingham
on August 29 and 30, and September 2 and 3, 1907.
66. Ruth Rosen's *The Lost Sisterhood: Prostitution in America 1900–1918* (Baltimore:
Johns Hopkins University Press, 1982) discusses popular attitudes toward prostitutes
(see esp. 46–48).
67. Sheffield to Gov. Braxton Bragg Comer, June 10, 1908.

speaking of Miss Crump[,] 'the star witness', that the 'nurses need have no fears of her testimony' as a 'prostitute[']s word was never taken.' ''[68] A year or so later, Sheffield told Dr. Lanford that, ''Prostitutes tell the truth sometimes—as little as Dr Partlow seems to think. I can't say that Miss Crump was, or was not a prostitute, but can say, after spending two years in violent [back] wards that her statement was true from start to finish.''[69]

In three of the ten letters in which Sheffield labels herself a prostitute, she also mentions Crump.[70] And, as we have seen, all but one of the ten appeared after the investigation occurred. The authorities' dismissal of what Sheffield considered to be Crump's true stories must have reminded her of those authorities' similar dismissal of her own claims to sanity—perhaps because they also viewed her as sexually disgraced. Both women bore a social stigma and found that unrelated dimensions of their character had been tainted by its pollution. In other words, it may have been the authorities' subjective assessment of her rather than any objective description of long-past sexual behavior that led Sheffield to use the attention-grabbing label of prostitute.

Sheffield's letters themselves provide some evidence which, though confusing, is against her seeming admissions of prostitution. In telling her story to Gov. Oates, for example, she calls his attention to her ''proud and prominent family'' but also describes herself in almost rote fashion as a ''prostitute'' and a ''criminal.'' She then proceeds to explain that ''had I wanted to have lived a disreputable life—I could have when young for when young, I passed for a very *handsome* woman. . . . ''[71] The contrary implication is that she had *not* been disreputable. Her ''prominence'' and her ''prostitution'' may thus have defined opposites in her discourse—opposites that describe status, not behavior.

On July 11, 1890, Superintendent Peter Bryce admitted Andrew (known to some family members as ''Dock'') Sheffield to the Alabama Insane Hospital (called Bryce Hospital after his death in 1892), which was

---

68. Sheffield to Samuel Will John, late 1908. This letter was intercepted and never mailed to John. It is possible that he read it on one of his frequent visits to the institution, however. Ironically, John was one of the Hospital's representatives who acted as counsel for the institution during the investigation. He was therefore present at the hearings and may have been partly responsible for the tactics which so angered Sheffield. For another reference to the Crump matter, see Sheffield to Searcy, ca. 1908.

69. Sheffield to Lanford, September 16, 1909. The exact nature of Crump's charges are not known. Her testimony has not survived.

70. Sheffield to Lanford, September 16, 1909; Sheffield to Samuel Will John, late 1908; and to Searcy, ca. 1908.

71. Sheffield to Gov. Oates, December 30, 1895.

located adjacent to the state's University in Tuscaloosa. A full record of her initial examination has not survived, but the *Case History Books,* a permanent record of most (but not all) notes kept on the wards, do provide a digest of her case. Read by the dozens of nurses and doctors who worked with Sheffield over the next thirty years, that record stated in straightforward style the following information: she was single and forty-one years old; she did not have an occupation; she was a criminal charged with arson; despite her status as unmarried, she was identified as a "House wife" (the irony probably was not intended); her family had considered her insane for fifteen years; she was depressed but not suicidal (one of her sisters, however, had committed suicide); she had a good education; and she was of "intemperate habits."[72]

In many of her letters, Sheffield refers to the year following her admission as the worst of her incarceration. Her case history hints at but fails to corroborate this sense of cruel treatment. On July 30, for example, the records show that she was "quiet, & getting along well since her admission. She is rational, & converses freely. . . . " But by August 10, she was "nervous" and complaining of bad headaches. She was also showing a measure of defiance by staying in her room during the physicians' morning rounds. Her doctor reported that she could be "found sitting at her window looking out, with her elbows resting on the window-sill, & her head in her hands. She answers questions readily, but does not turn around when addressed."[73] Seven months after her admission, on February 15, 1891, her doctor reported that she was "usually quiet, & always rational, but more or less morose & frequently asks to be sent home, becoming at times threatening." He also noted for the first time that she alleged bad treatment in letters to her father, but the physician discounted the charge as a "false statement."[74]

As far as it goes, this case history is accurate and insightful. But much that was routine either required no formal record or entirely escaped the notice of the attending doctors. Patients of the Hospital ordinarily saw their doctors no more than once a day, and they conversed with the medical staff only rarely. Nineteenth- and early twentieth-century insanity specialists employed no equivalent of modern talking therapies that brought them into intimate contact with their patients. Instead, the philosophy of

---

72. Entry for patient #3910. *Admissions Book,* Staff Library. Superintendent Bryce did not conduct the initial examination of Sheffield personally. Assistant physician W. G. Somerville actually processed her admission. She had been brought to the Hospital by Marshall County Sheriff M. G. Wells and her nephew O. D. Street.

73. *Case History Book #6,* p. 185.

74. *Case History Book #6,* p. 224.

moral treatment dictated that they minister primarily to the countless aches and physical illnesses of their patients. A physically healthy patient in these crowded quarters who gave his or her nurses little trouble would seldom have exchanged more than the amenities with a doctor during his morning rounds.

As Ellen Dwyer's study of New York asylums suggests, nurses more than doctors affected the patients' lives. These attendants in Bryce Hospital literally lived among the patients during their waking hours. Following an initial examination, newly admitted patients came immediately under the control of the nurses, who operated within established routines and according to the doctors' daily orders. Some patients went immediately to wards for new patients, where they sometimes entered "seclusion." This involved isolation in a room with no furniture except, in some cases, a mattress on the floor. Ordinarily, nurses put only the most unmanageable patients in seclusion, but new arrivals often presented special cases. Virtually all of the Hospital's inmates came against their will, and many rebelled at leaving loved ones or friends to enter a massive institution designed to hold them by force. Not surprisingly, many were bitterly resentful and decidedly uncooperative. Seclusion supposedly provided a haven of sorts where these new patients' resentment could dissipate and where neither nurses nor patients would be injured.

Sheffield's records do not show that she entered seclusion when she first came to the Hospital. Yet if such isolation was a routine practice, hers probably would not have been recorded. Sheffield's letters never say exactly what happened following her admission, but she repeatedly refers to brutal treatment during her "first year" in the Hospital. Her case history shows that she often made physical threats and, in May 1891, struck the supervisor of women nurses, Mary Buck, whom she held responsible for her treatment. Given the evidence of Sheffield's capacity for abuse—evidence not only from her keepers but from statements in her letters as well—it is a fair inference that she taxed her nurses to the very limits of their ability. In short, she resented her commitment and doubtless abused her keepers. Almost certainly she spent time in seclusion during this first year.[75]

Quite possibly her addiction to chloral hydrate contributed to her early troubles in the Hospital. She may not have completely broken the habit before coming to Tuscaloosa. Her letters speak not at all to this point. Any remaining physical or psychological dependence would have

---

75.   The first recorded seclusion of Sheffield occurred in May 1891, following her attack on Supervisor Mary Buck.

combined with her characteristic obstinacy to make Sheffield an especially unruly patient. Doctors at the Hospital often found it necessary to seclude patients with addictions to drugs or alcohol more often and for longer periods than other patients.

Even without the vagaries of her special case, Sheffield's early experience in the Hospital would undoubtedly have been traumatic. Most new inmates of mental institutions before and since 1890 have reported similar initial experiences. Sociologist Erving Goffman, a scholar in the tradition of ''labelers,'' addressed this process of beginning one's ''career'' as an inmate of a mental hospital in his seminal 1961 work on asylums as total institutions. He argued that, on admission, a patient ''begins a series of abasements, degradations, humiliations, and profanations of self. His self is systematically, if often unintentionally, mortified.''[76] For Sheffield, who had been considerably independent, confinement with no promise of release dramatically altered her personal horizons. It cut her off from familiar routines and familiar faces. More, it cut her off from control of her daily life and the prospect of her own future. Finally, it placed her in a role subservient to men and women whom she did not respect.

Sheffield's admission laid down an unmistakable boundary between her free past and a confined future. Her letters are mute on the point, but it is likely that she had heard stories of life in Tuscaloosa and had wondered at the mysteries of life within that giant institution before coming there. At the very outset, she underwent a physical exam which was conducted by a stranger in an impersonal, perhaps mysterious place many miles from home. In 1896 the Assistant Superintendent, E. D. Bondurant, described what this exam might entail: examination of ''the condition of the lungs, of heart, arteries and general system, and condition of abnormal viscera; a urinalysis is made; the nerve reactions are tested, including sensibility, motility, reflexes, speech, gait, etc. In many cases the blood is examined . . . ; the electrical reactions tested; when there is reason to suspect disease of pelvic organs a gynecological examination is made.''[77]

From such an exam, Sheffield quite possibly entered a seclusion room which her letters call the ''cross hall.'' Following a brief seclusion, she would have entered a ward populated by strange persons, most of whom seemed clearly less rational than she. There she would have noticed sights, sounds, and smells that were totally foreign to her experience. From that time forward, she would never again know perfect privacy.

---

76. Goffman, *Asylums: Essays on the Social Situation of Mental Patients and Other Inmates* (Garden City, N. Y.: Doubleday, 1961), 14.

77. *Biennial Report . . . 1896* (Montgomery: Roemer Printing, 1896), 15.

Doctors and nurses, not she, controlled the key to her room. She had but one trunk of her own clothes; the furniture was the Hospital's. She used the toilet and bathed in a room common to the ward and supervised by a nurse. At night her door was locked to keep her in—though, as her letters reveal, it could never completely keep out the sounds of other patients.

So, as Goffman observed of asylums nearly seventy years later, Andrew Sheffield experienced "abasements, degradations, humiliations, and profanations" of her "self." Despite the conscious efforts of the medical staff to make the process as humane as possible, it was inescapably traumatic to lose one's freedom and to enter the minutely managed world of a massive institution. Sheffield's frequent allusions to her cruel treatment in 1890 reveal clearly this process of "mortification." Indeed, her memory of abuse during her first year may have been an exaggerated recollection of her difficult adjustment to institutional life. Even the Hospital staff's best intentions could have mitigated only slightly the trauma of that adjustment for a patient as unwilling as Sheffield.

These letters reveal, however, that the "self" of Andrew Sheffield survived that first year. More than Goffman might have imagined, she remained an independent-minded, aggressive, and uncompromising person. The social controllers never managed to discipline her character or eccentricity for long. She clung defiantly to her "self" and went on to make a somewhat independent life within the Hospital. She outlived several generations of doctors, nurses, and patients. Indeed, within the narrow world of the asylum, the whole of her world, she reigned as an infamous persona that sometimes engendered fear and at times even merited respect. Prone to withdraw emotionally and to strike out physically, she managed to carve out a personal space for herself that few entered willingly.

———————————————————————————————

Most images of the asylum, as we have seen, come to us from the outside looking in. And architecturally this Kirkbride-style hospital impressed onlookers as did few buildings anywhere in the South. By the 1890s, it was the largest single structure anywhere in Alabama, probably anywhere for hundreds of miles in all directions.[78] No traveler on the busy Black Warrior River that flowed by the Hospital on the north, or on the railroad which stopped at its front gate to the south, could easily forget Bryce Hospital or the images of authority and permanence it projected.

Even those who never saw the Hospital knew of its operations and likely carried in their minds an imagined picture of what it was like. In his

———————————————————————————————

78. In 1907, for example, the Montgomery *Advertiser* identified Bryce Hospital as "the largest single building in Alabama" (*Advertiser*, August 23, 1907, p. 1).

Annual Report for 1897, Superintendent Searcy boasted that the asylum was ''by far the largest public charity in the State; there is hardly a hamlet or family that is not interested in us. . . . ''[79] Those who had never seen the Hospital or sent family members there acknowledged the institution's place in their society when they offered words of support or condolence to distressed friends, or when they gossiped about the hidden history of a neighbor's commitment to Tuscaloosa. Moreover, by the 1890s, hundreds of released patients had returned to the larger society, carrying tales and providing constant reminders of the institution's presence.

To those like Sheffield who never went home, the Hospital presented a different face. Through them, modern readers can see the asylum from the inside out. Not merely a massive and imposing building, it became, when viewed from this perspective, an interconnected world of rooms, front ''show'' wards, ''back'' wards, dining rooms, ''airing courts,'' an amusement hall, a chapel, and spacious, beautiful grounds. Having passed from outsiders to inmates, patients came to view the publicly imposing monolith as fragmented, reduced and personalized. It became to Sheffield a new world with its own special hierarchies, routines, and rules. To her, it seemed a different place from that imagined by Thomas Kirkbride or the Alabama doctors who hoped to give life to his vision.

In keeping with this Kirkbride plan, Bryce Hospital segregated its men and women patients. Sheffield and the other women resided in wards extending east from the administrative offices, while the men populated the west wing. Such separation of the sexes supported the genius of moral therapy by reducing the excitability of patients and providing proof of propriety to an often suspicious public.[80] But as a consequence, Sheffield lived in an almost purely women's world. She saw men only during the routinized morning rounds when the male physicians passed through her ward, at chapel, during rigorously supervised weekly amusements, or on evening walks when groups of women sometimes passed separate groups of men. For Sheffield, these chances to interact with men were rare. Her letters show, moreover, that she often ran afoul of the rules and lost her privileges even to attend chapel or amusements, or go on walks. Her world

---

79. ''Annual Report,'' 1897, unpublished typescript, p. 2, State Hospitals Collection, ADAH.

80. According to the Hospital's by-laws written in 1890, ''Interviews between the sexes in yards, laundry, shops, at entrances to wards, or in any other unsuitable part of the building are forbidden.'' This rule applied to patients and nurses alike. See *By-Laws, Rules, and Regulations of the Alabama Insane Hospital*, 69.

therefore differed greatly from the one beyond the Hospital's grounds, where men and women took each other's presence for granted. More than women in the saner society, she lived almost literally in a "separate sphere."

By the 1890s, when Sheffield settled into the institution's regimen, the doctors had nearly ceased to speak consciously of moral treatment's importance. But the inertia of thirty years' deliberate effort to establish the therapy carried into the twentieth century. Never in Sheffield's lifetime did the physicians experiment with, for example, the newer talking therapies which by 1920 had come to characterize the private-practice care of some of the mentally ill outside the asylums. Sheffield's care followed the older precepts and the rhythms of moral treatment. She lived according to a generations-old routine and received no medical intervention for her insanity. What we today would call "psychiatry" never touched her life.

But her treatment was more textured than this fact might suggest. Since 1880, earlier than most American institutions, Bryce Hospital had practiced a policy of "non-restraint." More in keeping with an English philosophy of moral therapy, Bryce and Searcy forbade the use of any mechanical restraints. Sheffield certainly never saw a manacle and likely never saw a straight jacket. Patients who were not subject to control by reason or authority ended up in the "cross-hall." Sheffield explains in her letters that she knew these seclusion rooms well, having been placed there for her occasional outbursts and actual attacks on nurses or fellow patients.[81]

Like most public institutions of its era, Bryce Hospital during Sheffield's years also followed a policy of what today might be called "occupational therapy." All physically able patients pursued some kind of work. The men labored largely outdoors—doing landscaping, moving earth in wheel barrows, building roads, making bricks for the continual expansion of the huge facility, tending the dairy, working in the stables, or practicing trades in various shops, such as printing and carpentry. Sheffield and the other women, however, had few such opportunities, restrained as they were by the conventional restrictions on women's work found in the wider,

---

81.   Her case history does not record all of her trips to the cross-hall but does show that the staff believed she sometimes needed this extra measure of discipline (see *Case History Book #6*, 224–25, 229, 234). For a contemporary discussion of non-restraint that places Peter Bryce among the first American superintendents to employ it, see Clark Bell, "Mechanical Restraint in the Care of the Insane," *Medico-Legal Journal* 10 (1891): 203–48, 384–99.

saner society.[82] Except for the few black women at Bryce,[83] female patients never worked outside, but remained indoors where they helped the nurses with housekeeping or engaged in sewing. Women patients in fact made most of the clothing worn by the poorer patients, whose families either could not afford to furnish it or had forgotten them. Many women, including Sheffield, produced fancy work which the nurses sold outside the Hospital. Nurses routinely took commissions for items such as tablecloths and pillowcases from families in the area around Tuscaloosa. Patients then produced the desired goods, which the nurses delivered on their days off. Patients and nurses both made a small sum in this way.[84]

Like the system of non-restraint, the requirement that all be busy fit well with the older tenets of moral treatment. Such labor, provided it was unhurried and disciplined, promoted values thought to be essential to a healthy mind. Superintendent Searcy told his Trustees in 1893 that, because of the exertion of physical labor, "The men are very much more quiet night and day than the women: less noisy and more satisfied." He even wished that social convention allowed him to put white women as well as black to work out of doors.[85] Judging from Sheffield's letters, Searcy's remarks were much to the point. In their separate sphere, women did suffer from the tedium of housekeeping and sewing, and the limited freedom indoors. More than once, these letters show, the stress got the better of Andrew.

Indeed, virtually all of Andrew Sheffield's letters show a woman under stress. The place itself, its physical dimensions and patterns of life, promised trouble for this independent woman who had lived alone before her commitment. The people who populated that place were also to make

82. *By-Laws, Rules, and Regulations* (1890), 48. See also *Biennial Report . . . 1890* (Montgomery: Brown Printing, 1890), 5–6, 25–26, 31–32. Virtually every biennial report included discussion of the patients' work.

83. After 1901, most black patients were kept in a separate hospital in Mt. Vernon, several miles north of Mobile. Before Jim Crow laws were enacted, significant numbers of blacks lived in the Hospital in Tuscaloosa. After 1901 only a few blacks remained. The staff kept a few black patients there largely because blacks could be used in jobs thought unacceptable for white patients.

84. *By-Laws, Rules, and Regulations* (1890), 68. Fancy work was a tradition from the Hospital's founding. The first by-laws of the institution stated that the Matron (later called the Supervisor) "shall have charge of fancy articles made by the patients, and for sale." *By-Laws, Alabama Insane Hospital* (Tuscaloosa: "Observer" Book and Job Office, 1861), 25.

85. "Proceedings of the Board of Trustees," October 4, 1893, *Trustees Minute Book 1:* [204], Staff Library, Bryce Hospital.

her life difficult—perhaps as difficult as she made theirs. Dr. Searcy and Sheffield never maintained a congenial relationship, for example. The son of a long-time Trustee and himself a past Trustee who had a general private practice in Tuscaloosa after graduating from the Medical Department of New York University in 1867, Dr. Searcy was Superintendent of the Hospital for almost exactly the same years that Sheffield was in residence there. In fact, all her letters in this collection date from his tenure, and about one-third of Sheffield's letters are to him. The two came to know one another very well.

In most of these letters, Sheffield complains repeatedly of ill treatment and Dr. Searcy's lack of cooperation in meeting her demands to be transferred to the penitentiary. (She always argues that as a sane criminal, her proper place of confinement was a prison not a mental institution.)[86] Searcy's letters clearly show that he found her exasperating. To Gov. Oates in 1896 he describes her as "incorrigible," "unapproachable," "disagreeable," and "hostile in her feelings towards all who have authority over her." But he also concedes that she is "highly intelligent in most respects." In language reminiscent of Elizabeth Packard's case thirty years before, Searcy tells Oates that his patient suffers from "moral insanity."[87] Significantly, by the late 1890s most insanity specialists considered this diagnostic category to be disreputable.[88] Indeed, it is the only time Searcy is known to have used the label. He usually prefers "moral imbecility," but that description may have seemed logically unfitted for someone as unmistakably intelligent as Sheffield, especially when one was describing her to a layperson such as the Governor. The mere fact that he resorted to this label pointed to his own exasperation and the troubling character of her case.

---

86. Sheffield repeatedly asked Searcy and the various governors with whom she communicated to have her transferred to the penitentiary. She argued that, as a sane woman, she should be confined there instead of the Hospital. The problem, of course, was that she had never been convicted of any crime, only charged. Before she could go to the penitentiary, she would have to stand trial in Marshall County. She, however, refused to do that. Her self-awareness informed her that she would behave as badly at a trial as she had at her preliminary trial in 1890. And if that happened, the jury would find her insane and send her back to Searcy.

87. See Searcy to Gov. Oates, January 1, 1896.

88. For discussions of the debates over moral insanity outside Alabama, see Charles Rosenberg, *Trial of the Assassin Guiteau: Law and Psychiatry in the Gilded Age* (Chicago: University of Chicago Press, 1968), and John S. Hughes, *In the Law's Darkness: Isaac Ray and the Medical Jurisprudence of Insanity in Nineteenth-Century America* (New York: Oceana Press, 1986). A helpful contemporary discussion is Percute Iterum [pseud.], "The History and Present Position of the Doctrine of Moral Insanity," *Medico-Legal Journal* 10 (1891): 249–64, 356–83.

Despite the usual tenor of their interaction—which was mutually suspicious—both were capable of kindness, or something like it. Searcy, for example, gave his permission on occasion for Sheffield to visit town to shop, allowed her better furnishings than other patients on her wards, and occasionally mailed her incriminating letters to governors and other dignitaries. For her part, Sheffield occasionally apologized for her intemperate behavior or for misunderstandings on her part. Each, it seems, essentially disliked the other, but nonetheless saw something to be gained by small reachings out. Searcy could hope for greater institutional harmony if this difficult patient were better pleased. And Sheffield had no other recourse to wider opportunity but through the Superintendent's authority.

In her daily life, however, Sheffield rarely dealt with Searcy. Assistant physicians, as the staff doctors were called, conducted the daily rounds and assumed immediate responsibility for the patients.[89] By the 1890s these doctors, all of whom had M. D. degrees though no special training in insanity, managed the daily routine and reported to Searcy, who supervised their activities. Both the men's and the women's sides typically had two assistant physicians, each with responsibility for certain wards. Patients therefore had one doctor whom they saw every day. Nurses also took their orders directly from one of these staff doctors and usually not from the Superintendent.

Sheffield once called these men "mere lads, scarcely emerged from their teens."[90] While this slightly exaggerates the case, it comes close to a correct characterization of the typical assistant physician. Most were young men who had just finished medical school but had not established a private practice. Almost none of these young staff doctors intended to make mental illness a lifelong specialty. And few of them did. They came to work at Bryce because of the vast opportunities for clinical experience there. Few doctors at the turn of the century worked in general hospitals. Such institutions had not yet come to play a central role in American medical care, especially in the South. A mental hospital therefore afforded

---

89. The title of assistant physician is today a bit misleading, suggesting that these men were not yet doctors. They were indeed physicians, though most had not practiced widely before taking the Hospital position. There were "internes" who also worked in the Hospital throughout much of the period. They were assistants to the assistant physicians, as it were. Those holding this position typically did not have their M. D. degrees yet and probably worked in the Hospital during those months when the medical schools were not in session, typically half or more of the year. The internes, unlike the assistant physicians, received no pay, only room and board.

90. Sheffield to Little, May 12, 1906.

young practitioners literally hundreds of sick people—physically sick people—on whom they could improve their skills of diagnosing and treating. Insanity itself remained a secondary interest for the great majority of these young doctors who, for the most part, set up general private practices when they left the Hospital's employment.

Sheffield complained that many of these assistant physicians came from humble backgrounds and undistinguished families. To some extent, this class-conscious impression corroborates what historians know generally about turn-of-the-century medical men. Many doctors of the period attended one of a wide variety of proprietary medical schools, none of which required college preparation.[91] Given this reasonably democratic access to medical education, many bright young men of humble origins did seek to improve their lot by becoming doctors. Quite possibly, then, Sheffield's description of these doctors, meant as a criticism, may well have actually offered a valuable insight into the profession's contemporary demographics. Moreover, the observation also suggested opportunism in the doctors, some of whom were using the Hospital as a stepping stone.

By rules of the institution, none of these young doctors could marry. From Sheffield's perspective, this regulation guaranteed that they would have too little experience with women to treat them properly. And surprisingly, for a woman who often described herself as a "prostitute," Sheffield showed remarkable sensitivity to propriety. In addition to their youthful ignorance of women, these doctors often had to treat the most delicate conditions, sometimes in women who were themselves young, attractive, and, according to Sheffield, not terribly crazy. Recall, too, that Sheffield's trouble in Marshall County revolved around her relationship with a physician who, though older, had allegedly taken sexual advantage of her. Needless to say, Sheffield would have preferred doctors who were married, older, and of a social station more like her own.

Regardless of these perceived shortcomings in the young doctors, it was the female nurses who controlled the tone of Sheffield's day-to-day existence. The doctors operated as managers from the central administrative hall, and necessarily left the actual care and treatment of the patients to the nurses. Thomas Scheff, the sociologist most often associated with

---

91. See, for example, Abraham Flexner, *Medical Education in the United States* (New York: Carnegie Foundation, 1910). Flexner discussed all the medical schools in the nation and found all but a handful woefully lacking in requirements and facilities. He discussed the two Alabama schools on pp. 185–87. The resumes of the hospital's doctors no longer exist, so it is not known where most went to school. Many probably were trained in Alabama or some neighboring state. According to Flexner, all Southern schools were inadequate, except Johns Hopkins in Baltimore.

labeling theory, explained nearly thirty years ago how such fragmented bureaucratic authority served to locate power largely in the hands of attendants rather than doctors. Basing his conclusions on the workings of a large institution in the 1950s, he explained that young ward doctors had usually received no formal training in managing life on the wards. "The typical ward physician," he said, "was not only a newcomer, but also, as far as most ward problems were concerned, an amateur." This usually left him at the mercy of the more practically experienced nurses. Attendants, Scheff argued, developed "a strong sense of solidarity" that often caused them to view doctors in adversarial terms.[92]

Sheffield's letters confirm Scheff's insights. She tells repeatedly of ways in which the policies of the doctors were undermined by the nurses. In particular, she believed that the female supervisor, Mary Buck, controlled and manipulated the younger, less experienced doctors. The rank-and-file nurses certainly exhibited what Scheff called solidarity, behaving, she says, one way when the doctors were on the ward and another way when they themselves were in absolute charge. If Sheffield's letters are correct, many of the nurses feared their female supervisor far more than any of the male doctors.

Like the assistant physicians, nurses were to be unmarried as a condition of their employment.[93] Because of this regulation, most of these nurses were extremely young. Sheffield's pet phrase for them was "pretty girls." Few were older than their early twenties and several were only in their teens.[94] None had experience in caring for the insane before coming to the Hospital, though many eventually graduated from a Training School for nurses that the institution operated after the mid-1890s as a way of improving the quality of nursing. Few who graduated stayed to make a career, however. They usually went on to better paying jobs in other hospitals or in private nursing.[95]

---

92. "Control Over Policy by Attendants in a Mental Hospital," *Journal of Health and Human Behavior* 2 (Summer 1961): 93–105; quotations, 95 and 98.

93. This is true at least as it applies to the white nurses who had care of Sheffield. Some black nurses, who worked in black wards, were married—usually to black male nurses or other employees of the institution.

94. According to data derived from Manuscript Census Rolls for Tuscaloosa County for 1900, there were 43 white female nurses ranging in age from 18 to 39. All were listed as single. The actual average age was 22.8 years. Data derived from Manuscript Census Rolls, Tuscaloosa County, 1910 shows that there were 65 white female nurses ranging in age from 16 to 39. All were single; one was widowed. The actual average age was 22.2 years.

95. A pamphlet prepared in 1902 by the Hospital as a recruiting device for nurses showed that a large number of the Training School graduates were either in private nursing or working elsewhere such as "Dr. King's Sanatorium in Selma." Of the forty-six men

Quite commonly, these young women left their families in the countryside to work for a few months or years at Bryce. In time, something like a stream of nurses opened between the Hospital and various locales in the surrounding area. The repetition of certain family names in the lists of nurses on the manuscript census rolls suggests that some families supplied several daughters or cousins to do such work. Indeed, occasionally, Sheffield's letters become confusing because several nurses, whom she usually identifies by their last names only, had the same name.

Hospital rules imposed few qualifications for employment beyond a good character, sometimes a reference, and a willingness to work for the sixteen to twenty dollars a month that women nurses usually received.[96] As a result, a variety of young women applied. In 1907 a physician who was practicing in Birmingham and teaching there at the medical school characterized the Bryce nursing staff. A former assistant physician at Bryce who now annually brought his students to tour the Hospital, he therefore knew the institution well: "some of the young women [nurses] come from the country, and some are educated; some of them have a good high school education and some of them employed there have not much of an education. . . ."[97] Most of these variously prepared young women probably never intended a career, but stayed only long enough to get a new and respectable skill or to save money before marriage. The persistently low average age from one year to another suggests a rapid turnover. A few probably came specifically to study at the Training School as preparation for work elsewhere. Much like the many young assistant physicians who came through the Hospital during Sheffield's thirty years there, these young nurses also seem to have viewed employment in the institution as a weigh station to something better.

Sheffield and her nurses seem never to have shared much common ground. More often than not, the relationships that Sheffield developed with her nurses reflected the vast distances between them. Gender, it seems, failed to provide any conscious solidarity, even in the face of a mutual adversarial pose regarding the male doctors. The letters suggest that

---

and women who graduated from 1896 to 1901, only twelve still worked in the Hospital—and seven of those were from the most recent class of 1901, who likely would leave soon. See *The Alabama Insane Hospitals: Notice to Persons Applying for Positions as Nurses . . .* (Tuscaloosa: Hospital Print Shop, 1902).

96. This pay may have been near but a bit below the average for asylums at the turn of the century. See a discussion of salaries in A. B. Richardson, "Nurses in Hospitals for the Insane," *Proceedings of the American Medico-Psychological Association, 1902* (Baltimore: American Medico-Psychological Association, 1902), 212–19.

97. Testimony of B. L. Wyman before the legislature's Investigative Commission of 1907, meeting in Birmingham, August 30, 1907, Official Transcript, p. 17, State Hospitals Collection, ADAH. Wyman had worked under Peter Bryce at the Hospital in the 1880s.

Sheffield saw her female attendants as all she was not. She had reached her later years; their lives were only beginning. She could point to a wealthy and prominent family; most of them could not. She was single; they most likely would marry. She bore the label "insane"; they did not. She never had to work; they did. She had received an education; many of them had not. She had little hope of leaving; they needed only to give their notice.

Repeatedly, Sheffield complained of "petticoat government," her placement under the authority of these other women.[98] She especially disliked Mary Buck, who held the position of Supervisor (formerly called the Matron), for nearly twenty-five years of Sheffield's stay in the Hospital. Sheffield had also charged, it will be recalled, that Buck was responsible for the alleged ill treatment she received in her first year. The Supervisor also controlled many of the younger doctors. Much as Scheff later explained, newly arrived assistant physicians had to learn the routines of the various wards from someone. To a great extent, it was Buck who told them about the "real" operation of the Hospital after Searcy had explained the "ideal." Far more than any doctor, Buck and the few older nurses possessed and handed down knowledge of the vast asylum's unwritten folkways.

Despite this ill ease with "petticoat government," Sheffield managed to accept the nurses' authority most of the time. She evidently did well in the fancy work industry that the nurses supervised, and thereby proved herself of value to them. She even had her friends among the attendants. Some nurses smuggled out letters that she knew the medical staff would intercept. While it is possible that they performed the service for money, they just as likely did it out of a sense of friendship or perhaps pity. Sheffield also formed attachments that her gruff character sometimes belied. Buck's assistant supervisor, Mattie Parr, often showed Sheffield kindnesses. "Miss Mattie," as Sheffield called her, allowed her to eat in her room, for example, rather than in the dining room. Sheffield appreciated the favor. When Parr died, the long-time patient remembered that she had been "Miss Mattie's pet" and admitted that she had loved Mattie Parr.

Parr's kindness could accomplish little more than small favors, however, without the agreement of the doctors and Supervisor Buck. And Sheffield was decidedly not their pet. She accused one doctor of trying to poison her. She alleged repeatedly that Buck had been drunk on the job. Such accusations hardly endeared her to those in authority. As a result, she

---

98. See, for example, Sheffield to Gov. Thomas G. Jones, June 15, 1893. The complaint can be found in many subsequent letters as well.

spent much of her thirty years at Bryce Hospital on the "back wards," some of which in later years were located literally behind the main building. This issue of back wards figures prominently in Sheffield's letters written after 1907. It was her view that her assignment there was a form of punishment. Hospital policy, however, technically forbade such a system of punishment. In fact, the non-restraint, moral-treatment approach prohibited punishment in any form as inappropriate for the mentally ill. In 1896 Superintendent Searcy explained Sheffield's ward assignments, saying to Gov. Oates that she "has been most of the time kept on the demented ward where she could not find patients to disaffect with her abuse of the officials, (she is exceedingly good at it) and where she could not frighten others with her horrible tales."[99]

In a paper he read several years later at the National Conference of Charities and Correction, Searcy expanded his views on ward assignments and the issue of punishment. He explained that "The moving of a patient from one ward to another, to a better or a lower grade, serves often as an excellent remedial measure. The discipline, if we may call it such, of these changes, is understood by most patients and has a beneficial effect. The principle, involved in it, is not punishment nor is it particularly a reward, but is a readjustment of class according to the varying condition of the patient."[100] So what Searcy saw as a measure to help Sheffield's condition and to assure institutional harmony, she interpreted as punishment. Again, perspective made all the difference.

The patients' view of punishment, as well as the many alleged abuses that Sheffield's letters discuss, became a matter of public scrutiny in the summer of 1907, when the state legislature undertook its major investigation of the Hospital. Sheffield, as we have already seen, ended up surprisingly playing no role in this investigation, which ended with a limited exoneration of the Hospital. The Commission sidestepped the difficult decision about whether to believe the negative testimony of insane witnesses. Its report criticized the Hospital indirectly, however, by recommending that higher wages be paid the nurses in order to assure a better class of employees, and that the quality of food given the patients be improved.[101] The Hospital thus weathered the storm and technically retained its good

---

99.   See Searcy to Gov. Oates, January 1, 1896.
100. Searcy, "For What Classes Should the State Make Provision?" in *Proceedings of the National Conference of Charities and Correction, 1903* (Boston: George H. Ellis, 1904), 425.
101. *Reports on the Legislative Investigation of the Alabama Insane Hospitals in 1907* (Tuscaloosa: Hospital Print, 1907). This is a reprint of the official report published in Montgomery. See also the Montgomery *Advertiser,* September 8, 1907, p. 1.

name. But the episode destroyed whatever public innocence had still attached to this vast home for the state's unfortunate insane.

Sheffield's letters include the period of the investigation and its aftermath. As a result, they supply valuable insights into this process of public scrutiny from the patients' perspective. Sheffield's letters reveal, for
example, that, far from being kept ignorant, intelligent patients like herself managed to keep up with the latest news throughout the investigation.
Newspapers still circulated among the patients. And nurses no doubt carried onto the wards tales and rumors of the investigation occurring on the
outside. Many patients, Sheffield claimed, feared to testify because of the
likelihood of punishment from either the nurses or the doctors. Indeed,
some of Sheffield's letters from 1908 and after allege that some patients
were later punished for what they had said. She also suggests that matters
got worse once the Commission vindicated Searcy and his management.
Instead of feeling chastened by criticism, the nurses were emboldened by
their having survived unpunished. Patients' morale suffered as a result.

Sheffield's view of events during and after 1907 may lack objectivity,
but it rings with authenticity. Like all of her insights about doctors, nurses,
and fellow patients, her impressions of the investigation reveal a sincere,
if perhaps a distempered, viewpoint. But was her construction of reality
insane? On the one hand, her family and the doctors who kept her in the
Hospital for nearly thirty years had certainly found reason to consider
her mad. On the other hand, unlike most Southern women of her generation, Sheffield had lived to middle age alone and beyond the daily protection of any man in her family. Until the public revelation of her crime,
her relationship with Dr. May, and her drug addiction, Sheffield's neighbors may well have considered her eccentric rather than insane. In any
event, the boundary between madness and peculiarity was at best a shady
one that often required the illumination of an extraordinary event to give
it definition.[102]

Once Sheffield was in the Hospital, her case history resolved few of
the ambiguities regarding her madness or sanity. Surviving physicians'

---

102. For a fuller discussion of these issues, see my essay "Commitment, Family Stress,
and Legal Culture: The Case of Victorian Alabama," in Donald Nieman, ed., *The
Constitution, Law, and American Society: Critical Aspects of the Nineteenth-Century
Experience* (Athens: University of Georgia Press, 1992), 133–61. An earlier version
of this essay was "Alabama's Families and Involuntary Commitment of the Insane,
1861–1900: New Solutions to Old Problems," Institute for Legal Studies, University
of Wisconsin-Madison, *Working Papers*, 2d ser. (May 1987), 1–58.

notes from the early months of her confinement report no clear evidence of insanity. On July 30, 1890, less than three weeks after her admission, her doctor noted that she "[h]as been quiet, & getting along well since her admission. She is rational, & converses freely concerning the charge of arson . . . as well as the killing of her paramour. . . . [S]he has no delusions as far as we can discover." The next case note, from about two weeks later, found her nervous and depressed.[103]

This depression, it seems, never lifted but sometimes transformed into rage. On February 15, 1891, her doctor reported that she was "[u]sually quiet, & always rational, but more or less morose & frequently asks to be sent home, at times becoming threatening." On May 12, however, the case history reported that "she became irritated by some trifling occurrence, became profane, obscene, & made dire threats against the officials of the Hospital, struck the Supervisoress, & swore she would kill her." After this outburst, the physician in charge ended his note with a sentence that may well summarize the institution's official view of Sheffield: "She seems to be a woman of considerable intellectual capacity, but devoid of moral stamina."[104] Significantly, this clinical judgment came only after Sheffield's aggressive outburst on the wards ten months into her stay. Apart from a possible veiled reference to her "prostitution" in this comment on her "moral stamina," it is a diagnosis based entirely on her life as a patient, not as a free woman.

Throughout her long career as a patient, Sheffield occasionally became physically abusive and used language that the doctors considered "obscene." She had, as noted, attacked Supervisor Buck on at least one occasion. Eighteen years into her commitment, she "knocked" a fellow patient with whom she was having difficulty.[105] A physician's note from 1898 describes her as having an "antipathy to the physicians & wishes them to keep out of her room, which they gladly do. She is extremely treacherous & not to be trusted from day to day."[106] Similar characterizations of her unpleasantness appeared in her file until shortly before her death. One of her doctor's last notes from 1918 describes her as defiant and unyielding, as well as "[p]rofane and vulgar."[107]

---

103. *Case History Book #6*, p. 185, entries for July 30 and August 10, 1890.
104. *Case History Book #6*, p. 224.
105. Sheffield to Searcy, ca. late 1908.
106. *Case History Book #6*, p. 229, entry for May 11, 1898.
107. *Case History Book #6*, p. 435, entry for October 8, 1918. By this time Sheffield was suffering from the diet deficiency disease pellagra, which was common in large institutions and was often associated with emotional depression. For a good overview of this disease in the South at this time, see Elizabeth W. Etheridge, *The Butterfly Caste:*

Apart from this consistent record of abuse, mean-spiritedness, and profanity—all of which, though disagreeable, are consistent with reason—there is little in her official record to validate any objective diagnosis of insanity. But there is *some* evidence. First, the doctors' case history frequently mentions delusions. Significantly, though, as noted above, her first case notes state quite clearly that "she has no delusions, as far as we can discover." The first mention of a delusion comes in a note from March 8, 1893, almost three years into her confinement. The physician entered the note in a discussion of her many letters to prominent persons which criticized some of the doctors and nurses. At the end of his entry, he states: "Exhibits some delusion at times." He describes no specific delusion, however, and thereby leaves the impression that her perceptions of poor treatment were chimerical.[108]

Later case notes repeat this judgment that Sheffield suffered from delusions. But no doctor ever describes a single example.[109] As her letters reveal, Sheffield herself had read this case history on several occasions. On the back wards, where most patients were insensible, the nurses sometimes kept the physicians' case notes unlocked and on their desktops where anyone could see them. One nurse even read Sheffield's entire case history to her.[110] In letters to outside officials in 1906, for example, Sheffield quotes from memory that her history reported "no discoverable delusions."[111] But in letters to officials within the institution, she acknowledges that the case history does label her as frequently delusional. And the characterization infuriated her. In a letter from late 1908, she asks Superintendent Searcy for an explanation: "I want you to tell me some time what are my Delusions, as every Dr except [E. D.] Bondurant [one of her physicians in the 1890s] has me charged with delusions."[112]

A Social History of Pellagra in the South (Westport, Conn.: Greenwood Publishing, 1972).

108. *Case History Book #6*, p. 225.
109. See, for example, *Case History Book #6*, p. 229, entry for March 8, 1899; and *Case History Book #6*, p. 234, entries for August 12, 1904, and September 28, 1905.
110. Sheffield to Searcy, ca. October 1908. In this letter, Sheffield explains that a nurse on one of the back wards (No. 14) who had left the Hospital's employment read to her the case history. As this example shows, Sheffield was careful not to inform on friendly nurses until after they were beyond the Superintendent's discipline.
111. Sheffield to Dr. Jonathon Little (Hospital Treasurer), May 12, 1906; Sheffield to Gov. William D. Jelks, September 25, 1906. Both of these letters were intercepted and kept in Sheffield's file. Neither reached its intended correspondent. The phrase here "no discoverable delusions" does not exist in the surviving case history, but its import comes from the earlier notes cited above (which says "no delusions as far as we can discover").
112. Sheffield to Searcy, ca. October 1908.

Though Sheffield's official case history lacks the details of any specific delusion, some surviving letters hint at its possibility. In a letter from June 1898, Sheffield states that Superintendent Searcy deliberately prevented her from having her requested audience with Gov. Johnston. She was so angered that she made what, on its face, seems an outrageous threat: "I'm going to write the 'Grand Master' of the Masonic Lodge. I am a Mason myself—and I've suffered long enough at the hands of you so-called Masons, when I can have every one of you *expelled from Masonry*." What makes the quotation plausibly delusional is that the Masons barred women from membership, something that Searcy certainly knew, for as Sheffield states, he *was* a Mason. Yet Sheffield was clearly familiar with Masonry. The father with whom she so strongly identified long served as the Worshipful Master of the Masonic Lodge in her hometown of Warrenton. Her half-brother, Judge Street, was also a prominent Mason in Marshall County.[113]

Andrew Sheffield, it also should be remembered, was a woman with a man's name. More than in any other instance, these allegations about Masonry suggest the possibility of unresolved gender issues in the shaping of her identity. She not only bore the masculine name, but she lived independently and was clearly male-centered in her family loyalties and identification. The daughter's role was at best muted for her and arguably may have shaded into aspects of a son's role. In any event, her insistence that she was in fact a Mason suggests the possibility that her profoundest sense of identity was troubled or uniquely complex.

More outrageous, though less delusional, was a personal attack on Gov. Johnston the year before. She wrote to him, as she did to all governors, to ask him to remove her from the Hospital on the grounds that she was not insane. She believed that Johnston should transfer her to the women's prison in Wetumpka.[114] Like earlier governors, Johnston wrote back to say that he had no authority over the commitment process and that she could go to the penitentiary only after a conviction on the charge of arson. So, having no authority in her case, he told her to "be cheerful, pleasant, agreeable, and contented."[115]

---

113. Owen, *History of Alabama and Dictionary of Alabama Biography* 4:1540, 1633.
114. See Sheffield to Gov. Johnston, July 17 and July 23, 1897. These letters are located in ADAH.
115. Sheffield to Gov. Johnston, August 3, 1897, ADAH. Johnston's letter to her has not survived, and the quotation above from Johnston is actually a quotation from Sheffield's letter of this date to Johnston. Sheffield often quotes directly from her correspondents back to them, and in every case which can be corroborated, her quotations are accurate. The content of Johnston's letter is inferred from Sheffield's letters to him.

By most accounts, including her own, such docility had never been Sheffield's way, and seven years of forced confinement had clearly failed to nurture this character trait. As a result, Johnston's condescending advice simply infuriated her. In a rash outburst reminiscent of her father's killing of Buck May, she fired off an angry letter that told the Governor his unwillingness to help her was "proof positive that you are not a friend to white weomen, [and] instead [of] favoring the mobbing of negroes for rapeing [*sic*] and murdering little white girls and weomen throughout the State, you are doing all in your power to shield, protect, and defend the negro rapeist."[116]

It was a potent insult which conflated her region's deepest racial fears with the masculine imperative to defend white womanhood. Hardly could Sheffield have constructed a more unladylike or desperate attack on Johnston's honor. Even she soon regretted the assault. Less than a month later, a much chastened Sheffield wrote the Governor and apologized. "I have for several weeks," she said, "felt very much grieved over the insulting note which I sent you. If you will accept an appology [*sic*] from a disgraced and friendless woman I make it." Significantly and characteristically, she tied this apology to the memory of her father (whom Johnston had known): "Were my Father living and knew that I had written such an insulting note to a nice good old gentleman he would be very much mortified over it. Hope you will pardon me and let it pass unnoticed."[117]

But was her initial racist attack on Johnston evidence of insanity? It certainly illuminated the ambiguous and often confusing line between anger and madness. In later years, Sheffield apologized to Dr. Lanford, to whom she had written an insulting letter. "[A]ll my life [I have] had a mania for writing letters—when any of the family or neighbors would offend me in the least—not a word would I say—but would write them a letter." Betraying considerable self-awareness, she continued by saying that the Hospital's doctors and nurses "all think it meanness of me—innate meanness that cause[s] me to write such letters. I don't attribute it altogether to in[n]ate meanness—I hardly know now to account for it— my crave for writing such letters—unless it comes from my sensitive nature[.] I'll admit that I am and always have been very sensitive, and when any little thing worries me, I want to write. I am also revengeful, and when ~~any~~ any thing goes wrong or not to please me I feel that I must

116.   Sheffield to Gov. Johnston, August 3, 1897.
117.   Sheffield to Johnston, September 1, 1897, ADAH.

avenge it.''[118] This penchant for indirect confrontation rather than face-to-face conflict, her "mania for writing letters," is the only madness she ever admitted.

Her doctors understandably viewed the case differently. In his 1896 letter that diagnosed Sheffield as morally insane, Superintendent Searcy reassured Gov. Oates, who was impressed with Sheffield's lucidity, that she had "a constant 'delusion of persecution' on the part of the officials of the Hospital." He then misinformed the Governor that "it has been the case ever since she came." It will be recalled that her initial case notes, made before Searcy worked at the Hospital, clearly found her without any delusions. But during the time that he had known her personally, he found her to be "the most incorrigible and inapproachable woman I ever saw. I have made all sorts of advances to assure her of my kind and best intentions toward her, but have invariably met the most abrupt rebuffs, and most generally abuse and cursing.''[119]

The letters which follow do not allow for easy conclusions. At their heart is the key relationship between Superintendent Searcy and his most troubling patient. Both Sheffield's sanity and Searcy's humanity emerge from this long association a bit blemished. But neither quality is ever totally disproven. Both antagonists, it seems, struggled to defend themselves in a case that not only was frustrating for them, but one that tested the very limits of appropriate institutional care. At a deeper level, the struggle probed the limits of what their lives or life's work meant. In the final analysis, however, there was a vital difference. The Superintendent possessed both power and freedom. Sheffield held but little of either.

118. Sheffield to Lanford, ca. 1910; strikeout in the original. In this letter, she tells Lanford that she will not write any more letters, except an occasional postcard to let others know that she has received their letters. Yet evidently her mania for letter writing continued. Long and sometimes mean-spirited letters from the period after 1910 have survived.
119. Searcy to Oates, January 1, 1896. Gov. Oates had written to Searcy on Dec. 26, 1895, and was deeply impressed with the evidence of sanity he found in Sheffield's letters. Searcy's response was designed to convince him of her insanity.

"I WAS SENT HERE A SANE WOMAN"

1893–1900

During her first decade as a mental patient, Andrew Sheffield tried to convince state authorities, mostly governors, to release her from the Hospital in Tuscaloosa. Her premise was one common to most rebellious asylum patients: she was not insane. But as the letters in this chapter suggest, her similarity with other patients ended there. In none of her letters does she ask for an outright release. Freedom is not the object of the personal crusade found in these letters. Instead, Sheffield insists that as an accused arsonist she should be transferred to the state's penitentiary for women at Wetumpka. So, for the governors she petitioned, the doctors who held her against her will, and the family who sent her to Tuscaloosa, her case presented an odd and troubling face.

Contrariness comprised the metal of her character; rebellion, its chief alloy. During the 1890s, Sheffield lobbied her case before the highest officials of the state—and unfailingly got their attention. Time and again, the state's governors, Joseph F. Johnston in particular, found her rational and articulate. "She is a remarkable woman," Johnston observed on July 29, 1897. But only five days later, angered over his inability to transfer her to the penitentiary, Sheffield wrote the governor an irrational and insulting letter that accused him of favoring the raping of white women by black men. Lucidity and fury thus coexisted in this contrary personality.

This chapter introduces the details of this peculiar woman's life story and charts the dimensions of her character. Sheffield's focus in the following letters is nearly always on herself. But in telling her story to various governors, she reveals much about the routine and folkways of this large Southern asylum. In particular, the nature of her antagonistic relationship with Superintendent James T. Searcy emerges in these early letters. Apart from a fellow patient or two, Searcy was the only person whose tenure spanned the twenty-six years of Sheffield's correspondence.

&

June 15, 1893
SHEFFIELD TO GOV. THOMAS G. JONES[1]

In this, Andrew Sheffield's first surviving letter, she sets a tone and outlines a basic argument that changes only subtly over the next twenty-six years of her confinement. Apart from revealing her deep-seated dislike of those in authority, she also suggests much about the asylum's social arrangements among the various classes of patients.

& &

> Tuscaloosa. Ala.
> June 15th 1893.

Gov. Thomas. G. Jones.
   Montgomery.
      Ala.

     Sir;

     I have been informed by Dr Bondurant[2] that my letter reached you safely.[3] In reply to my letter, you requested Dr Bondurant to write you my true condition *mentally*. When the Dr informed me of this, I remarked to him, what will be your reply? his answer was, ''I shall write him you are Insane.''[4] I beg to be excused for the liberty I take in annoying you with

---

1. There is no evidence that the Governor ever received this letter. So far as can be determined, it is not a copy. The governor may have returned it with his reply as was occasionally the custom of correspondents at the time. It is now located in Sheffield's file in the Medical Records Office of Bryce Hospital in Tuscaloosa.
2. Eugene DuBose Bondurant was the Assistant Superintendent of the Hospital at the time that Sheffield wrote this letter. He had been as assistant physician from 1885 to 1892 and had served briefly as Acting Superintendent in 1892 prior to Searcy's election to the Superintendency. He left the Hospital in 1897 and moved to Mobile, where he had a private practice and served as the dean of the medical school there. He served as a Trustee of the Hospital from 1902 to 1923.
3. Sheffield's earlier letter has not been found. It did reach the Governor, however. A letter in Sheffield's file, dated June 5, 1893, from Jones's personal secretary, J. V. Jemison, to Dr. James T. Searcy acknowledges its receipt.
4. No letter from Bondurant to the Governor has survived.

my many complaints. I have been so unjustly treated here in the Hospital that "Patience has ceased to be a virtue". As I am entirely under your administration, and believing you to be a just and honorable man, I implore and beseech you to send a *disinterested* physician to interview me in person; one that will be governed altogether by principle, and I will willingly abide his decision. If I have been so unfortunate to violate the laws of Moral Society and deserve Capital punishment, please commute my case to the Penitentiary instead of the Insane Hospital. If there, I hope I would be dealt with justly, and that the Warden of the Penitentiary would not allow his empty vanity to get complete controle of his buisness affairs. The physicians here are very, very superficial characters; will give instances of it here in the Hospital. When a patient come here, matters not how poor—what her condition may be financialy, if her personal appearance is all right, a genteel pair of kid gloves on, a No. 2 shoe, and a *gaudy, butterfly* colored necktie, (matters not how crazy she may be) she is placed on a front first class ward, to blaze a paragon of some fashionable Metropolitan; and is seated at the diet table[5] as a special, private, patient; Their diet is next to that of the Dr's and Supervisors, which is perfectly superb, live like Kings and Queens. The nurses have a table set apart for themselves, and have respectable poor "folks" fare. And now come the poor old state paupers,[6] (as we are called) who bear the burdens of the day. Similar to that of a poor old private in war, who does all the work and fighting, receives no pay and get nothing to eat, and subject to the whims of those who have been placed over them. The physicians here carry their personal feeling too much into business affairs. They avail themselves of every low, petty way of taunting and iritating patients causing them to do and say all manner of things, and, for the time, appearing to be *somewhat demented themselves.* They congeal together, swear the patients are crazy to keep them here. If the Penitentiary is bossed altogether by men, you would do me a favor to send me there, for I could willingly be subservient to those in authority having the *master* mind, and competent to order and direct; but I cannot and will not succumb to *petticoat government.* The so called Supervisor[7] is allowed to rule from cellar to garret. If she takes a dislike to a patient (excuse my slang expression) the patient had better be in *Purgatory.* She monopolizes half of their time, twisting her witts as to

5. The diet of the private patients included more variety than that supplied to the indigent inmates such as Sheffield. This included fresh fruits and vegetables and what the staff called "delicacies."
6. The indigent patients, like herself, who were maintained at state expense. Such comprised the overwhelming majority of the patients.
7. Mary Louise Buck.

the best way to taunt and iritate those whom she has taken a dislike for. Is it just that human beings should be thus annoyed in an institution entirely under your controle? All I ask is justice. If I am to remain here, I wish to be treated as well as all low, common uneducated paupers, regardless of what I was sent here for; justice demands it. I am forced to remain on back wards with filthy patients, at the same time, quiet, give no trouble. I ask you as Gov of the State to give me some relief, have me removed from the Hospital or have me put in a quiet part of the house.

A. M. Sheffield.

Guntersville, Alabama
August 21, 1893
JUDGE T. A. STREET TO SEARCY

Sheffield's half-brother is probably responding here to a now-lost letter from Searcy protesting Andrew's ability to mail complaining letters to governors and other authorities.

Dr. J. T. Searcy
Tuskaloosa Ala

Dear Sir: Your letter with inclosure of letter to me from my unfortunate sister was received only on the 19 inst.[8] It was delayed in the mail by some course or others
But in reply to your questions say that I am satisfied her treatment is as good as she will permit her keepers to treat her, and I fully agree with you that she should not be permitted to write letters to whomsoever she wants to, for it can do her no good and I know her well enough to know that she will denounce and abuse any one with whom she comes in contact. I would certainly suppress her letters. She has been insane from childhood and it could do her no good to let her exhaust her dislikes in writing letters.

Yours truly,   T. A. Street.

---

8.   Neither Searcy's nor Sheffield's letter has survived.

Montgomery
December 13, 1895
GOV. WILLIAM C. OATES TO SEARCY

Gov. Oates had been a friend of Sheffield's father and, perhaps out of a sense of obligation, wrote to the Superintendent for more information about Andrew's peculiar case.

Dec. 13th, 1895.

Dr. J. T. Searcy, Supt.,
  Alabama Insane Hospital,
  Tuscaloosa, Ala.

Dear Doctor:

I enclose to you a letter from Miss A. M. Sheffield, which I received last Spring, but it was mislaid and I overlooked it. I have also written to her.[9] Is she the daughter of the late Col. Sheffield of Marshall County? With what crime is she charged and what is her mental condition? Please give me the status of her case? She writes with great intelligence.

Very truly your friend,
W^m C Oates

PS. Please return her letter?

Montgomery
December 26, 1895
GOV. OATES TO SEARCY

---

9. Neither Sheffield's nor the Governor's letters have survived. At the close of this letter, Gov. Oates asks that Searcy return Sheffield's letter. If he did, it has not survived in the Governor's papers.

Searcy's response (now lost) evidently failed to satisfy the Governor. Moreover, Oates had received another letter (also lost) from Sheffield which had deeply impressed him on the question of her sanity.

⅋ ⅋

Dr. J. T. Searcey [*sic*],
        Superintendent Insane Hospital,
                Tuscaloosa, Ala.

My dear Doctor:

I have just read a long letter from Miss A. M. Sheffield,[10] one of your criminal patients, who insists that she is not insane, and from the character of her letters if she is insane a good many people outside of the Hospital would be blessed by a streak of her insanity when it comes to writing letters. She writes splendidly and with great intelligence. She says she had rather go to the Penitentiary than remain any longer in the Hospital. I would like to have her in the Penitentiary as I am trying to establish a reformatory and would like to have her for a teacher, if she is all the time as sane and intelligent as she is when writing me a letter. I knew her father well in the army and after it, and we were good friends. Don't you think that she is entitled to a discharge from your hospital even if she should have to be remanded on the charge of arson? I think she could defend herself decidedly better and more ably than a majority of lawyers could do for her. What were the facts in her case? Was she tried and acquitted on that plea, or before the trial was she committed to the hospital for treatment. You know more about her case than I do, but i am strongly impressed with the idea that she is not insane at this time and if so ⟨according to the circumstances of the case, she⟩[11] is certainly entitled to be discharged or remanded. Please write me, Doctor, all you know about it and your opinion of her case.[12] I feel deeply interested in it and wish to know all about it.

---

10. The letter to which he refers no longer exists. The first surviving letter to Oates is Sheffield's next one, dated December 30, 1895.

11. This material was interlineated in the Governor's hand after the letter was typed.

12. Searcy's formal response to the Governor follows below, but after reading Oates's remarks, he wrote the following notation in pencil at the bottom of this letter:
     Above answered by sending Miss Sheffield's reply to the Governor [her letter of December 30, 1895, that follows], and several of her letters in file, with an opinion of the physicians, since she has been here, of her's being a most typical case of moral insanity,—the most typical in the house.
            Dec. 31. 95.   J. T. S.

I have mislaid you[r] letter about the appointment of a trustee in the place of the late Col. Hargrove. I will find it soon and act upon it.

Very truly yours,

W^m C Oates

Dictated.

PS. Miss Sheffield says that sometimes when a woman of good family goes wrong it is a good dodge to save the family name to send her to the insane asylum. I want her case investigated & thoroughly tested as to her mental condition.[13]

December 26, 1895

SHEFFIELD TO SEARCY[14]

At the same time that Searcy received Oates's preceding letter, Sheffield evidently got one of her own from the Governor, which may have emboldened her. In the following, she negotiates with Searcy about the means of mailing her response to the Governor.

Dr. Searcy,

Read my letter and return it. If you are willing that one of the nurses go with me to town and mail my letter—I'll answer it, otherwise I cannot. I do not object that you read what I write, but I cannot give Gov Oates the full particulars of my scandal & disgrace & send it out there for these Dr's to "giggle" over. If you are willing to do this Send me 4 sheets of large paper.

A. M. S.

---

13. The Governor added this postscript after the letter was typed.
14. Dated by a notation in Searcy's hand: "Received Dec. 26th 95. J. T. S."

≥•

December 30, 1895
SHEFFIELD TO GOV. OATES

Searcy wrote the following notation on this letter: "After two or three days composing it, Miss S. handed me her letter to the Governor—rather more pleasant and less abusive than usual. Dec. 31ˢᵗ." Sheffield provides here the fullest history of her case available from any source. It is important for its details of both fact and emotion.

≥• ≥•

Tuskaloosa. Ala.
Insane. Hospital
Dec 30ᵗʰ 1895.

Gov. W. C. Oates.
Montgomery.
Ala.

Sir;

I have received your letter of the 26ᵗʰ inst.[15] The contents of your letter is all that I could ask. If from the heart, you are a conscientious man. I have never met you, but I know of you through my father. Since your election, I have often thought if you were the Oates I have so often heard him speak of? Often, often, have I heard him speak of you in connection with the war, "Oates of South Ala." You ask that I make a "full disclosure of all the facts in the case, withholding nothing". The question arises, where shall I begin? The trouble with myself, is, that I have to say so much to express a *little*. In justice not only to myself, but to you also, I will make a truthful disclosure—stating positive facts to the best of my knowledge. My incarceration as an insane woman, was not only because I was of a proud and prominent family—that was as I stated in my first letter to you—gotten up here in the Hospital, came to me as Dr. Bryce[16]

---

15. Gov. Oates's letter to Sheffield has not survived. Only Oates's letter to Searcy is in the file.

16. Peter Bryce was the Superintendent of the Alabama Insane Hospital when Sheffield was admitted in 1890. Following his death in 1892, the institution was named Bryce Hospital in his honor.

having made such statements. While I have never known a time that I thought I was insane, those who sent me here, were honest in their confession—firmly believed me insane. Without a doubt I passed for an insane woman in Marshall Co. for ten years previous to my imprisonment here. To commence at the first—the spring of 1880 I had as many have, a disappointment in love, which was the first disappointment, the first cross of my life, consequently I was not prepared for it—and being naturaly of a very high temperament—of a nervous and excitable nature, I was not able to hold up under it—and was raving and frantic—*not with insanity*—but from grief and trouble, heartbroken; and, the only cause I can assign for not being sent to the Hospital at that time was my fathers *love* for his child—not wanting to throw me off at the mercy of others— and, stain my life with the Insane Asylum. He did all that money could do to heal my broken heart, gave me travel—spent his money with a lavish hand—and from this trouble I became adicted to the bad habit of taking opiates—and was for four years a chloral drinker[17]—drank it until it almost destroyed my life, and when taken from me at the end of four years I was no more than a walking skeleton, except that I was breathing. Of course, during this time, I did many things that caused my relatives, friends, and neighbors to think me of unsound mind; and I suppose I was—from the effects of opiate—I don't suppose that one could feel, or be perfectly natural under the influence of an opiate. And in the midst of this trouble another (the worst of all) unexpectedly came, my fathers financial failure having failed in his mercantile buisness in 1882. In his old age—his declining years, reduced to poverty (mans worst enemy) thrown *financialy* on a level with the common herd. I again sought relief through the *chloral* bottle, drank it for a year—and taken from me again, but my troubles remained with me, steadfast. In the spring I think, of 1885—my father got employment in the State Superintendents office at Montgomery under Maj Sol Palmer.[18] I was comfortably situated and well provided for at my home in Warrenton Marshall Co. In the fall of 1888 my health failed—was in wretched health. My father wrote Dr. L. D. Lusk of Guntersville Ala to mind me, and, give me the best medical attention possible, he did so—but he was five miles away, and I was situated so that I

---

17. Chloral hydrate was a drug commonly used in the late nineteenth century for its sedative effects. It sometimes became addictive. See, for example, Dr. T. D. Crothers's discussion of "chloralism" in *The Drug Habits and Their Treatment* (Chicago: G. P. Engelhard, 1902), 86–92.

18. Solamon Palmer, a long-time friend of the Sheffields from Marshall County. He was elected State Superintendent of Education in 1884 and served until 1890. James Sheffield stayed in the State Superintendent's office until his death in 1892.

could not call him in when needed—a distance of five miles; and from mere necessity and convenience Dr Wm May[19] of Warrenton was called in—and although a practicing physician and *Dr* for his title—was a man devoid of gentlemanly principals—low traits of character and while I felt it degratory to my high standing to have him attend me, necessity forced it. His prescription was—much to my joy *chloral* having been deprived the *much loved stuff* for several years, my father having notified Dr's May and Smith of Warrenton that if they sold me an opiate he would prosicute them. During his visits he furnished me with chloral by the quantity. Not wanting to *smooth* or *plaster* over, (for the stain on my character will remain,) I can truthfully say that he accomplished my ruin in, and through the chloral bottle alone; proof is this, I was 39 years of age—at that time—had for years been of age, my own woman, and had I been passionately fond of men—I could have gone astray while younger. Now for the *crime*, after he had accomplished my ruin and had me (as he said) "where he wanted" me—proposed that I seek revenge for him by applying the torch to my nearest neighbors dwelling a Mr Richard Anderson whose family I had all my life been intimately associated with—and entertained the greatest of kind feeling for, and would not of my own will have harmed a yard dog of his, for having been raised up togather—gone to school together—played when children together—I loved him as a brother. He, Dr May and Mr Richard Anderson had for years been at "daggers points["]— and "armed to the teeth" for each other. A refusal on my part to apply the torch enraged him so much, that I through fear of the man almost abandoned my house entirely for several months; and when at home even in day time—I for months sit with closed and locked doors to avoid him. When convinced that I would not willingly seek revenge for him, as an inducement he proposed to pay me—after having my word for it that money would be no inducement—he then resorted to *threats,* that if I failed he would "expose me publicaly and leave the country[.]" Would come to my house intoxecated, and when in a rage several times drew his pistol from his pocket, and I beged him to use it and I realy wanted him to kill me—he all this while keeping me well supplied with chloral, took special interest in the chloral bottle—to see that it was kept filled, and at his own expense. He paved and planned the way that I should go to the house—prepared the kindling on the back porch of my house—loosened a panel of Mr Andersons garden fence; unwilling to go with me—I must

---

19.   Note that this is only a partial account. Sheffield leaves the impression that she had not known May before this, but in fact she had known him at least since 1880, when, according to the manuscript census, he boarded in her and her father's house.

go alone, and apply the torch. You said in your letter that you supposed that my "devotion for the man was such that induced me to commit the crime". Such was not the case, for I was not devoted to him in the least; for realy he and myself were not and had not been for years, good friends—for I never like him as a man, but on speaking terms. I was not without protection my brother Judge Street and his son O. D. Street, and my father, but I knew what the result of an exposure of the matter would be—and I knew not who—would receive the load of lead—as for Dr May I would not have said one word or taken one step to have saved his life, but my *relatives* exposed, for as a matter of course, I knew that to expose the matter would end in the shedding of blood. After it was all over I could then see very plainly that he planed it all in a way that I would be suspicioned, and was—; arrested and taken to Guntersville and placed behind the bars—and several days afterwards I was taken to the court house and given what I *think* was a *preliminary trial,* returned to prison—and afterwards tried for lunacy and sent here. My father came from Montgomery visited me in prison—the morning afterwards killed Dr Wm May in my sisters house at Warrenton. To the very best of my knowledge I have written you the positive facts concerning the whole affair. I want you to distinctly understand that. I did not appeal to you thinking that I could, or wanting to gain my liberty, freedom through you, for I am not entitled to my freedom—neither do I want it. My only reason for writing you was this; I have been here almost six years, Superintendents and the physicians agreeing with me that I was not an insane woman, but of sound mind[.] In that respect they have been my friends—and now if they would only declare the same to the outside world—they could give me a lifetime home at Wetumpka[20]—where I had rather be, than here a *criminal.* Their word for it, that I was of sound mind when sent here, and my treatment in some respects, has long since convinced me, that I'm not worthy a cell in the Insane Asylum, but justly desire a lifetime home a Wetumpka. In some respects I have been treated in a way to cause me to feel that my presence here, will reflect on the better class, and rob them of their *virtue.* I have no desire whatever to set at liberty, there is no inducement in the out world for me, for if out and free, *I'd* be a penniless prostitute—and—as a matter of course *friendless.* I have no friends in the out world, no more than I have here. If tried I could only be acquitted on the grounds of having been demented at the time the crime was committed, that I object to, for one reason, I know that I was not insane—besides I've had the Supt & Dr's word for it that I was not. All I desire is to be placed before the grand jury

---

20. Site of the state's prison for women.

of Marshall Co—the Supt Dr's Somerville,[21] Bondurant and Wright
forced to appear in person, and swear there, what they have often said
here; I can't say positively that Dr. Somerville ever told that I was of
sound mind—but he heard Dr Bryce tell me that I was not insane. No jury,
if I could prevent it, should acquit me on the plea of insanity. I have, and
I always had a greater horror for an Asylum than for the Penitentiary.
They, of course have it in their power to make it either pleasant or unpleasant for sane patients—and do make it pleasant for some of the sane
indigents. The newspapers speak of Dr Searcy as being a good man—and
I have no right to dispute it, and if I did it would amount to nothing for as
he told me this morning that there was no rein over him—that he bossed
this institution as he pleased regardless of law. I do not know that their
unkind treatment to *aged* prostitutes and criminals is any evidence whatever of meanness on their part—for I don't say that we deserve even humane treatment. You say you have known many "good weomen to be
guilty of indiscretions, and still be good weomen," would to God that the
officers of this institution were of the same mind. As for my character—I
do not want the sympathy of no one, for I know I'll never get it—my age
and sense would not admit of any plastering over—farther than I can say
that had I wanted to have lived a disreputable life—I could have when
young for when young, I passed for a very *handsome* woman—although
no traces of beauty to be seen now—that I'm old. I do not reflect on the
citizens of Marshall for sending me here—and although my brother Judge
Street has made no inquiry as to my condition, taken no notice of me since
my imprisonment here, I do not reflect on him, for he believed me an insane woman. The Dr's here very soon decided that I was not of unsound
mind—and I blame them for keeping me here, for if I have to spend my
remaining years in prison, I'd like to be *legally* imprisoned. If I was a responsible being as the Dr's here claim—I'm no better to suffer the penalty
than many others, guilty of the same offense. I'm for justice in all things.
I want you to write Dr's Somerville—Wright Bondurant and the Supt have
their word for it—as to whether I'm an insane woman or not. If not insane,
and was not when sent here then you have me sent to Guntersville—placed
before the grand jury—tried for arson—in first-degree. This is all I ask of
you. I never want to be tried unless the physicians here, testify to my sanity *when sent here*[.] There is but one way that I would *willingly* go to
trial—and that is for the Dr's to swear that I was *sent here* a sane

21.   William G. Somerville was the assistant physician who had examined and admitted
      Sheffield on her arrival at the Hospital in 1890. He left the asylum in 1891, but later
      served as a Trustee from 1893 to 1910.

woman—otherwise I do not want to be tried. I do not want to go out of the Hospital, and sent back to it, no I do not—neither do I want to be tried and acquitted on the grounds of having been demented at the time the crime was committed. If insane when sent here, I'm so yet. I repeat, that all I ask of you to do for me is to write—Dr's Searcy, Somerville, Bondurant and Wright making inquiry as to the condition of my mind when sent here, and through my six years here—if they say I came here a sane woman and remained sane, the whole of the six years up to the present time, then have me sent to Marshall. I never want to see Guntersville or be tried unless I'm hanged or sent to the Penitentiary. And I'm satisfied with my charge to the jury that they would not acquit me; for I could give my charge as well as the Judge give his. So far as my brain is concerned I had not had a friend—for ten or twelve years—until I came to the Hospital, these men are right, they agree with me—that my brain was, & is yet in a healthy condition. I thank you kindly for your sympathy expressed for me in your letter—you are the only one I've had a sympathetic word from since from my Father. If the officers here have entertained any sympathy of kind feeling for me they have managed well to keep it hidden—for I've had no evidence of it. With many good wishes for your happiness and welfare. I am.

A. M. Sheffield

Tuscaloosa

January 1, 1896

SEARCY TO GOV. OATES

The following is Searcy's response to the Governor's letter of December 26. He probably mailed it with Sheffield's preceding letter. In it, he supplies the most concise known diagnosis of Sheffield by any doctor.

Jan. 1st. 1896.

To Gov. William C. Oates,
    Montgomery, Ala.

My Dear Sir:—

I am glad that you seem interested in the case of Miss Sheffield. You are not the first one that she has interested. She was one of the first patients in the Hospital whose case I investigated when I took charge. She has written numbers of letters to prominent men over the State, and has been writing them ever since she came to the Hospital. Some of them have been placed on file; numbers of them have been sent, until stopped by request of her family.[22] I send you some of them, from which you can see the tenor of her mind. Those not sent as addressed, have been sent to her brother, or have been placed on file; we have quite a number of them. I will be glad to have you return those I send you, as they are kept on file.[23] All stopped correspondence is placed on file.

She has a constant "delusion of persecution" on the part of the officials of the Hospital; it has been the case ever since she came.[24] Besides that, she is the most incorrigible and inapproachable woman I ever saw. I have made all sorts of advances to assure her of my kind and best intentions toward her, but have invariably met the most abrupt rebuffs, and most generally abuse and cursing.

Because she has been so disagreeable to the other patients and to the employes, she has largely been let alone. No one can enter pleasantly her room without violent attack of abuse. At some intervals, and to some persons at intervals, she is approachable. She is very violent toward any one in authority in the house. This had, I learn, been her character for years before she came here.

She does not seem to have the least regard for public or private opinion. Her accusations against the officers of the Hospital and her statements of abuse are utterly without foundation, in every instance of which I have heard. She misconstrues every statement made to her, to suit her points.

If by insanity you mean such an inherently defective mental condition that the person cannot live outside of a house of restraint, without being a menace and a danger to themselves or others, she certainly fills that construction. She is always cited in the Hospital as a most typical case of "*moral insanity*".[25] Highly intelligent in most respects, she is bitterly insensible to all attempts at kindness to her, and hostile in her feelings towards all who have authority over her. We have not a more unpleasant patient in the Hospital to deal with. She has seemed some better in deportment of late, so last Spring we had her placed on one of our best wards. She has always had a good comfortable room, and as good fare as

---

22.   T.A. Street's above letter to Searcy, dated August 21, 1893, may have been the source of Searcy's statement here.
23.   There is no way to determine which letters Searcy sent to the Governor.
24.   Searcy is inaccurate here. Sheffield's case history states that she had no known delusions when she came to the Hospital. See *Case History Book #6*, p. 185.
25.   Nowhere in her surviving file did any of the doctors diagnose her as morally insane. Neither was moral insanity a diagnostic category commonly used in this Hospital.

any of the other patients. At her own instance, and because she is so ir-
reconcilable with others, she has had a seat and plate at a side table in the
dining room.

She seems entirely insensible to any kindness shown by me or others,
and puts a wrong construction on it. I believe at large she would be a constant danger. Her relatives all know her; write to them if you like. [S]he
has some full brothers and sisters, who never write about her. Judge Street,
of Guntersville, is her half-brother. He is a most excellent man, and writes
very feelingly about her. She will probably give you any amount of correspondence. Something may at some time occasion her displeasure, when
you will get her abuse. Of late she has been in her most pleasant mood.

She has been most of the time kept on the demented ward[26] where she
could not find patients to disaffect with her abuse of the officials, (she is
exceedingly good at it.) and where she could not frighten others with her
horrible tales.

> I am
> Yours very truly,
> J. T. Searcy SUP'T

Ward No. 14

July 17, 1897

SHEFFIELD TO GOV. JOSEPH F. JOHNSTON[27]

*This is the first in a revealing series of letters that Sheffield wrote to
Gov. Johnston, who, like Oates, had known her father.*

> Tuscaloosa. Ala.
> Insane. Hospital.
> July 17. 1897.

Gov. J. F. Johnston.
    Montgomery.
        Ala.

  Sir;

---

26. The back wards.
27. This letter is in ADAH.

I have heretofore appealed to Ex Gov's Jones and Oates, and of no avail. I will now try you; from what I can gather from the newspapers, it seems that you are interesting yourself more in prisoners, and prison affairs than any Gov heretofore, (that is the convicts and penitintiary)[.] I am a daughter of Col. J. L. Sheffield who died at Montgomery 1892. The Spring of 1890 I was charged with *Arson* in first degree, adjudged insane; and sent to the Hospital to remain until recovered from what the *incapacitated* physicians of Marshall Co claimed to be insanity. Gov Oates wrote me very encouraging, asking that I give him a "true and full account of my case;" in my very ignorant and simple way, I explained to him as best I could, "from start to finish." I heard no more from him except that the "Supt had sent him a copy of my history as given at the Hospital." The Supt afterwards told me that he ("Gov Oates["]) did not ask that he or the physicians give their opinion as to my mental condition." It was doing me a great injustice to use my history as given in here—from the fact, when I came here—I passed the medical board[28] as a sane woman. The Supt and his physicians have repeatedly told me that "I was not an insane woman when sent to the Hospital;"[29] but not withstanding this I have been detained here, on top of my many pleads and earnest solicitations to be sent away. According to what the Supt and physicians say I should have spent the past seven years at Wetumpka, undergoing a life sentence. As a matter of course it will seem strange to you, (as would to many others,) that one should prefer a home in the Penitentiary, rather than in the Hospital; and so it would seem strange to me, had I not spent seven years here as a "deep dyed criminal." I am not wanting to berate the Hospital—I can say a great deal of good for it; it is a nice good home for a crazy woman who cannot be kept at home; and, a nice good home for a sane woman if sent here for insanity, and under a good character, for that class, as a general thing, have the sympathy, respect, and kind feeling of the authorities; unfortunately for me, I came to them for crime, and down into the lowest depths of *prostitution* and *degradation*. As for the crime for which I'm charged I'm guilty—but not of my own will. It was not the insane workings of an unbalanced mind that caused me to commit the crime, neither

---

28. There was nothing so formal as a medical board that evaluated incoming patients. The admitting physician, who in Sheffield's case was W. G. Somerville, did examine carefully their patients' states of mind. Certainly in difficult cases that involved prominent persons (as hers did), all the doctors, including the Superintendent, would have taken an interest.

29. While Sheffield is clearly quoting the spoken word here, no existing written document supports this statement.

was it committed through ignorance; I'll admit my ignorance, at the same
time, I'm not one of dense—impenetrable—and unwholesome ignorance.
I am not wanting to be removed from the Hospital, with a hope of gaining
my freedom and liberty, no such thoughts enter my mind—I'm aware that
I'm doomed to prison, but as I am not guilty of deliberate, premeditated
murder, I think justice demands my punishment be lessened by giving me
a lifetime home at Sprigness Farm[30] or a "hemp necktie" either of which
is preferable rather than spend the remaining years of my life here, locked
in with filthy incurably insane weomen—As a matter of course the patients are classified as near as can be, and as a matter of fact, the crime for
which I'm charged, has thrown me on the back wards with the filthy, dirty
faced, browsy headed lunatics, nothing to hear but the unearthly shrieks of
the maniacs, nothing to see but the poor incurably insane beings, nothing
for the mind or body to feast upon, deprived of books or papers, in fact
deprived of every thing which might lighten confinement and pass the
dreary hours. The Supt told me two years ago that I was not insane but "if
sent out of the Hospital and sent to the Penitentiary would disgrace my
kin". His sympathy is running in the wrong channel. I'll acknowledge my
ignorance in regard to law, but it does seem that if a Gov could pardon a
man murderer undergoing a life sentence, that he could have a sane criminal removed from an Insane Asylum.[31] When a criminal is sent here, and
pronounced sane by these eminent insanity experts, and the criminal not
contented to remain here, (and prefer the Penitentiary) and the Supt refuse
to send the criminal out, I think the Gov should interfere, have them removed from the Hospital, placed before the grand jury, and given the full
benefit of the law. I would gladly go into any county jail—and contend
with all the *filth* and *vermin* which might be placed there, my meals served
on a tin plate and iron fork, than remain locked in on the back wards of
this Hospital, to be worried, agrevated and tormented by the crazy. I know
what the Penitentiary is as well as you do; it is hard work, starvation, and
mean treatment, but I would gladly accept all of that to be freed from this.
If I must spend my life within the walls of brick and mortar, for God Sake
let it be at Wetumpka. There are worse criminals than I, who have escaped
the penalty of the courts, and gone free through the schemes of a shrewd
lawyers work, but I dont expect that. You will remember when here,[32] you
passed through a ward off from the main part of the building, a desolate,
gloomy, dismal place—entirely surrounded by a high brick wall—(the

---

30. Sprigness Farm was the correctional facility for women located at Wetumpka.
31. Alabama's governor had no such power.
32. The Governor, who was an ex-officio member of the institution's Board of Trustees,
     evidently had visited the Hospital recently.

criminal ward)[33] I occupy a cell on that ward, have not seen outside the walls for days, weeks, and months, and can't say that I ever will unless sent out of the Hospital. These men treat the disgraced class as well as most men would, and no doubt better than some would, but I know from very sad experience, that they have no sympathy for an aged prostitute or criminal. Will you please let me hear from you if you can or cannot have me removed from the Hospital, be positive, plain, I dont mean that I want you to write to the Supt but to me—I am thoroughly competent to attend to my own affairs, without the aid or assistance of any one on the Hospital grounds. Should you write to the Supt have him and his assistants to spend their opinion as to my mental condition, and if they say to you, as they have boldly said within the walls of the prison, you will have no reason for not having me removed from the Hospital. Hoping to hear from you at your earliest convenience. I am Miss. A. M. Sheffield.

Tuskaloosa.
Insane. Asylum.} Ala.

≈●

Montgomery
July 19, 1897
GOV. JOHNSTON TO SHEFFIELD

Like Oates, Gov. Johnston attempted to show some personal concern for Sheffield.

≈● ≈●

July 19th 1897

Miss A. M. Sheffield
Tuscaloosa Ala

Dear Miss

      I have just finished reading your letter of the 17th inst. I knew your father and knew him to be a gallant Confederate soldier and a

---

33. Sheffield is referring to a building usually called the Annex, also known as Ward No. 14, that was originally built for black inmates. The "criminal ward" is Sheffield's name for the ward, which included many who had committed no crime; it is not the name used by the officials of the institution.

good man and citizen. I know nothing at all of your case. If I ever heard any particulars they now escape me. I am here to see that the laws are faithfully executed, and our laws are sufficient to protect every one in life, liberty and property if faithfully enforced. I gather from your letter that you were charged with Arson but before trial put upon trial for insanity, pronounced insane and sent to the Asylum. *You will understand of course that what Dr Searcy would say about your case would have great weight, because he is a man of such high character that one would be very reluctant in believing that he would report other than the matter as he sees it.*[34] I will by this mail request a report from him: under §8 of the Act approved Feb 27th 1889 the Com^n of Lunacy can examine you and when [with] their recommendation I discharge you or take such action as may seem best. If you desire your case examined in that way let me know and I will consider it in connection with the report of Dr Searcy.

Yours Respy
Jos. T. Johnston Govr

You may rest assured that any doubt I may have shall always be resolved in favor of the unfortunate and distressed.[35]

Tuscaloosa

July 22, 1897

SEARCY TO GOV. JOHNSTON

In the following letter, Searcy betrays a sense of exasperation with his difficult and articulate patient.

Tuscaloosa, Ala., July 22^d. 1897.

To Governor Jos. F. Johnston.

---

34. The italicized material was not emphasized by the Governor, but by Sheffield. This sentence evidently upset her and in the right-hand margin of the letter, she wrote: "For God sake let the truth come that I was sent here a sane sound minded woman and to keep me out of the Penitentiary."
35. The Governor wrote this sentence in the left-hand margin of the letter.

My Dear Sir:

    I sent you Miss. Sheffield's letter several days ago. I think she wrote it more for my benefit, than for you; for the same reason, she has just now sent me her reply. . . . I have not heard from a person, who knows them[36] at their homes, who is at all willing for them to be at large. If I offer to give them a trial,[37] at once I have protests against it. I would be very glad to let either go, if I thought I could safely do so.

Very respectfully,
J. T. Searcy
Supt, &c.

July 23, 1897

SHEFFIELD TO GOV. JOHNSTON

This letter encapsulates Sheffield's dilemma. She interprets her options very narrowly: the asylum or the penitentiary.

Tuskaloosa. Ala.
Insane. Hospital
July 23. 1897.

Gov. J. F. Johnston.
    Montgomery.
      Ala.

    Sir;—

    Yours to hand[38]—Dr Searcy informed me three years ago, that I could not be examined by a commission of lunacy, from the fact, that I was not tried for Arson before sent here. And I think it unnecessary, and object to it for this reason; the Sup't and physicians of this institution are

---

36. This letter also refers to another patient, a man with a history similar to Sheffield's.
37. In other words, if he would allow them to return to stand trial on the charges pending against them.
38. Johnston to Sheffield, July 19, 1897.

considered eminent insanity experts—having had many years experience with the insane, made *insanity* their study for years; besides I read the papers[39] sent here with me stating that when recovered the Supt was to send me out. (They say I was "not insane", for that reason there has been no recovery[.]) Dr. W. G. Somerville now a resident of Tuskaloosa, was a physician here, in charge of the weomens department for a year after I came here. Dr. E. D. Bondurant who is now in charge of same, and has been for thirteen years has seen more or less of me every day for the past seven years—had daily conversations with me, as has also Dr's Searcy and Wright. Have they not a better idea as to the conditions of my mind, than a commission of lunacy would have after questioning and crossquestioning me for fifteen or twenty minutes? I want Dr's Searcy, Wright[,] Bondurant and Somerville to seal my fate, they are the men to pass sentence upon me, so far as concerns the condition of my *brain*. And you are the man to force them to do it. Force them to state to you the condition of my mind when sent here, and through my seven years stay; Dr Searcy has never given me any reason for keeping me here except that I was not insane when sent here, and if sent out could "disgrace my kin for I'd be sent to the Pen"—And again Supt and Dr's would tell me that if "sent back to Marshall would be sent back here, rather than send me to the Penitentiary". I would naturaly dread to come here a second time—more than did the first; "A burnt child dreads the fire." They tell the truth when they say that I was sent here a sane woman—for I was—and my mind is the same now as was when sent here—perfectly sound, my brain in a healthy condition—no change except in my personal appearance—as a matter of course I've lost all my pride as to my personal appearance—having dragged round on the filthy back wards of this institution, and slept, eaten, and associated altogether with the incurably insane for seven years. I'm not fishing for freedom and liberty—I'm wanting to be removed from among the filthy, incurably insane of this institution. I'm forty-eight years of age, have spent the best part of my life, consequently I'm perfectly reconciled to prison—if the Supt will only aid and assist me in getting a lifetime home at Sprigness farm. My treatment is my objection to the Hospital, although I've made but little complaint, for as you say—the Supt is a "man of such high character"[40] that no one would credit a complaint coming from any patient entrusted to his care; And besides I have had such treatment as is given other weomen criminals, but the best of treatment given the insane—such as their condition calls for, is compelled

---

39. Commitment papers. Sheffield's original commitment papers have not survived.
40. This is a direct quotation from Johnston's letter to Sheffield, July 19, 1897.

to be punishment to a sane sensible woman, more especially one reared far above the common herd. If I'm sent to the Penitentiary I want the evidence of these Dr's to send me there—if I'm hanged I want their evidence to hang me, if I'm held a prisoner here, their evidence must hold me. If you favor me with a removal from the Hospital, I've one request to make of you, see that the supt and Dr's are sworn in the presence of Sheriff that I was "sent here a sane woman and to keep me out of the Penitentiary." I *never* did approve of sending sane criminals through by the insanity route, and did not in my own case, and the Supt and Dr's have talked to me in a way—(and in my treatment also) until I'm convinced that I justly deserve an imprisonment here, and that it would be the greatest sin of my life did I allow a jury to acquit me. I'm *perfectly* reconciled to prison, but I want the prison that I justly deserve.

> A. M. Sheffield.
> Tuskaloosa.
> Asylum. Ala.

July 23, 1897
SHEFFIELD TO SEARCY[41]

Sheffield probably handed this note to Searcy on his morning rounds. Searcy later sent it to Gov. Johnston as evidence of her mental state.

Dr. Searcy.

This is the last effort I'll ever make to get out of the Hospital, and for heaven's sake tell the truth that I was sent here a sane woman, and to keep

---

41. Across the top of this note is the following, written by Searcy in his own hand:
> Hospital. July 23d /97
> Dear Governor:—
>   Enclosed find other communications from Miss Sheffield. She has been told all along the opinion of the Doctors about her. She has selected her line—to go to the Penitentiary as a delusion & will hear nothing else.
> Respy,
> J. T. Searcy
Searcy evidently sent the note which Sheffield had written to him along to the Governor, who then returned it with his answer.

me out of the Penitentiary. The Gov as good as says that your word will be
the law, and as my future is in your hands I hope you will favor me by
aiding me in getting a home at Sprigness farm. You know that as long as
Dr Bondurant lives, he will be here, and you also know that as long as I'm
here he will keep me on the back wards. You know that I've had a hard
time here, and you know that it has gone hard with me—as much so as
would with one of your daughters if forced to spend seven years on the
back wards of this Hospital, with exactly the same treatment that I have
had. He kept me on [wards] 9-7-10 and 12 five years and nothing particular against me, now, that he has cause to dislike me I cant expect anything
else. Had you sent me from 12 to [ward] five four years ago or even sent
me from 8 to 5 two years ago when I asked you I would not have been here
today. Mrs McDonald[42] can sit on No. 5 and curse to her hearts content
and it is all right, for Dr Bondurant is her friend. Were I called on to give
in my reasons for claiming to have had mean treatment here, (aside from
every thing else) I'd only give in that one reason keeping me on the filthy
back wards; refusing me a cell on No 5 convinced me that I justly deserve
an imprisoned life. Now let the truth come, and favor me with giving me
a home at Sprigness farm. Do by me as you would want one to do by one
of yours if here in my place, and you know they were treated as I am.
Some day you may be better prepared to sympathize with poor Judge
Somerville[43] than now—little do you know what your boys and girls will
do for you before you die.

A. M. S.

Montgomery

July 29, 1897

GOV. JOHNSTON TO SEARCY

*While the Governor continued to voice tacit agreement with Searcy's
views, he also rises to Sheffield's defense in this letter. Searcy could hardly
have read it as a ringing endorsement.*

---

42.   A fellow patient.
43.   A local judge whose children had him committed.

ze ze

July 29 1897

J. T. Searcy
Tuskaloosa Ala

Dear Doctor   I thank you for the full reports in the cases of Miss Sheffield and Hickman: She is a remarkable woman. What do you think of trying her in some of the better wards and see if she appreciates: I will write her and Hickman both by this mail, and give them some good advice, and I trust that it will do them good.[44] I am quite sure that you would give them the benefit of any doubts; of course I would not presume to advise one of your great skill and wisdom and experience, but it seems to me that in some cases the reports attach too much importance to some acts. I mean as evidence of insanity; e.g., getting mad and raising cain. We all do that sometimes and possibly with just as little cause as the insane.

Yours very truly
Jos. T. Johnston
Gov[r]

ze

Ca. July 1897
SHEFFIELD TO SEARCY[45]

In the following, Sheffield betrays her emotional life, showing especially the delicate line between anger and depression that she nearly always walked.

ze ze

44. Hickman was a male patient who, like Sheffield, had complained to the Governor.
45. Dated by Sheffield's reference to the "past five years" under Searcy, who took over the Superintendency following Bryce's death in 1892. Later in the letter she also refers to the "past seven years" that she had been in the Hospital.

Dr. Searcy.

If you have not sent my letter to Dr Somerville,[46] I'd like that you
send it, for if I do not hear from him, I will write him through the papers.
I did not write it for yours or Dr Bondurants benefit. If you are willing,
and will send the letters out, send me six or eight sheets of paper today,
and I will write to others. I wish you would send me away, or, quit having
me to write so many letters, for I'm tiard [sic] of it; have a perfect horror
of paper and pen. You told me friday that I ought to go out and make my
support—had you done your duty I would have been in the Penitentiary at
work—earning my bread for the past five years. You also said that you
would write the Sheriff to come for me, take me back, try me, and turn me
loose, *I'll be there at* the turning loose. I'm not afraid of being turned
loose. No jury will acquit me after hearing my charge. The men of Marshall had the advantage of me, sent me here against my will—but as for an
acquittal I have the advantage—and I will use it. I dont want to be acquitted, and I will not be. I want to be dealt with as though I was a "nig-
ger" or poor white mans sister, given a home at the Penitentiary. You
order the Sheriff to come for me—have a justice of peace, and Dr Somerville to come out, and you, Somerville, and Bondurant, swear in the
presence of the Sheriff, that I was sent here a sane woman—responsible—
and for no cause but to keep me out of the Penitentiary. I have gone
through with too much the past seven years, to think that I deserve any
thing except punishment, I justly deserve lifetime imprisonment in the
State Penitentiary, and there, I want to go. My punishment here has confirmed that belief. When you came here I could have liked you, I wanted
to like you as a prison master. I even made my *brags* that when you were
Supt I'd get off the back filthy wards; it was reasonable to suppose that as
you had children of your own,[47] you would be merciful on other peoples.
Had you sent me from No 12 to No 5 when I asked you five years ago I
would to day have been a free woman. I have never given a nurse any trouble, gotten along with them—better than most of the patients—kept myself and cell in order—made no noise or filth—but still you allowed me
punished with the filth and insanity of the Hospital, until I'm now com-

---

46. Probably Dr. W. G. Somerville, who was an assistant physician between 1889 and
    1891. He was the physician who received her into the Hospital. This is not the "Judge
    Somerville" mentioned in the preceding letter.
47. Superintendent Bryce and his wife never had any children. Until 1900, all the other
    doctors were required by institutional policy to be unmarried, and therefore they too
    had no children. After 1900, it was rare that a married doctor worked at the Hospital.
    Searcy had twelve children.

pletely *demoralized—dehumanized*. I say that any woman, who is not good enough to occupy a cell on No 5 ward dont deserve an acquittal. I attribute all to my treatment here. I dont think that you have allowed me punished with the filth and insanity because you thought I deserved it, I think it was for an effect. I think that it was done to drive me out a fugitive, or reconcile me to an acquittal, I am not a subject for a pet or favorite here—and I have not expected any favors—and have not asked for any. I am under no obligations to any of you, except, you, have allowed me to work for nurses, make a little money,[48] to clothe my back, and you may be assured that I appreciate & thank you for that privilege, for it has enabled me to wear decent clothing. I will ever feel grateful to you for that. Now Dr Searcy I'm at your mercy, and it is your duty to send me back to Marshall and when you wish to do so you order the Sheriff for me—and be sure that you have Dr. Somerville and justice of peace here, for I propose to go out right—or not at all. Please never mention an acquittal to me again,[49] for it makes me mad, causes me to write letters, for no good—for Jesus Christ, and all the Angels of Heaven could not change my head, so far as an acquittal is concerned; I would if acquitted stick fire to the new twenty five thousand dollar courthouse at Guntersville, I'd burn out every juryman, if acquitted, and I'd tell them so before tried. You do your duty and you can put me where I will have to earn my living and never have an opportunity of burning a house. No woman, not good enough to stay on No 5—attend service at the chappel, attend the picnics, and amusements dont deserve her freedom. If Dr Bondurant should throw Mrs McDonald off on a filthy back ward (while in one of his fits of temper) would you allow him to keep her there ~~five~~ seven years? No—for so far as you know, her character is spotless—here for insanity. My life here has been one of punishment—privation, have not been comfortably situated in my cell. Deprived of every comfort. I am ready for the Penitentiary—and I want to go there, for it is the propper place for me. I have shared all the bad—been deprived the good of the Hospital—but I know from experience that the filth and insanity is far the worst punishment given sane patients. I have had enough to make me mean—associated with the crazy, filthy, low-raised, ignorant of this Hospital. My treatment—punishing me with the filth and insanity of this prison has determined me against an acquittal. It

---

48. A reference to her participation in the "fancy work" industry run by the nurses.
49. Searcy evidently told her that she could be acquitted on the charge of arson on the grounds that she was insane at the time. Such an acquittal was unacceptable to her, because the trial judge would simply have remanded her to Searcy's custody in Tuscaloosa. The procedure would have vindicated Searcy and Sheffield's family, but not her.

was a mistaken idea of Dr Bondurants that to punish me with the filth and insanity of the prison, would send me out a fugitive, or reconcile me to an acquittal; (the smartest of men some times make the broadest mistakes)[.] No patient ever wanted to leave the Hospital as much as I do, but I must leave right. I want justice and will have it if my tongue and hands will give it. I hope you will do me the favor, never to mention an acquittal, or, "turn loose" to me again. I'll be there at the "turning loose".

A. M. Sheffield.

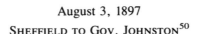

August 3, 1897
SHEFFIELD TO GOV. JOHNSTON[50]

Sheffield's response to a letter from the Governor that has not sur-vived, the following note, colored with both anger and racism, reveals her at her most irrational.

Tuskaloosa. Ala.
Aug 3rd. 1897.

Gov. J. F. Johnston.
Montgomery.
Ala.

Sir;—

Unasked for kindness is not every time unthankfully received by myself—but I'm sorry to say that the advice given me in yours of the 23rd [51] was little appreciated.
I'm much oblige for your sympathy (if from the heart) but, you may be assured that the sympathy of the people is not what I am wanting. Of what good is the sympathy of others to me? In what way could it be of benefit to me?

---

50. This letter is in ADAH.
51. This letter no longer exists, but in his letter to Searcy of July 29, 1897, Gov. Johnston does say that he is also writing to Sheffield in order to give her some "good advice."

It is an easy matter for one to say what they would do if in anothers place; were you in my place, and, I in yours, holding the highest office within the gift of the people of the State of Ala, a four thousand dollar salary, wearing, eating, and drinking the very best, riding round in fine carriages, sailing round on the cars from one place to another, all at the States expense, I could well offord [*sic*] to give you the same advice you gave me, "be cheerful, pleasant, agreeable, and contented." I had but little hope that you would favor and befriend me, but that little hope caused me to call on you. Were I a man (more especialy a negro,) undergoing a sentence in the penitentiary for *rapeing* some white child or woman, my appeal would have met your approval, you would have had me out of the penitentiary with the hope of getting my vote, and influence hereafter. Upholding such is proof positive that you are not a friend to white weomen, instead favoring the mobbing of negroes for rapeing and murdering little white girls and weomen throughout the State, you are doing all in your power to shield, protect, and defend the negro rapeist. No answer required.

A. M. Sheffield.

September 1, 1897
SHEFFIELD TO GOV. JOHNSTON[52]

Sheffield soon regretted the preceding letter and offered this apology.

Tuskaloosa. Ala.
Sept 1st 1897.

Gov J. T Johnston.

Sir;

I have for several weeks felt very much grieved over the insulting note which I sent you. If you will accept an appology from a disgraced and friendless woman I make it. Dr Searcy wrote you that I was "brood-

---

52. This letter is in ADAH.

ing over the past,'' that angered me and caused me to write as I did. The past gives me no trouble, neither does the future, any farther than being here is concerned; the present occupies my mind, no time to think of the past or future. You gave me good advice—and I appreciate it. Were my Father living and knew that I had written such an insulting note to a nice good old gentleman he would be very much mortified over it. Hope you will pardon me and let it pass unnoticed. With best wishes for your future welfare—I am Miss A. M. Sheffield.

Ward No. 14

Early September 1897

SHEFFIELD TO SEARCY[53]

Perhaps feeling empowered by Gov. Johnston's attention, Sheffield issues an ultimatum to the Superintendent in this letter and, in the process, suggests much about the texture of asylum life.

Dr Searcy,

From what the Gov says I suppose he will see me this fall, that is, he will be here.[54] If I am under punishment when he comes here, I will not see him, will not speak to him, neither shall he send me from the Hospital. So if you want this matter to go off all right you had better draw in—withdraw your punishment. If I am not on a decent ward, with my *trunk*[55] and every dime of my money he shall not see me. You are only depriving me of my trunk and money with a hope that I'll go out to be acquitted when it will only keep me here.[56] The plain truth is, that Dr Bondurants leaving here would come nearer driving me out to be acquitted than *any thing else;* not that I have ever been a ''favorite or pet'' of his, neither have

53. Searcy sent this letter to Gov. Johnston for his information. It has remained in the Governor's papers in ADAH.

54. It is likely that in a letter which has not survived, the Governor told Sheffield that he would visit the Hospital.

55. Unlike most patients on the back wards, Sheffield was often allowed her own trunk of clothing and personal items.

56. Acquittal on the grounds of insanity would have resulted in Sheffield's return to the Hospital in Tuscaloosa. There was no other state institution for the insane.

I been in love with or *lusting* after him as many sane patients are;[57] but I know what it is to be here under "petticoat government,["] at the mercy of an ignorant woman.[58] I have'nt forgotten my first year here. I've had no cruel brutal treatment under Dr Bondurants administration, he is the only friend the patients have ever had, and no man will ever keep the weomen employes in their right place, as he has. Do just as you like about it, but just as certain as I am not on a decent ward with my trunk and money, Johnston will not see me. [N]either shall he send me from the Hospital, so now, just do as you like, if you wish to withdraw your punishment do so— if not, all right. Punishment will keep me here; *punishment* will give Miss Sheffield her "free papers".

A. M. S.

You and Wright[59] & Mary B. need not think that because I hate you, that I also hate Dr. B[60]—Dr. K[61] and Miss Mattie.[62]

Ward No. 14

September 7, 1897

SHEFFIELD TO SEARCY[63]

Searcy, it seems, refused to bend under Sheffield's pressure. She had to abide by the self-imposed terms of her ultimatum.

---

57. The evidence of another patient seems to corroborate Sheffield's opinion here. In August 1891, a female patient wrote to Bondurant of her "passionate love" for him, signing it "By, By, Love" and "With much love & one kiss." See letter of patient #4224 to Bondurant, August 20, 1891, in patient's file.
58. A reference to Mary Buck.
59. R. A. Wright, an assistant physician from 1890 to 1896.
60. Bondurant.
61. J. B. Killebrew, an assistant physician from 1896 to 1898.
62. This postscript was actually written upside-down across the top of the first page of this letter, giving it the look of an afterthought.
63. This letter, in ADAH, probably accompanied the following to Gov. Johnston. In keeping with his habit, the Superintendent sent letters intended for himself to the Governor, probably in order to provide evidence which he believed supported his position.

Dr. Searcy.

Send this to Gov. Johnson.[64] for I do really believe that he would come here to see me; and I would hate for him to come and it so that I could not see him, for under no circumstances would I now see him.[65] I did not want to see him, thinking that perhaps he could influence me to do what I know would be best for me, go and be freed.[66] I see that you are determined not to remove the punishment, and if he should come I'd certainly regret it, for of course he would expect to see me. I wrote you a note last Sunday asking you to remove me to a quiet ward[67]—give me my trunk, and money, and I again asked you yesterday morning and you still refuse me; I'm now convinced that you do not intend giving me a chance to get in a good humor, and I don't intend to ask any more. You are as anxious that I go out to be acquitted, as I am anxious to get out of your *clutches,* at the same time use *contrariness* with me, which you know only keeps me here. My experiences with this place is, that *contrariness,* and *punishment,* is the best medicine that could be given in many cases, but in my case the rule had not worked to a good advantage, has only pinned me to the prison. If the Gov come you must be sure and talk to him as you say you talked to Oates, but now don't tell *my side,* for God sake don't tell him that you have kept me on a *filthy back ward* for *seven years,* and that I have not heard a *prayer* or *sermon* during the seven years—have not been allowed to go out with the others, to *any* of their places of *amusements*—or *entertainments of any kind,* no be sure and don't tell him any of *this,* fix up a pretty tale for *yourself,* as all men in *public business* should do. The gov has said to me in one of his letters that you were a man of such "*high character*" that no one would "doubt your word."[68] Had you favored me in this, I know it would have been best for me, for I intended trying to give under to an acquittal, rather than remain here under "petticoat government." I never will stay on middle floor, unless I was kept locked in all the while. I'm sorry that you did not put me from under punishment. The matter is settled now, I will not see Johnston, under *no circumstances whatever.* You can keep my trunk, money & also keep me under punishment.

A. M. S.

64. The following note to Johnston, dated September 7, 1897. As was her practice, she handed both letters to the Superintendent on his morning rounds.
65. It is possible that Johnston came to the Hospital at the annual meeting of the Trustees held in late September.
66. In other words, return to Marshall County for trial.
67. Probably the note immediately preceding this one.
68. In his letter to Sheffield of July 19, 1897, Johnston said essentially this.

September 7, 1897
SHEFFIELD TO GOV. JOHNSTON[69]

*Following the failed negotiations with Searcy over ending her "pun-
ishment," Sheffield wrote this brief and cryptic message to the Governor.*

Tuskaloosa. Ala.
Sept 7ᵗʰ 1897.

Gov. J. F. Johnston.
    Montgomery.
        Ala.

Sir;—

I feel very grateful for the interest you have taken in me; and, I'm
sorry to inform you of the fact, that under the circumstances I could not
see you were you to come to the Hospital—facts which I could not well
explain.

A. M. Sheffield.

Ward No. 4

Early 1898
SHEFFIELD TO SEARCY[70]

*Following a favorable change in her ward assignment, Sheffield
found that her reputation preceded her.*

---

69. This letter is in ADAH.
70. This letter refers to the "last eight years," which would date it in 1898.

Dr. Searcy.

My understanding was when I came from No 14, I was to make no more threats. I came to No 4[71] full determined to carry out my promise, make no more threats, behave myself, and force myself to be more pleasant. I was in perfect good humor this morning, and Dr Killebrew came in mad, wanting to know what I had against Miss Brown,[72] when I had forgotten that she and myself had ever had a "fuss". What good can he accomplish going through here raking and scraping up all of my old threats and "fusses" made the past eight years? I can't see his motive, unless it is to pick a fuss out of me, & keep me on No 14. He told me this morning that his word was the law, that it was useless for me to complain to you about any thing. He has been very kind to give me medicine, and furnish me with something to read, but he does not like me, because I expressed myself so openly as to Dr Bondurants leaving here, and I yet boldly & openly say, that had I had that small amount of money in my own possession Killebrew would not have sent me to No 14 last week, for I would not have been here after Bondurant left. It never hurt me for Dr Bondurant to misstreat me, for I knew he was far my superior intellectualy, & inteligently, if I have to be misstreated for God sake let it be by my *superiors*. [A]nd another thing Dr Bondurant did not allow himself influenced, when he misstreated me, I knew that it was of his own will. Dr Killebrew has no right to dislike me or to want to abuse or misstreat me, for I have *never* said one word of abuse of him, never spoken a harmful word of him. His conversation this morning was proof, that he is not going to give me a *chance* to stay on No 4. raking & scraping up all of my old threats & fusses, will very soon put me on No 14. You have given *many* patients protection, and interfeared, I've known you to do it, why not do the same by me and have him to let these old threats go—and treat me in a way that I can stay on No 4. There is no need Dr Searcy of his picking at me, and bringing up all of these old threats & fusses, keeping me irritated is a good way to get me back on No 14—Will you please do me the favor to see that he lets these old threats and fusses go—and not bring them up any more— I have been in a perfect good humor since I came back to No 4, but he came in mad this morning and threatening me with No 14. [I]f he keep that up he can soon put me there. Dr Killebrew only dislikes me because I expressed myself as I did about Dr Bondurant leaving here, I had a right to regret his leaving, for I knew that Mary Buck did not like me, & that it

---

71.   One of the front wards.
72.   A fellow patient.

would come to this. I think you might favor me in this & have him to let
these old threats and fusses go—no need of him bringing that up. I had
better be on No. 14 than here & him coming in every morning & threatening me with 14. & bringing up old threats & fusses. He says his word is
the law, & if he is not willing for me to stay on No 4 he can put me back
on 14, and if he is going to keep on bringing up old threats & fusses he can
very easily do it. If you are willing for me to stay on 4, as you are lawfully
head I think you might have him to let these old threats and fusses go.

A. M. S.

Ward No. 14

Spring 1898

SHEFFIELD TO SEARCY[73]

*The following letter was occasioned by another anticipated visit to the
hospital by Gov. Johnston. In it Sheffield's angry mood toward Searcy, in-
spired by her return to the back wards, continues. Her distemper extends
as well to Supervisor Buck, who increasingly became an object of
her fury.*

Dr. Searcy.

Heretofore the Gov has visited the prison[74] during university commencement; if Johnston should come he would, as a matter of course,
want to see the worrying criminal.[75] ([A]s much through curiosity as any
thing else.) If he should ask to see me, loose [*sic*] no time passing word

73. Sheffield probably wrote this letter in the spring of 1898. She refers to Assistant Su-
    perintendent Bondurant as having left. Although the exact date of his departure is un-
    known, it is certain that he left sometime in 1897 but was still there in late July 1897.
    Another letter, dated in early September 1897, makes clear that Bondurant had already
    left. This letter makes clear he has been gone for "several months." She is also an-
    ticipating the University's commencement.
74. The Hospital.
75. Herself.

about that "sitting room",[76] I have'nt been in it since I parted there with my Father, and I will never be in it again. I will be as pleasant as possible with him provided not one of you come round me with your *deceit*. He is no better to sit a few moments in my cell than I am to sit in it a life time. You need not fear to trust him alone I will not ask him for *Tobacco* or *money,* neither will I ask him to have *intercourse* with me, so you need not have him *guarded*. A conversation with him, under the circumstances, will amount to nothing, for my self-will, and unbending disposition will not admit of my coming under to you. I can't say that I am willing to an acquittal, but can say that a great change has taken place in my mind, since Bondurant left here—and, would not have been here now, but for your contraryness. Just what you think will force me out will keep me here. Had I, a million dollars, and been treated about it as have been about the *seventy* I would not want it. [A]t the same time I regret that it will keep me here. You shall never say that I "left to get the money".[77] I had 40 cents when I went to No 14, after all of Bucks and Mattie Parrs threats, I have so far had money. You claim that you refused me the money on account of the letters written Buck and Mattie Parr. I've never heard of you saying that the *lies* they told caused me to write the letters.[78] Could you see the letters written in Bucks name, sent out by Emma Huckabee and Twilly[79] I expect you would *mob me*. It is strange that Turner the photographer of Tuskaloosa did not answer, as his was a little love note. Did she ever get an answer from Miss B. M. Spaulding of Birmingham? (I got her address from Cora Milton,[80] she knew every *lewd* womans address in Birmingham). Did she ever get answers to letters written Mr. J. L. Laughlin of Huntsville, G. C. Burgess of Anniston, B. S. Walden of Decatur, B. M. Harris of Union Springs? Left no doubt on their minds as who she was, her full name signed, and Supervisoress of the Asylum, not satisfied with her salary, and wanted to get out to make "lots" of money. It is a penitentiary offense to forge a name, I wish you would have me arrested, tried for *forgery,* swear me sane and have me sent to penitentiary. I am not

---

76. A room in the central administrative hall that families used when they visited patients at the Hospital.
77. Money that she had earned or that relatives had sent to her. She preferred to keep this money in her room locked in her trunk rather than on account in the main office. Technically, it was a violation of rules for patients to have money on the wards, though Sheffield and others commonly had some. For an example of another patient with the privilege of keeping her own money, see file of patient #4289, especially Mrs. M. E. S. Posey (a former nurse) to W. D. Partlow, November 2, 1912.
78. No letters from this period to Buck and Parr have survived.
79. Nurses who had probably left the Hospital's employment. Sheffield seldom revealed names of her collaborators while they were still liable to the Superintendent's disciline.
80. A patient.

boasting only wanting you to know that your supervisors did not "out do" me so much after all, with their lies. They can far excell me in *lying* but in nothing else. Neither one of them are the devil that I am for they have not the sense to be. To tell the truth I have never failed to do any thing that I wanted to do except to go to a *decent, quiet ward.* I have sent letters out independent of you for more than seven years, Miss Farr and Mrs Branch[81] mailed my letters in center building letter box for years. Not boasting only wanting you to know that you have not kept up with me. If you doubt that letters were sent in Bucks name to the above named, you write them, then you will know. I expect to forge more if I have cause to do it, 14 or no 14. If Killebrew[82] ever sends me to 14 again only to set an example I will handle him publicaly. If it suits you to encourage prostitution here, it is your buisness, but I will certainly handle it, if I'm given cause to. He may be competent to boss a plantation of work men, but that is all. There is only one way to get rid of me, let me tear up the money, or give it away, and *you* know, that it is done. Several months ago I sent a note out by a nurse going from here, a note to the Sheriff of Mobile county to collect the seventy dollars from Bondurant,[83] so (I guess he snap[p]ed his beautiful eyes). As a matter of course the Sheriff presented the account. I can do with out money as well as others. I have been here so long, that I do not object to wearing hall dresses,[84] for my pride is all gone, never give my personal appearance a moments thought, feel better in rags, patches, and filth. It is not to your interest to keep me here, at the same time you will never get rid of me under contraryness. I was never completely "out done" in my life, until Talley[85] sent me here instead of the penitentiary. Had he sent me there I would have worked and behaved and now Johnston would have pardoned me. As it is he can do *nothing* for me. Jesus Christ could do nothing for me under your "*spite* work" and contraryness. I'm not going to talk with the Gov on the subject for he has told me that he could not send me to the Penitintiary.

A. M. S.

---

81. Nurses.
82. Dr. J. B. Killebrew.
83. Bondurant settled in Mobile, where he helped to found the medical school there.
84. Clothing assigned to patients who had no money or whose family failed to send clothing was commonly referred to as "hall" goods. These "hall dresses" were usually made by patients themselves of sturdy material.
85. John B. Talley was the circuit judge who presided at her preliminary hearing and ordered her committed to the Hospital.

❧

May 14, 1898

SHEFFIELD TO GOV. JOHNSTON[86]

*After a recent return to the back wards, Sheffield in this letter appeals
yet again to the Governor. In the process, she denounces Searcy in the bit-
terest terms she would ever employ.*

❧ ❧

Tuskaloosa. Ala.
May 14. 1898.

Gov. J. F. Johnston.
   Montgomery.
      Ala.

Sir;—

First, allow me to congratulate you upon your renomination, if
an honest, faithful, and capable discharge of duty will insure your reelec-
tion, you will be Alabamas next Gov.
I hope you will pardon my obtruding myself upon your notice at this time,
when things of more importance demand your attention, but, "sorrow is
always selfish".
   You will see from the heading of this, that I'm still in the Hospital,
and I fear will remain here, since my release depends upon what you
termed Dr Searcys "*high standing*[.]"[87]
   Now, that you have seen the Supt, and heard through him, concerning
myself, I doubt that any thing I may say, would add to, or detract from the
information conveyed by him.
   I was brought up to respect age, and it does violence to my feelings
to speak disrespectfully of any old person, at the same time it is my disposition to be out spoken and tell the whole truth when the occasion demands it.
   Yes, the Supt is a man of very "high character", and all that I might
say of him, would go for nothing, from the fact he has money, station, and

---

86. This letter is in ADAH.
87. A quotation from Johnston's letter to Sheffield, July 19, 1897.

is a social and religious ornament. I know him from having spent six years in his care, and I unhesitatingly say, that he is the most artful and cunning piece of flesh that I ever had to encounter with; is deceitful, hypocritical, fond of *praise*, and, works for the approbation of others, and nothing else; deceit is the foundation and capping stone of his character.

I am ignorant as to the full power and authority of the Gov, should I ask any thing out of your power to grant please attribute it to ignorance on my part. The crime with which I'm charged calls for life imprisonment or death, I prefer the latter, but, will not get it at the hands of the law, therefore the only desire of my life, is, that I be placed in the penitentiary for the term of my natural life. I infinitely prefer that, to this.

The English language is inadequate to the expressions of some situations, mine is one of them; on the back wards with the incurably insane and Epileptics, only because as they say, I'm here for crime, while many other indigents, reared less tenderly—and accustomed to less wealth, in fact to none, have choice of wards, rooms, and allowed many privileges.

Had I been insane, I would not have incured the ill will of the Supt, Drs, and Supervisors; the insane cannot understand them as I can.

Can you as Gov of the State, have me sent from the Hospital to the penitentiary? Be plain, positive, (I like candor) say whether you can or cannot, if you cannot I will not bother you any more. I know what the Penitentiary is as well as you do. I'm willing to be guarded with *shot guns,* wear the stripes, and drudge and delve from morn until night. Write me whither you can or cannot have me removed. I don't deserve freedom and liberty, neither do I want it. The head ones of this institution have from the first, and do yet say that I was only "sent here to escape the Penitentiary". If you cannot send me there, you can do nothing else for me. Hope you will not think me troublesome. I will not bother you any more.

(Miss.) A. M. Sheffield.

May 14, 1898
SHEFFIELD TO SEARCY[88]

Sheffield attached this brief note to the preceding letter to Johnston.

---

88. This letter is in ADAH, not the Hospital's Records Office. Searcy enclosed it with Sheffield's letter to Johnston on May 24, 1898.

Dr. Searcy.

Please send my letter out.[89] I have written twice to Gov Johnston within the past month, the letters were mailed, and he received them, no answer yet; perhaps he will answer this, as I've flattered him a little.[90]

I cannot account for why he failed to answer my notes, it may be that you gave him such a terrible account of me, that he has become prejudiced, and lost interest in me. If I knew that to be true, I'd be very far from writing to him again; if he fails to answer this, I will then know that you prejudiced him towards me, and will not bother him any more. Realy I have no idea he is any better than any of the rest of you.

A. M. Sheffield.

May 23, 1898

SHEFFIELD TO GOV. JOHNSTON[91]

In this, her last letter to Gov. Johnston, Sheffield reveals a mood of exasperation and resignation. There is also a tone of gratitude that probably surpassed any desire to flatter.

Tuskaloosa. Ala.
May 23. 1898.

Gov. J. F. Johnston.
    Montgomery.
      Ala.

Dear. Sir;—

---

89. The preceding letter to Gov. Johnston.

90. No other letters to Johnston from the spring of 1898 remain in his papers. Contrary to Sheffield's belief stated here, there is no proof that the Governor ever received these letters.

91. This letter is in ADAH. In a brief note to Searcy accompanying this letter, Sheffield says: "Please send my letter out, and you can scratch my name off your list of *letter writers,* for this winds up my letter writing, for Gov Johnston has very kindly, in a very feeling way informed me that he could not have me remooved from the Hospital. I know my doom, I can but submit."

Your letter[92] received, read, and put aside with a sigh, for there is no moment in our lives when we feel less worthy the sympathy of others, than when we receive evidences of kindness which we feel we do not merit.

I regret that it is out of your power to have me removed from the Hospital. I can but submit. No one who has never been a sane uncared for patient in an Insane Asylum, can imagine what it is to be immured within its walls for years, subject to the power of prejudiced physicians, calling themselves insanity experts, and without hope of ever getting out. It is a life of repression and depression, it is the acme of weariness; the life is narrowing, the thoughts run in one channel so long. It is worse than death, it is a living death. It is an indescribable situation. Job, realized something of its horror when he exclaimed "Perish the day in which I was born." You said in your letter that the "law made no distinction between the criminal insane and any others, that there was no warrant for any difference in treatment because of any crime committed". Whether the law makes a distinction or not, the officials here do, and no power can legislate it away while human nature is what it is, for we, the criminals are treated with insolent disrespect, and are a second consideration in every thing. I am accounted sane, a woman of sound mind, is it not incongrous that I should be expected to study the whims and bigotries of these people, and fritter away my own mental and spiritual force, in vain and useless efforts to adjust my conduct to their despotic, usurpatory sway? Dr Searcy is a man of high prejudice, he makes his plans, and cuts them in iron. I could bid prison walls farewell tomorrow if I would only agree with Dr Searcy;[93] unfortunately for me I'm for what is just and right.

I have for you the respect due my Fathers friend, the many good deeds done during your two years administration assure me that you are worthy the admiration of the people, and that you are a man of true goodness, kindness of heart, and a hearty sympathy with every shade of suffering humanity. It is only the pure and good who are in sympathy with the disgraced.

I again thank you for the information given me, now, that you have so kindly given it, I shall not trouble you any more, this letter closes our correspondence. With best wishes for your welfare. I am

                                                            A. M. Sheffield.

---

92. This letter has not survived.
93. That is, agree to return to Marshall County for trial.

Late May 1898
SHEFFIELD TO SEARCY[94]

The following was prompted by Gov. Johnston's last letter (which has not survived), in which he said that he could not remove her from the Hospital.

Dr. Searcy.

I have received quite a lengthy letter from Gov Johnston,[95] he has authorized me to write the local Trustees.[96] Please send me their names and three sheets of paper.

The Gov says he is fully convinced as to my sanity, also says that two distinguished physicians of Montgomery read my letter, and they concured with him, that I was sane, and that my writing and composition was perfect. So you see your villiany [*sic*] is exposed.

A. M. S.

Ca. June 1898
SHEFFIELD TO SEARCY[97]

Sheffield's mood of resignation or depression failed to last. In the following, her anger leads her to irrationality.

---

94. Sheffield probably wrote this letter, now in ADAH, in May around the time that she ended her correspondence with the Governor. Searcy sent it on to the Governor, perhaps with his letter of May 24, 1898. This would account for its being in the State Achives rather than in Sheffield's file at the Hospital.
95. This letter has not survived.
96. See Sheffield's letter below, June 1898, to Trustee Williamson.
97. Judging from its content, this letter precedes immediately the dated letter to Williamson which follows.

Dr. Searcy.

I am not dependant on you, to send my letters out, if you fail to send this out,[98] I will write another, and send it out the first opportunity. It will pay you to send this, for if I have to write another to Williamson[99] it will be one that you would not want to send out. Gov Johnston wrote me, that the "first time he came to Tuskaloosa he would certainly call to see me"—I sit up here *four* days punished myself to wear my clothes, had my gray hair frizzed, my face chalked, expecting every moment for the Gov to come in; he was here and you forbid his coming to see me; because you knew that it was my intention to expose you all, and also to have Mr. Perkins[100] sent out of this Hospital. I want you to send me a sheet of paper tomorrow, I'm going to write the "Grand Master" of the Masonic Lodge. I am a Mason myself—and I've suffered long enough at the hands of you so-called Masons, when I can have every one of you *expelled from Masonry*.

A. M. Sheffield.

June 1898

SHEFFIELD TO J. L. WILLIAMSON

Despite Sheffield's request that Searcy forward this letter to Williamson, a Trustee of the Hospital, Searcy kept it and placed it in her file.

Tuskaloosa. Ala.
June. 1898

Dr. Williamson

Sir—

You will excuse my uncourteous introduction when I make known to you my object in writing you. I'm a patient confined in the Insane Asylum

---

98. The following letter to Williamson.
99. J. L. Williamson, a resident Trustee of the Hospital.
100. W. C. Perkins was the Hospital's Steward and, as such, was responsible for, among other things, the patients' money.

("deep dyed criminal.") I was charged with arson in first degree, adjudged insane by the incapacitated physicians of Marshall Co, and sent to Hospital June 7, 1890. When I came here I passed the medical board as a woman of "*sound* mind," and have been often told that I was only "sent here to escape the *gallows* or *penitintiary*".

I, of late wrote Gov J. F. Johnston thinking that through him I could exchange my home here, for one at the penitintiary. He wrote me that he was "powerless to do anything for me, but that the Trustees had authority to have me removed from the Hospital['"]; and he also said that according to rules laid down by Trustees, it was the duty of the Resident board of Trustees[101] to attend to such matters, that they had the "right and authority to have any patient removed from the Hospital even without *concuring* with the Supt."

While I am not wanting freedom and liberty, I am more than anxious to exchange my home here for one in the penitintiary. I infinitely prefer that to this, rather than remain here subject to such treatment as female criminals receive at the hands of these so-called "nice, good men", ("world renowned eminent insanity experts")[.] The crime with which I'm charged calls for life imprisonment or death, I prefer the latter, but will not get it, for that reason I am anxious for life imprisonment at the penitintiary. Dr. W. G. Somerville received me into the Hospital; he knows, and, I'm satisfied will say, that I was of sound mind when sent here. Dr's Searcy, Bondurant and Wright have repeatedly told me that I was "not insane when sent here", and I agree with them. The Supt (Dr Searcy) has often told me that I was only sent here because I was of a "proud and respectable family, and that he only kept me here, because if sent to the Penitentiary, would disgrace my *kin*". Dr. Bondurant often told me that if sent back to Marshall that I would be sent back here, even if acquitted, for that reason I beg to go back in a way that I would be sent to the Penitentiary. Will you please condescende to give my case a little attention,? more especially as the Gov has said that it is your duty to do it. Will you please have Dr's Searcy, Somerville[,] Bondurant and Wright to give their *sworn evidence* that I was of sound mind when sent here? If you will do me this favor, say so, if not, say so, Let me hear from you.

> (Miss) A. M. Sheffield
> Tuskaloosa.
> Ala.
> "Insane. Asylum".

---

101.   The Resident Board was comprised of the Tuscaloosa Trustees, who, because they were nearby, could deal with emergencies. The full Board generally met in Tuscaloosa only once a year.

Ca. 1900
SHEFFIELD TO SEARCY[102]

Anger over her being denied access to her money and the news of yet another possible visit from Gov. Johnston led Sheffield to use the harsh language of racial hatred once again to dramatize her plight.

Dr. Searcy.

It is useless for you to say one word to me about the Gov, he wrote me two years ago, that he could do nothing for me, consequently I've no buisness with him. And if he could do any thing for me, he should not do it—now, that you have tried to controle me with a little money.[103] No—if the Gov could send me to Heaven I would now refuse to go. Have you forgotten that I wrote you when Bondurant left here, that if you did not want me to have the money, if you would let me dispose of it, that I would go back to Marshall, and let the jury acquit me, rather, than remain here under "petticoat government."?[104] I meant it.—You, did not believe it, you, thought I wanted the money and not my freedom and liberty. You should have given me the money, let me dispose of it in any way that I liked, and gone back. With Bondurant here to protect me, I prefered to remain here, rather than let a jury acquit me, but of course I felt different about it after he left. Had I known that he intended leaving here I would have given the money up. I thought that he, like yourself, had frozen to his position. It was worse for myself, and none to your good, that you

---

102. Dated by Sheffield's reference to the Governor's telling her "two years ago" that he could do nothing for her. This probably was Johnston's missing letter of May 1898, to which she refers. Sheffield addressed the envelope containing this letter somewhat sarcastically to "Dr. J. T. Searcy. 'Paradise.' " Searcy also wrote on the envelope: "Miss Sheffield had accumulated over $50 in money, sent her, & which she had otherwise made by sewing since in the Hospital, which was taken & deposited in the Steward's Office, which occasioned this letter. Patients are not allowed money in the wards."

103. She believed that Searcy had tried to discipline her by having her money taken and placed on account with the Steward. See Searcy's note on the letter (footnote 102, above).

104. The letter to which Sheffield refers no longer exists. Letters to Searcy from 1897 refer to the matters discussed here, but in none does she agree to return to Marshall if her money is returned.

undertook to controle me with the money, for you only pin[n]ed me to the prison. Nothing except Bondurants leaving here would have brought me under—and had you not sent me, I would have sliped off & gone back to Marshall—had I had the money. When you failed to accept my proposition I vowed that I would never make another effort to get out, would never write another letter—I have been true to my vow. I do not think any the less of you on account of the way you have treated me about the money— has not increased my hatred for you. You refused me the money—with a hope that you could controle me, that if you deprived me of a dime, that I would after awhile "tuck under," & let a jury acquit me; a mistaken idea of *yours*. I am more fully determined today, than was two years ago, that you shall not controle me with it. Time will convince you that I am not to be controlled with a little money—two many *devils* in me for that. It is nice to have a little money, but I can do without it as well as any other woman. Now that I have no pride as to my personal appearance, I had as soon be dependant on the house for clothing, as to have my own. I can wear the ragged, patched, and thrown aside garments, and the clothing of dead weomen, and will, rather than be controlled with a little money. You keep the money, you keep me—had I one million dollars out of here, and knew I would get it by going out, and only had one copper cent in the center building[105]—I'd refuse to go without the copper cent. No, under the circumstances I have no buisness with the Gov—I do not want to see him—neither will I see him.[106] He can do nothing for me—now that you have undertaken to controle me with *spite work, and contrariness.* You need not ask me "why don't you write to your brother"?[107] My brothers did not disgrace me, they would have protected me rather than not; as little as you think it, they are unlike yourselves, gentlemen—high toned honest and honorable and I feel that I would be doing them a great injustice to even ask anything of them. You had as well try to turn the warrior river[108] up stream as to say one word to me now, about an acquittal. My will is good to go to jail, penitentiary or any where rather than here—and rather than remain here, if no other chance for me, I had rather go out and live with negroes, or be a cook in any lewd house in the united States—in fact I had rather marry a nice, clean, genteel looking mulatto negro rather than

---

105. The Steward's Office, as all administrative offices, was located in the "center building."
106. Searcy probably told Sheffield that the Governor was coming again to the Hospital, perhaps in conjunction with the Trustees' annual fall inspection.
107. A reference to T. A. Street.
108. A reference to the Black Warrior River, which flows past the Hospital grounds.

remain here. Please take my word for it that you will never controle me with the money. I never intend to ask for any thing of you, for I have never asked any thing of you that you have not refused me.

A. M. Sheffield

Chapter 2

"MY SENSE OF RIGHT AND WRONG IS VERY ACUTE"

1903–1907

Sheffield's crusading of the first decade bore no fruit. Her letters from the early years of the new century acknowledge this fact and reveal subtle changes. Her frequent correspondence with governors declined noticeably, due partly to her own choice and partly to the Superintendent's. As the letters in this chapter make clear, Searcy began limiting Sheffield's contact with outside dignitaries. It took three years of trying for Sheffield to succeed in contacting Gov. William D. Jelks, for example. While her rebellion remained, it lost its tone of urgency. Ironically, rebellion was thus mixed with resignation.

Resignation to Searcy's authority, however, was not rapprochement. Sheffield's position never softened. If anything, it hardened. Sheffield directs most of her correspondence in this chapter to doctors within the Hospital: Searcy and her new ward physician in 1907, John A. Lanford. As a consequence, these letters are less formal and polished than those in the previous chapter written to governors. They also provide greater insight into the daily workings of the Hospital. Her letters to Searcy early in this period focus on reestablishing contact with outsiders. But once she succeeded in reaching Jelks in 1906, and received no relief, her letters turned almost exclusively to internal affairs such as relationships with doctors and nurses, and the social geography of the wards.

By these years, the range of Sheffield's life had narrowed. Denied access to outsiders and more than a decade removed from her home and family in Marshall County, she saw the scope of her horizons shrink. The difficult personality remained, maybe even sharpened, but its field of experience was increasingly limited to the grounds of the Tuscaloosa asylum.

Ca. 1903

SHEFFIELD TO SEARCY[1]

Sheffield makes a proposal to the Superintendent that he probably ignored.

Dr Searcy.

I have been thinking for some time that I would write you telling you my intentions, that is, what I have been thinking of doing. I don't know that you will approve of it, at the same time I have no fears of your punishment, for there is no need punishing me a sane sensible woman, qualified to ''look out'' for herself. I have sense enough to know that it would be unlawful for you to send me to the Depot,[2] unless you knew that I was going to Marshall. It is a settled and confirmed fact that I will never go to Marshall—unless taken by force. I want out of the Hospital, and there is but one way that I am willing to go—What I would like to know is this, if I should leave, that is, if I had an opportunity of leaving, would you make an effert [sic] to get me back? Would you send a telegram to Birmingham, Cottondale, Montgomery, Mobile, Selma, Meridian and many other places, to be on the lookout for an escaped patient? Would you have nurses to get on their bicycles, and go out on every road leading out from Tuskaloosa. No patient can make their escape from here, without exposing themselves to danger, unless they go aboard the train, and that is the only way I would go. I have been thinking of going to one of my brothers in California. He wrote me some time ago, (last fall,)[3] that if I would come he would send me the money to defray my expenses.
I don't know whether you could give me permission to do this or not. I'm aware as to how I was sent here. I don't think you would make yourself liable, for I'm sure I would never expose you. I could make my escape in spite of your telephone messages and men on bicycles, but I would have to

1. Dated only approximately by the style of the handwriting (especially the way Sheffield wrote her capital ''S'' which changed over the years) and the stationery on which it was written.
2. The railroad depot in nearby downtown Tuscaloosa.
3. No letters from her full brothers in California have survived.

lie out in the woods, and I don't want to do that, and *would not* do it. Even if I did not go to my brother, I'm a sane sensible woman, well competent to take care of myself, and if I prefer to be out in the world to "beat my own way," I see no reason why you should object. Now there is no need making this public, this is mine and your affair, and does not concern the Dr's in the least, it is none of their buisness. Now I don't want you to think that I am going to do this any way. I am not going to do it under any circumstances. I want assurance from you that you would not molest me. If I knew that an insane patient was wanting or trying to make their escape from here, I would do what I could to prevent it, while I don't think it would be right for you to interfere in my case, and I can't believe that you would, at the same time I do not know it. I only want some assurance from you. If I can't go aboard the cars at Tuskaloosa I can never go, for I would never expose myself to danger by walking the country roads, at night. I've to [*sic*] much sense for that. All I want to know is that you would make no effort to bring me back, and put me on a violent ward for a twelve months punishment. I don't say that I have a notion of leaving today, tomorrow, or next day. I only say that all I want is a little assurance from you that it would be all right. Why Dr Searcy why should you care? I'm sane, sensible, sense enough to care for myself. I can assure you that I would take no patient with me, no, indeed, too glad to get out from among them. If you do not approve of this, there is no need taking any offense at it, just tell me in a pleasant and gentlemanly way that you do not, and I will drop it. This is I hope confidential.

A. M. Sheffield.

Ca. 1903

SHEFFIELD TO SEARCY[4]

Sheffield tells the Superintendent in this letter that she is planning to write to Gov. William D. Jelks, just as she had done to his predecessors. To Searcy, it may have seemed a promise of repeating the experience with Gov. Johnston in the 1890s.

---

4.   Dated by the reference to her "thirteen year stay" in the Hospital.

Dr. Searcy.

I have said that I would never write to any one again in regard to my leaving here. Jelks is a villian [*sic*], but I'll try him, I am going to try to get out of here one more time through the Gov—and if I fail, it will not be my fault. My reason, for telling you of this is to ask you for God sake, be not a stumbling block. You, are a man of sound mind [*sic*], good judgement, at least I take you to be. You know your business, and I am far from wanting to dictate for you in any matter except in my own case; being a woman of sound mind I think it just and right that I be allowed to do that. You have all the while had a very mistaken idea of this matter, that to aid and assist me in getting justice at the hands of the law would reflect on you; a mistaken idea of yours. Were I an educated woman of refined and polished manners, young, beautiful, of good character, and money, and guilty of this crime, then it would reflect on you publicaly—as it is, I'm old, homely, ignorant, poverty-stricken, friendless, homeless, and disgraced, for this reason I can but think that the public would applaud you. My sense of right and wrong is very acute. I love justice, I crave it, I want it—and would gladly make any sacrifice in order to get it. I am going to write Jelks send you writings authorizing you to release me, and then if you will furnish me with writings stating that I was sent here a sane woman, and that my way and manners throughout my thirteen year stay here was that of a well balanced woman, then for one time in my life I will be elected. I can go to Guntersville alone (no need of the sheriff in my case) give my self up to the sheriff and walk into the jail; with the negroes and low born whites, where I ought to be, and where I had rather be than in any insane hospital.
Now give this matter a little thought, put yourself in my place. You and every Dr who has been here since my imprisonment here, know me only as a sane sensible woman. Were I in your place I would stick to the truth in criminal cases if it put me out of my position, and sent me to the field to follow the plow.

A. M. Sheffield

I will write Jelks this week.[5]

---

5. No letter to Jelks from this period has survived.

May 3, 1906
SHEFFIELD TO GOV. WILLIAM D. JELKS[6]

*As suggested in the previous letter, this was not Sheffield's first to Jelks.
Searcy had intercepted her earlier attempts to contact the Governor, just as
he clearly intercepted this one, which was never posted. Jelks never saw it,
unless Searcy showed it to him on a visit to the Hospital at some later date.*

Tuskaloosa, Ala—
May 3rd 1906.

Gov Jelks,

Dear Sir

You will please excuse my obtruding myself upon you, when matters
of more importance demand you attention.
I am a daughter of the late Col James L. Sheffield, a criminal patient in
the Ala Insane Hospital. Was charged with Arson in first degree—wrongfully adjudged insane—and sent to the Hospital from Marshall Co—June
3, 1890. My detention here has been unjust and unlawful, from the fact I
passed the Hospital medical board as a sane woman when I came here.
Have only been detained because the Sup't is unwilling to publicaly state
that my mind was not disturbed when sent here, and that my deportment
throughout the fifteen years has been that of a sane woman.
I am unwilling to go to trial, from the fact, I know that if the Supt and dr's
failed to make the same statements in the presence of a jury, that they have
repeatedly made here that my trial would result in an acquittal.
My whole desire is that I be dealt with as having been perfectly rational at
the time the crime was committed, and be given the full penalty—life sentence in the Penitentiary. I crave it, I yearn for it, I pray for it, and be
assured that I deserve it.

---

6. This is not the letter to which Sheffield refers at the close of her previous letter from
    1903. This one remains in the Medical Records Office of the Hospital, not in the papers
    of the governors in ADAH. Searcy evidently intercepted and never mailed it. For some
    reason, the Superintendent reversed his earlier practice, as with Johnston in the 1890s,
    of sending on Sheffield's letters to the governor.

I am ignorant as regards the law, and it may be that it would be out of your power to grant my request—however I will ask it. It is this, have you the power, holding the governmental reins within your own hands to have me removed without trial, and placed in the Penitentiary?

I want just, and nothing short of a life sentence in the Penitentiary would be just. My treatment here is humane, better than I deserve—I want to hear from you—please address me—I am competent to attend to my own affairs without the aid of the Sup't and Dr's.

(Miss) Andrew Sheffield
Tuskaloosa
Box 268.} Ala.

May 12, 1906

SHEFFIELD TO DR. JONATHON LITTLE

Searcy intercepted this letter to the Hospital's Treasurer (whom Sheffield mistakes for one of the Trustees).

Insane Hospital.
Tuskaloosa. Ala.
May 12. 1906.

Dr. Little

Dear Sir.

I write you as one of the resident Board of Trustees.[7] You will please excuse my uncourteous introduction when I inform you of the circumstances which induces me to write you.

You are aware that for many years I have been an inmate of the Ala Insane Hospital, criminal, charged with arson. You of course are ac-

---

7. Jonathon Little was not actually one of the Resident Trustees. He was the Treasurer of the Hospital, who had a local private medical practice. Sheffield's mistake is understandable, however. Little was a former assistant physician (from 1869 to 1875) as were a good many of the Trustees. As an officer of the Hospital, he also would have been present during all the visits of the Trustees.

quainted with the circumstances surrounding my case, which brought
about my being incarcerated in the Insane Hospital.

I propose to state the facts to you.

My detention here, has been very unlawful, from the fact, the Sup't
and the physicians who composed the board when I came, pronounced me
sane, my mind not in the least disordered.

The late Dr Bryce—Dr's. W. G. Somerville, E. D. Bondurant and
S. W. Wright composed the board when I came to the Hospital.

Dr. T. J. [*sic*] Searcy present Supt and all physicians who have been
under his administration, up to the present, agree with the above board.

Within the walls of this institution the Sup't and physicians have
openly stated that my mind has been and is up to the present that of a sane
person, they stoutly assert that I have at no time since my imprisonment
here been the least unbalanced; that my conduct and deportment throughout my stay here has been that of a well ballanced woman, and *no discoverable delusions.*[8]

I am compelled to look to others outside my relations, for aid and assistance in procuring a life sentence in the Penitentiary, for had my relations
wanted me there, they would not have had me sent here.

Any assistance you can give me in way of forcing the Sup't. and Dr's
Bondurant, Somerville and Wright to make a truthful statement as to my
sanity when sent here would be thankfully received.

Besides the Sup't, the present board of physicians, is, as you know
composed of four physicians, (mere lads, scarcely emerged from their
teens,) all of which agree that I'm well ballanced mentally and have been
since they have known me. The evidence of no one would amount to anything except the physicians who were here when I came, from the fact,
fifteen years have elapsed since the commission of the crime, the question
is, and would be; was I, or not insane at the time the crime was committed? It is not reasonable to suppose if insane, that I could possibly have
recovered in so short a while, as to have been pronounced sane when I
arrived at the Hospital, as it was scarcely two weeks from the time the
crime was committed until I was imprisoned here.

It would be absurd to put up a plea of *emotional* insanity, from the

---

8. The existing case history corroborates Sheffield here—at least in part. Her history from
   July 30, 1890, nearly two months after her admission, says: "she has no delusions, as
   far as we can discover" (*Case History Book #6*, p. 185). On March 3, 1893, the case
   history says that she "Exhibits some delusions at times," but it describes no particular
   delusion (p. 225). Again, exactly six years later, on March 3, 1899, her history reports
   delusions in the same vague manner: "She has many delusions, talks pleasantly, and
   intelligently" (p. 229). But even then, the history describes no single delusion.

fact, the the crime was not committed on my own will, but from force of circumstances.

I would willingly accept an exchange from this place to county jail or Penitintiary. Words are inadequate to describe my situation and treatment in some respects. It is such that I have almost gotten to where I doubt the existence of a God, for if a just God existed he would surely awaken to his duty and relieve me a miserable and wrecked piece of humanity from the clutches of so called Dr's.

While the law does not warrant any difference in the treatment of her so called criminal insane and others, that difference is made[.]

Patients here otherwise than of good standing are subjected to many wrongs, forced to submit to the taunts and jeers, and all manner of hard hurtful things from Dr's.

In my own case it is simply beyond description. The physicians have lain aside my real name—am addressed as the "prominent woman." I have been, against my will, forced on public exhibition in the Hospital, forced to be gazed at by the curious, (those coming and going,) as the most "prominent woman in the State". Exhibited and gazed at as though I were a curio in a museum, and if fashionable dressed, one would suppose that I had been placed here, not only to be gazed at, but to blaze as a paragon for some fashionable Metripolitan.

The newspapers containing my fathers trial were placed on file[9] and I have all the while been treated according to evidence given in against me—by the dead Dr's[10] relations and friends. I want imprisonment in the penitentiary, and the only way to get it is to force the Sup't and Dr's to make truthful statements as to my sanity when I came here. The greatest mystery of my life is, why that Dr Searcy is not willing to aid me in getting justice, a life sentence in the Penitentiary, when he has from the first of his coming here entertained the greatest ill will for me—besides claims that I am very objectionable in association with other patients, and that my leaving the Hospital would be a good ridance. I am ready and more willing to bid adieu to the Hospital, provided I can leave armed with writings that I was of sound mind when I came, and only "sent here to keep me out of the Penitentiary"—the writings signed by Supt—Dr's Somerville, Bondurant—Wright, and sworn to in the presence of an officer authorized to administer an oath. I hope you will give this your attention.

> (Miss) A. M. Sheffield.
> Tuskaloosa.
> Box 268.} Ala.

---

9. These newspaper accounts, if they ever existed, no longer remain in her file.
10. A reference to Dr. William May.

Ca. 1906
SHEFFIELD TO SEARCY[11]

Sheffield asks for permission to go to the dentist in Tuscaloosa without an escort.

Dr Searcy.

Suppose you let me go to Dr Hassells[12] alone, what you say? I did not want to go alone, and that was why I proposed going with "Aunt" Laura.[13] Now I prefer to go alone, and no reason why I should not. As for "running away," there is no where I want to run to except to the Penitentiary, and they would not receive me, and you have told me repeatedly that if I should go a fugitive, I would be brought back to Marshall, so no reason why that I should think of "running away." To go alone I would feel at ease, speak to no one except Dr Hassell, and to tell the conductor that I wanted to get off at station in front of Buck residence.[14] Could behave myself as nicely as any woman in Tuscaloosa Co. To have one of the nurses go, I would feel "ill at ease," that my presence was a disgrace to them—a terrible feeling, no one know the feeling except those who have experienced it.

Would not have any talk to Dr Hassell except about my teeth. The Dr's of course would oppose me going alone, for they unlike yourself are evil minded. ("Evil to him who evil thinketh[.]") Would not go up in town, no buisness there.

No reason why I should not go alone, no reason why I should be guarded, could and would behave myself as nicely without, as with a guard. Would appreciate being allowed the privilige and pleasure of going alone.

---

11. Dated only approximately by the handwriting style and stationery.

12. A dentist in Tuscaloosa.

13. Probably one of the blacks who worked in the Hospital. For example, according to the 1900 manuscript census, Laura Cole was a ward attendant employed in the Hospital. The 1910 census shows her as still employed. She would have been fifty-four years old in 1906. Laura Dodson, another black ward attendant, would have been sixty-nine in 1906 and does not appear on the census rolls for 1910.

14. In other words, she would tell the streetcar conductor to let her off at a familiar landmark on the Hospital side of downtown Tuscaloosa.

But if you think I would not behave myself you need not allow it. But I certainly could go and come alone, as well as to be guarded.

A. M. Sheffield.

Ca. 1906[15]
SHEFFIELD TO [SEARCY]

This sarcastic note indicates that Searcy decided not to give her permission to go to town.

Had I not wanted Dr Hassell to have received the note I am sure I would not have written it.[16] If allowed to go alone I would have the teeth. I am the ''prominent''woman of the state, and will not degrade any one of the young lady nurses, by going to town with them. It would be an unpardonable sin for me to allow any of the officials to force any of these girls to accompany me to town, (the prominent woman)[.] Were I allowed to go alone I would go & come all right, and would have no desire whatever to go in the neighborhood of the *M. and O. Depot,* for I would have no buisness, there.

''Prominent woman''

Ca. 1906
SHEFFIELD TO SEARCY[17]

Aware that Searcy seized her earlier letters, Sheffield pleads with the Superintendent here to forward her next letter to Gov. Jelks.

---

15. Dated by the content, which is about the visit to Dr. Hassell's office. There is no greeting on the letter at all, but, given the content, it was clearly intended for Searcy.
16. No letter addressed to Dr. Hassell has survived.
17. Dated by references to letters to Jelks and Little, both written in 1906.

ði ði

(Confidential.)

Dr Searcy.

I'm satisfied my letters to Jelks, Little, Haralson and Timberlake[18] went to the "waste basket." I intend writing Jelks again and if I get no answer, I will write again, and send the letter out myself. I can do it. I do not want to do that, do not want to take the advantage of you, had rather do openly, but if you force me to sneak to do what is my right and duty to do, I can do it. It is a privilege that should be allowed me, to write the State authorities, for the state sent me here. I was well convinced many years ago that it was useless to write any of my "use-to-be" kin on the subject of going out of the Hospital—much less to the Penitintiary. If I touch on that subject in writing to any of my kin I get no answers to my letters. You will remember a year ago (only to gratify you, for I did not want it done, for it would not be right) I wrote Oliver Street asking him to have my case "nol pros"[19] he did not answer the letter. Have had three letters from him the past three months but said nothing about it. I've written every Gov since my imprisonment here, and expect to write every one hereafter. I do not know the full power of a Gov but am under the impression that the Gov could act satisfactorily in any case—having been pronounced sane when I came here, I remained perfectly sane all these many years.

Besides I've been tried, my Father's trial[20] was more mine than his. To do as *you* have all the while wanted me to do, would amount to nothing except in the sending of me back here, the jury could not dispose of me otherwise. I do not want an acquittal, but, if I did I could not conduct my self in a way to justify them in acquitting me; I am one woman who could not be tried, too much temper and resentment. I could not sit in the court five

---

18. Jelks was the Governor to whom she wrote in May and September 1906—letters which Searcy never posted. Likewise, Hospital authorities never mailed her letter to the Hospital's Treasurer Little. Jonathon Haralson was an associate justice of the state Supreme Court. Timberlake was a prominent resident of Jackson County, which neighbored her home county of Marshall.
19. *Nolle prosequi* is a statement filed by a prosecutor that he or she will not prosecute in the future. It is usually discussed in its abbreviated form, *nol pros.* The letter to O. D. Street, to which she refers, has not survived.
20. James Sheffield's trial for the murder of William May; he was acquitted in November 1890.

or six days and quietly listen to sensational stories told by a low class; that the dead man[21] was so very popular with. At the preliminary trial I was only in the court house one hour and half; when the witnesses told the truth it mattered not how bad it was I said nothing, but every time they told a lie, I give them the lie, and Judge Tally calling me down did not amount to any thing. I paid no attention to his raps. Besides I'd be asked five hundred or a thousand questions by the very filthy mouthed, vulgar minded lawyers, things that did not concern them and no buisness of theirs. At a final trial I would be in the court house at least five or six days—and I'd create forty scenes a day consequently my trial would result in my being sent back here. A thousand Judges, and ten thousand jurymen could not controle my tongue, and my brother Judge Street knew that, and that was why he arranged it so as not to have me present at my Fathers trial. If I could go there and sit quietly and say nothing, but I could not do that even if I wanted an acquittal. I have expressed my self now, only because you have never been willing to any thing except for me to go to trial. I'm one woman that could not be tried, my temper would not admit of it. You think because Mrs Garner[22] went to trial that I should do so. I read her trial—it was very scandalous and disgraceful (but not near so bad as mine would be) she sit and listened, said nothing—and was acquitted—but she and I are different weomen altogather, she was of a very sensational nature—loved notoriety—know it to be a fact that she was proud of her prominence won as a disgraced woman, while I am not proud of my prominence, but ashamed of it. It would be right for me to go the Pen—and if you want to favor me use your influence with the Gov—to send me there, then use you[r] influence for him to pardon me. I deserve going there and deserve pardon. I will write Jelks and ask if he can have me sent there. Jones, Oates, and Johnston, were good friends of my Father I think that was why they did nothing for me.

You would do me no favor in having me sent to Guntersville for you would only get me back here—they could not acquit me and I don't suppose they would send me to the Pen—and I know there would be no such *good luck* as hanging me. I have only expressed my self as to a trial, only because you have never approved any thing else. I hope you will send my next letter to Gov. Jelks.

A. M. Sheffield.

---

21. Dr. William May.
22. A former patient.

Tuscaloosa
September 24, 1906
SEARCY TO GOV. JELKS[23]

In the following, Searcy reveals the extent to which Sheffield's correspondence with the state's governors had been a commonplace. His tone also mirrors her own tenor of resignation in letters of the same period.

Sept. 24, 06.

Gov. W. D. Jelks,
    Montgomery,
       Ala.

My Dear Sir:—

      I have a patient here, a Miss Sheffield, from Marshall County, who has written to every Governor since she has been in the Hospital, (admitted in 1890) demanding or begging that she be sent to the Penitentiary. All the Governors, I believe, have had correspondence with her and about her. Your time has come with the others. All have told her that there is no way of her being sent to the Penitentiary except after trial by the court in Marshall.

      She is just such a character as she portrays she is in her statement of how she would act before a court if brought to trial.

      I judge you will have to answer too to the same effect.

Truly,
J. T. Searcy. M. D. Supt.

      P. S. Will you kindly return these letters they are kept on file with many others.[24]

---

23.   This letter is identified in the Hospital files as a copy.
24.   The particular letters that Searcy sent are unknown.

————————————————— ❧ —————————————————

September 25, 1906
SHEFFIELD TO GOV. JELKS

Fully aware that her earlier letters were intercepted, Sheffield once again introduces herself to Jelks and explains the history of her case.

❧ ❧

> Tuskaloosa, Ala.
> "Insane Hospital"
> Sept 25. 1906

Gov Wm D. Jelks.

Dear Sir:—

Will try to make my letter as brief as possible. I am a deep dyed criminal (from force of circumstances) confined in the Insane Hospital at Tuskaloosa.[25] Was "sent up" from Marshall Co sixteen years ago for an unsuccessful attempt at house burning Was placed before an inexperienced set of physicians, declared insane, and sent to the Hospital, instead of being tried for house firing and given the benefit of a piece of *hemp* or a life sentence in the Penitentiary, as would have been, had I been a negro or a white woman of low class family, destitute of *moneyed relations and influential friends.* When I arrived here I was pronounced sane by the "Hospital Medical Board" which was composed of the Supt, the late Dr Bryce, and three physicians—Dr's Somerville of Tuskaloosa, and Wright and Bondurant now of Mobile. Dr Searcy who has been in charge here for the past fourteen years, has all the while (within the walls of the Institution) stoutly asserted that I was "not insane", but that he "could not send me from the Hospital as it would be a disgrace to go to the Penitentiary".[26] Every physician who has had charge of the female department, has agreed with me, that my mind was not in the least disordered, but well balanced, no discoverable delusions, and that my deportment was that of a sane sensible woman. I have all these many years felt keenly the injustice of my

—————————————————————————

25. Given this explanatory introduction, Sheffield was evidently aware that her earlier letters to the Governor had been intercepted.
26. Sheffield is quoting Searcy's spoken word here. In no written document does Searcy say this.

having been sent here, (through by the insanity route) and felt more keenly the great injustice of having been detained here, only because the Supt is not willing to make a truthful public statement, that I was not insane when sent here, only sent here to keep me out of the Penitentiary, and also for fear that some one might censure him for having been instrumental in having a woman of a respectable family sent to the Penitintiary. I have beged and plead for justice, until I have almost despaired. My only wish and desire, is that justice be meted out to me, given a term, even if for life in the Penitintiary. I crave justice, I yearn for it, I pray for it, for that alone will *attone* for the crime. As for the crime, I would do the same again tomorrow, under the same circumstances, even did I know as I now do. After detaining me here all these many years, and declaring me sane when sent here, the Supt would be perfectly willing that I go to Marshall for trial, knowing that a jury would be more than apt to discharge me after having been detained sixteen years. One would hardly think Dr Searcy so disloyal to the State as to detain a rational, "deep dyed criminal" all these many years. The fact of my having been detained here sixteen years, would satisfy the jury that I was thought to have been insane when sent to the Hospital. While I am by no means an ignorant woman, yet like most women, I'm not posted as to law, more especially as to the power of the Gov—If I ask any thing out of your power attribute it to ignorance on my part.

Before sent here I had what I think was a preliminary trial (besides being tried for insanity)[.]

This, is what I wish to know, could you have me sent direct from the Hospital to the Penitintiary—sentence me yourself? Or if I should go to Marshall for trial, could you force and compel Dr Searcy to furnish me with a written statement as to my *sanity* when sent to the Hospital, signed by Dr's Bondurant, Somerville and Wright, and sworn to in the presence of an officer authorized to administer an oath? If you can do this say so, if not say so, be positive and plain. I have been underminded and baffled with until I want nothing but candor. Have had the wrong thing put upon me by men, had to shoulder so much wrong, until I have a horror of the wrong. I tax my brain daily trying to separate right from wrong. Have tried to explain my case, as but I would. It is not necessary to address the Supt, write me at your earliest convenience.

I am a daughter of the late James L Sheffield.

                                              (Miss) A. M. Sheffield.
                                              Tuskaloosa.
                                              Box. 268.}   Ala.

Montgomery
September 28, 1906
GOV. JELKS TO SHEFFIELD[27]

At last, a letter Sheffield wrote to Jelks had reached him. The Governor's response, however, is reminiscent of those of his predecessors.

ॐ ॐ

Miss Andrew Sheffield, Montgomery, Alabama, September, 28, 1906.
P. O. Box 268, Tuscaloosa, Ala.

My dear Miss Sheffield,

I habe [*sic*] received your letter of May 3d, and also your longer letter of September 25th, and have carefully read the contents of both of them. Your letter certainly does not read as if it might have been penned by an insane woman. Your statement of your case is very clear and very explicit, and your letter, on the whole, is unusually lucid. I will have to say to you, however, that I have no authority to take you out of the insane asylum, and put you in the penitentiary. The only way you can get into the penitentiary is after a trial in the Courts of Marshall County, or in the county in which the offense is said to have been committed.

I am sorry that I cannot meet with your wishes. It would gratify me to accomodate you if I could see my way clear to do it.
I am,

Faithfully yours,
Wm. D. Jelks,

May 25, 1907
SHEFFIELD TO SEARCY[28]

Sheffield was ill when she wrote the following and believed that she

---

27. Identified as a copy.
28. Dated by a notation on the letter: "Received May. 25th/07. J. T. Searcy."

*was dying. As a result, she adopts an uncharacteristically contrite tone
and attempts to settle accounts with her longtime antagonist.*

ह॰ ह॰

Dr Searcy.

This, no doubt is my last letter for my eyesight is fast failing. I realize
my awful condition, for of course when my sight is entirely gone, then I
will be in a far worse condition than if dead, at least I feel so, I'm under
the impression that when blind I would be put on a violent ward, but it is
only the *body* that can be hurt here. I am not only loosing my eyesight but
my general health is failing, my mind is also weakening, at least I think
so. When I die I do not object to you letting my relatives know it, but of
course I do not expect any thing but to be buried in the Hospital grave
yard. When gone I hope you will throw the mantel of sympathy and charity over all my missdeeds, and attribute every thing to a troubled, if not to
an insane mind. You have been kind to me, in many ways, have allowed
me many priviliges and I have all the while appreciated your kindness
more than my disposition would allow me to show. If I have ever wronged
you I ask forgiveness. I am trying to prepare for death, for I have felt impressed for several months that I would not live long, and I believe that
God has impressed that on my mind for my good. While I feel that my
mind is weakening I am not altogether unbalanced. I did not write you the
letter yesterday[29] in bad humor—or through ill will to any one, when my
fifteen dollars came up missing I was in good health and I enjoyed having
money, and the loss of it worried me, it troubled and grieved me, and of
course I talked about it, but if I live I hope I can feel different about this
and reconcile myself to it, that is, if she[30] did butcher me. I had the money
and I knew that if I put my money in the center building that you would
have every dime of it spent in burying me. I have long since forgiven Miss
Mattie and Miss Buck for the loss of fifteen dollars, and left it all with
them and God, I must forgive if I expect forgiveness. Miss Mattie for years
has been as kind to me as one could have been, and I appreciated it, and
loved her for her kindness to me, at the same time I know hers and Miss
Buck faults and weakness, and had my mind been natural I would not have
placed the money in their hands. The weak condition of my mind caused

---

29. This letter is missing.
30. Probably a reference to Mattie Parr, the Assistant Supervisor.

me to do it, and while I am not mad with her, it does hurt me a little, to think she would take the advantage of my weak mind, for she knew that if natural I would not have trusted her—for they know I have cause to doubt them; and when I put the money in the envelope, a week before I gave it to her, it was my intention to give it to Dr Lanford[31] to take to you, but would forget it, every morning. I had eighty dollars in gold, I kept out ten and put seventy in the envelope—God knows that I did—would say that I did, if I knew I would die before night. I gave it to her I think, on Monday and my mind was not in a condition to realize my mistake in giving her the money until Thursday. Fate has been against me in money matters, you have been so kind to let me have my money, and spend it as I liked, and although I try to keep it out of Miss Matties and Miss Bucks hands, they get it. My kin do not send me, any big amount but a little at a time, and I do not spend it foolishly, besides I do fancy work for the nurses, and had saved up that amount—, I cannot say that Miss Mattie opened the envelope and took any of my money, but if there is not seventy dollars in the envelope, she did, and I would say it, if I knew I would die in less than an hour—and I am very scared to die. If I loose my sight, I will not need money, blind people need nothing; and if I live and get well, if the money comes up less than seventy dollars I will try to forgive, and not let it worry me, for if she can live with it and get to heaven, I can live without it and get there but I cannot help feeling a little hurt with Miss Mattie to think she would take the money from my hands, knowing that I knew her weakness. Don't get mad with me Dr Searcy, I like you, I am one criminal that cannot say as Bob Watts[32] did that you have had me cruelly treated, for if on the stand in the court house, I could say that you had never had me cruelly treated. But the Bible teaches us to tell the truth, and for that reason I say there was seventy dollars in the envelope when I gave it to Miss Mattie, and I do not know that she opened it, and took any of it, but I know their weakness and if there is any thing short of seventy dollars, she did do it, and God knows it. Don't get mad with me, for God knows I am telling the truth when I say there was seventy dollars in the envelope, whether there is now, or not.

A. M. Sheffield

Dr Searcy don't let Dr Lanford punish me for writing this.

---

31. John A. Lanford, who became her ward doctor in 1907.
32. Another patient from Marshall County who was sent to the Hospital as unable to stand trial for reasons of insanity. He was later released, tried, and executed.

October 12, 1907
SHEFFIELD TO SEARCY[33]

Sheffield's health improved, and as it did, her tone of contrition disappeared. In the following, her anger resurfaces. She tells Searcy she plans to write the legislator who had headed the Investigative Commission that looked into alleged abuses in the Hospital during August 1907.

Dr Searcy.

You will not listen to any thing I say, so have to write, regardless the consequences. When the Legislature meets I intend writing Mr King[34] and have him put my case before the house, and know what can be done for me—if any thing. Will not ask any of you to post my letter, for you would not do it. Do not like to take the advantage of you, but when it is so much to my interest to do so, I feel justifiable[.] I will not abuse the Hospital, have no cause to do that, will plead my own case, beg and plead for justice. You will never do your duty in my case unless you are forced by law, so I feel it my right to appeal to the Legislature[.] The word of the Hospital authorities broke Bob Watts neck, (that is, the newspapers stated that the authorities pronounced him sane)[.] He had to suffer the extreme penalty for a crime some other man committed; he plead innocence to the last, and he was innocent, while I openly acknowledge my guilt, and you not willing to do your duty in my case. Why the difference? The difference is in the rank and station of the two families. You are only throwing words away to say anything to me about my kin taking me out of the Hospital. I was not sent here for any one of them to take me out—not one of them have ever mentioned the subject or expressed themselves, I have sense to know that they do not want me out. Why should they want me out of the Hospital? What could they do with me? now what do you think they could do with me? They could not keep me in their homes—I am not worthy of eating one meal from the swill buckets in the homes of any of my kin, I am

---

33. Dated by a notation on the outside of the folded letter: "File Miss Sheffield Oct. 12./07."
34. Jere C. King was the Chairman of the legislature's Investigative Commission of 1907 and the person most responsible for getting the legislature to examine alleged abuses at the Hospital. No letter to King has survived.

not worthy of sleeping one night on the kitchen floor in the homes of any of my kin, and you know it as well as I do, so what do you think they could do with me? Were they a low class, it would be quite different, but you must remember that my use to be kin, rank as you and yours do, why yes, indeed, consequently they could not have me in their homes, neither would I want them to, I think too much of them for that. When Oliver Street comes to see me, not one word will I say to him, or he to me on the subject of going out of the Hospital. Was not sent here for them to take me out, and they should not, even if they wanted to, although I would give my hope of Heaven to be free from it; (every one, even I have a little hope, although the Bible says I will not get there.) I thought I would die last winter, so I phoned to Tuskaloosa for Oliver Street to come out to see me, but he had gone, so he wrote me when he got home that he did not come, only because I had often written him not to come.[35] Had a letter from him six weeks ago, stating that he would be in Tuskaloosa soon and would come to see me. I do not want him to come now, but I will let him come, as he stoutly asserts that to visit me would not reflect on his family. All my kin are well posted as to my wishes and wants, they all know I want the Pen—and that if I can't get that, I prefer to remain here, rather than be acquitted of a crime that the Hospital authorities have all the while claimed that I was responsible for. I think sometimes, that the trouble with you is, that you do not believe I want to go to the Pen—Of course it seems unreasonable to you that a patient should want to leave the *Hospital,* even to go to their houses. I will admit that it is an earthly Heaven for employes, but I have never known but one patient who I thought had any cause whatever to want to remain in the Hospital, but if I was worshiped, and idolized by the authorities as she is, and fared as she does, I would beg for the Pen. No I will not abuse the Hospital in my letter to the Legislature, will only plead my case, for if you can be forced to send me to Marshall Co in a way that the jury could not acquit me, I want it done. I do not know that my letter would amount to any thing for the Legislators might treat it according to Dr Wymans knowledge of the patients—"all liars, and proof against telling the truth;"[36] however I will try it, so if you want to punish

---

35. As the U.S. District Attorney for the northern district of Alabama from 1907 to 1914, Street came to Tuscaloosa fairly frequently.

36. B. L. Wyman was an assistant physician in the Hospital from 1881 to 1884. He later established a private practice and taught at the medical school in Birmingham. In 1907 he testified before the legislature's investigating committee. Sheffield's remarks here refer to his comments before that committee. While he did not say word for word what she attributes to him here, he did testify at length that ex-patients' testimony should be viewed skeptically. When one Commission member asked him whether the testimony

me for writing the Legislators you can do so, I am willing to go to any violent ward on the grounds. I feel that it is my right to do it.

A. M. Sheffield.

Ward No. 4

Ca. 1907

SHEFFIELD TO SEARCY[37]

This brief note suggests that Sheffield's relationship with Searcy had continued to worsen.

Dr. Searcy.

Had much rather talk than write, but you will not listen to any thing I say.

I have been told that you were getting up a crowd for the alms houses throughout the state.[38] What about the Criminals for the Pen? There are two sane criminals on 4, and many others scattered throughout the building, suppose you favor us—the most unfortunate class in the building. I had a long talk with Col. John[39] when here, not about the said to be crulties [sic] of the Hospital, but about my own case. He told me that the law could force you to make a truthful statement as to my sanity when sent

---

of a former patient who was completely recovered could be trusted, Wyman answered that "because of the [former] confused state, [such ex-patients] get things mixed up." He went on to discuss what he called "paranoics" who have fixed delusions, often about their treatment, and make statements about bad treatment that they genuinely believe but that are nonetheless false. See typescript "Official Report," Investigative Commission, Session of August 30, 1907, pp. 20–24; quotation, p. 20, State Hospitals Collection, ADAH. Sheffield surely never read this transcript, but did read newspaper reports which covered and perhaps paraphrased the testimony. See, for example, the Montgomery *Advertiser*, August 31, 1907, p. 1.

37. Dated by references to ward assignments. Sheffield wrote this letter before being sent to Ward No.14 in November 1907. Further, the letter refers to the charges of cruelty leveled against the Hospital, also in 1907. It also refers to a conversation that she had with Trustee Samuel Will John of Birmingham. Out-of-town Trustees usually visited the Hospital only in the fall of each year.

38. On occasion Searcy returned chronically insane paupers to their home counties for custodial care. In this way, he could free up bed space for more acutely insane patients

39. Samuel Will John, a Hospital Trustee from 1899 to 1922.

here, that you could be forced before a grand jury same as any other man. That the same law was for you that was for all other men.

A. M. Sheffield.

Ca. 1907

SHEFFIELD TO DR. JOHN A. LANFORD[40]

This letter, to her new ward doctor, recounts her troubles with a former physician, Thomas F. Taylor, who had recently left the Hospital. It has a tone of introduction about it.

Dr. Lanford.

I am not speaking to you, but it is not because I am angry with, or hate you. You have given me no cause to hate you. For a year I have been worried and agrevated by Dr Taylor coming to my room, to my door, speaking to, and picking at me, throwing my prominence up to me, sending me to the "cross hall", and giving all kinds of orders concerning myself, besides giving me something in my medicine that he should not have given; kept me worried and agrevated beyond measure. I only want to be let alone in health, and when sick pass me by, for I deserve to suffer intense pain, am not worthy even one dose of medicine at States expense, unless it be a *fatal* dose.

A. M. Sheffield.

Ward No. 4

Ca. October 1907

SHEFFIELD TO SEARCY[41]

---

40. Dated only approximately. Sheffield says here that she had been recently upset with Dr. Taylor. The letter is to Lanford, however. Lanford probably replaced Taylor in 1907.

41. Dated by the reference to "Crenshaw's statement," testimony before the Investigative Commission in August of 1907. Also, Sheffield was still on nurse Lil Curry's ward (No. 4) at this letter's writing. From later, dated letters, it is known that Sheffield was moved from Ward No. 4 to No. 14 on November 3, 1907.

The following begins a series of letters in which Sheffield discusses her troubles with Lil Curry, the nurse in charge of Ward No. 4, a front ward where Sheffield had resided for much of the past ten years (with occasional brief stints on the back wards).

ટ્ઠ ટ્ઠ

Dr Searcy

You must give me a change, for I cannot, and will not stay with Lillie Curry any longer. I am willing to go to any lower floor, or to a cross hall,[42] if you think I deserve punishment for disputing her word. Did you read Mrs Crenshaws statement?[43] Did she tell any lies on you? Yes, she told two positive lies, so did Lillie Curry lie on me. I have never tried to distress a patient since I have been here, and when I fall out with any of the employes I never try to influence or turn other patients against them. I am not entirely destitute of principle and good qualities, if I am as Tom Taylor said "the most prominent woman in the State.["] This year with Lillie Curry has been the most miserable part of my stay here. We have gotten on badly all the year, only because I would resent her mean treatment, and go to Miss Buck to settle matters—and Miss Buck doing her duty by me, caused Lillie to dislike me more. I see there is no hope of her being changed, so I must go, for as we have not gotten on so far, we could not get on peacably hereafter, and I am tiard of having to fuss. She dislikes me, and I dislike her, I am high tempered—so is she, and she is so very exasperating that she might cause me to do something in heat of passion

---

42. A cross hall, sometimes called a "strong room" or a "seclusion room," was a separate room to which uncontrollable patients were sent. New patients often spent time there before being assigned to a regular room. When Sheffield came to the Hospital, it was common for these rooms to have no furniture, except in some cases a mattress. There was a box in which patients could relieve themselves. Windows were above eye level so that the patient could not see out. In 1893 the Superintendent reported to the Trustees that the Hospital had improved the sixty strong rooms by enlarging their windows to "as much as possible destroy the jail-like appearances. . . . " See "Superintendent's Report," Trustees Meeting, October 4, 1893, *Trustees Minute Book 1*:[214], Staff Library, Bryce Hospital.

43. Mrs. M. F. Crenshaw, a patient from January 1903 to June 1904, testified on August 21, 1907, when the Commission took testimony in Montgomery. She was, like Sheffield, very critical of Mary Buck, calling her an "old maid who never had her heart expanded, and [who] is cruel to the feminine sex." She testified to being placed in a cross hall, being sent to violent wards as punishment, being denied her Bible, and never being given enough to eat. See the Montgomery *Advertiser*, August 22, 1907, p. 8.

that I would regret a life-time so I think it best that we separate. Had rather stay on No 4 than any ward, suits me best, but I will go to any lower ward to get away from Lillie. I wish you would make the change soon, for I am sick, have had neuralgia a little in my shoulder several days. I am very sorry that she caused a disturbance between Dr Lanford and myself, for he has been kind to me, and I have tried to be nice and pleasant with him, he has been better to me, and did more for me when sick than all of the Dr's—but here, it is "friends today, and enemies tomorrow."

I could not stay on any of the upper floors[44]—for many reasons—one is that it hurts my back and side to go up the steps. Lillie has wanted me off the hall all the year—and I asked Miss Buck a month ago to change me[.] Some time ago, she said a good deal about my being here as I was—and of course that caused me to dislike her more, she should not throw stones—she has two sisters of disreputable character.

Dr Searcy you must change me I am willing to go back to the violent wards and never ask to leave them although I don't think I have done any thing to justify my going, but I cannot stay with Lillie.

I have never said that there was *nothing* the matter with Mrs Williamson[45] have been here too long with the insane to say that. Change me as soon as you can—don't care where you put me—or what punishment you give— I'm at your mercy. You can't expect a nurse to get along with patients that can't get on with nurses—Lillie can't get on with any one on the same ward with her. The other patients would be as glad to leave her as I would be—but you could not get one to say so—afraid.

A. M. Sheffield.

Ward No. 14

Ca. November 1907

SHEFFIELD TO LANFORD[46]

Sheffield's troubles with Curry worsened, and on November 3, 1907, the staff moved her to Ward No. 14, a "punishment" ward which she had occupied in the 1890s. This letter throws light on the patients' role in the

44.   The Hospital had three stories.
45.   A patient.
46.   Dated by Sheffield's reference to her having been recently sent to Ward No. 14. She moved there November 3, 1907.

recent legislative investigation. It also levies a serious charge at Supervisor Mary Buck.

કે કે

Dr Lanford

You men had as well stay away from me, for I will not speak to any of you, will not multiply words with you. You have done what Lillie Curry and Buck wanted you to do. I am under *punishment* on account of being *willfully* and *maliciously lied* on by Curry and Buck and I think you ought to be willing to let me alone. Had I gone before the committee[47] and *berated* the Hospital, and told the committee about Mary Buck drinking whiskey as Mrs Barnwell[48] did no doubt I would have been on No 4 now. This is the pay and thanks Dr Searcy has given me for writing up *only* the *good* that could be said of it.[49] Who has been benefitted on account of my punishment, Buck and Curry, it has given them pleasure. I don't suppose your pet Mrs Williamson[50] feels any better by it, and is no doubt *flat on her back* today, the same "*old crazy woman*", she was the day I came to No 14. It matters not how much you pet and "doll baby" her she will remain the same "old crazy woman" and you cannot make any thing else out of her. You get no praise from any of the employes from mistreating me on account of Lillie Curry's *lies,* she is very unpopular among the nurses, for many, very many nurses have *wilted* under Mary Bucks *tongue clash* on account of a lie told on them by Lillie Curry, so you see they are prepared to sympathize with the patients when mistreated on account of her *lies.* The foundation of this matter is, that Lillie Curry told Buck after the committee left that I advised Mrs Barnwell to tell them that she (Buck) drank whiskey. Mrs Barnwell told the truth but I *did not* tell her to do it. A few sundays after the committee left, I, as well as many others, saw Miss Bagwell[51] come in at No 1 door (from the annex) with a glass of whiskey, for Mary Buck—I said to Lillie Curry that a girl who would stay here and "trot round" for whiskey for Mary Buck was no account. Lillie Curry told Buck of what I had said, and she quit speaking to me. Soon after, I was talking with you about the whiskey being voted out of Tuskaloosa Co, and

---

47. The Investigative Commission of 1907.
48. A fellow patient.
49. Sheffield evidently wrote a statement for the Commission which was never presented. Neither did she testify.
50. A "private" patient whose family rather than the state paid her expenses.
51. A nurse.

I told you that I hoped not a drop could be brought here, that I never saw a *drunk woman* until I came here, Lillie told Buck of what I had said, the cap fitted her, so she got furiously mad with me, and went out, so I was told, and told you that I wanted to go to No 14. I had not said one word to her about going to any ward, you failed to send me, so when you went away, she went out so I was told, and told Dr's Searcy and Partlow that I wanted to go to No 14, which was positively false. I never said one word to her about going to any ward, for she had not spoken to me for three weeks, not since Curry told her of what I said to you about the drunk woman. I wrote Dr Searcy and you that I was willing to go to any cross hall or violent ward in the building to get away from Curry (No 14 is not in the building)[.] It is not reasonable to suppose that I would have asked to have gone to one of Dr Partlows[52] wards, to suffer under his treatment when sick, as did two years ago. No indeed I did not want to go to one of his wards. Mary Buck was mad about what had been said about whiskey, and wanted me on No 14. Lillie Curry told me when she first came on No 4, about Mary Buck sending her with another nurse to annex for whiskey after nine o clock at night, but Curry took care not to tell any thing she had said. It is no new sight to see a nurse coming from some ward with a small glass of whiskey, I have seen it ever since I came here, but I never saw a drunk woman until two years ago.

I told Mary Buck a year ago, that so long as she treated me half way right I did not care how much she drank. She claimed that she bathes her feet in it. Mary Buck being mad about what had been said about whiskey was the cause of her telling Dr's Searcy and Partlow that I wanted to go to No 14. I had made up my mind that I would settle down, and bother no more about Lillies *lieing* on me, when the nurse came sunday morning and told me that Dr's Searcy and Partlow said I must go to No 14, but did not know for several days after that she had told them that I wanted to go. Had Curry told Buck previous to committee coming here that I was distressing Mrs Williamson she would have given it no attention, for Buck knows that it is not my nature to want to distress any one, but as she was mad with me about the whiskey, she told Curry to tell you, for Buck knows that a *lie* will stir me up. Though it would have amounted to nothing had you entered my room in a good humor and given me the benefit of a doubt. Had Lillie told you that I was distressing any of the poor indigents, I doubt that you would have given it a moments thought. Mrs Williamson is private— educated, very intelligent, an income of her own, and a family interested in her, and a son in Birmingham to write you letters, thanking you for your

---

52. W. D. Partlow.

kind treatment of his mother—I am destitute of all that—am friendless, ignorant, poverty stricken, homeless, and disgraced. But after all I'm not destitute of feeling? Has it ever occured to any of you that a prostitute and criminal was not entirely destitute of feeling? Have you ever thought that I even I, was not destitute of feeling? Tom Taylor throwing my prominence into my face did not hurt my feelings, for that was true, it made me mad, but in this case it was a *lie* that give me trouble. I was just as far from wanting to distress your *pet* as the east is from the west, and any one man or woman who says that I wanted to distress Mrs Williamson tells a *lie*. You men have done your do, had me put on 14 for punishment, and were you men of feeling and principle you would be satisfied with what you have done and let me alone. I think your object in coming into my room is to get me stired up so that I will go on the ward and "bless you out" as I did Tom Taylor, giving you an excuse to have me put in a cold cross hall, so that I will get down with rheumatism and suffer under Dr Partlows treatment as did several years ago. I have often said that 14 ought to be only for prostitutes and criminals. You have three very prominent ones out here now. But the trouble is a *lie* put me on it. If any nurse here had told a *lie* on me and caused me punished, except Lillie Curry it would not have hurt me so much. She is the most ignorant, heartless, unfeeling and un-principled woman I have ever been with, and of one of the most disrepu-table families in the state, and that was why it made me mad, that she had so much to say about my being here as I am, she with two sisters living open immoral lives, mothers of illegitimate children, and living with other weomens husbands, for *that reason,* she should not have expressed herself so freely about me, when she first went to No 4. I am not bothering any of you, the beautiful Miss Curry, or the *loveable* Mrs Williamson, so I think you, Dr's Searcy and Partlow should be satisfied to stay away from me and let me alone. I am under punishment on account of the *lie* Lillie told on me about Mrs Williamson, and for what she told Mary Buck I had said about whiskey. If every woman was punished for talking that—none would escape. What people see with their own eyes they know to be true, and they will talk it. I have had as little to say about the whiskey as any woman here, but as Lillie did not like me she told Buck of what I said. Not a nurse would owne to it, for fear of loosing their positions. I mean they would not owne it to any of you, no indeed. I hope you will be merciful enough and have just enough pity for me to let me alone, and not come in to worry and agrevate me every morning. Dr Searcy will be more than apt to get rid of me this winter, for I could not live through a severe attack of rheumatism under Dr Partlows treatment, that is, if he should let me suffer as did two years ago. You all should remember that when you are picking at me, you are worrying a *"nothing* and *nobody*[.]'' Who have you mis-treated & punished? just think for a moment, a friendless, homeless, pov-erty stricken outcast—criminal and prostitute, unworthy the notice of the lowest vagabond in the state. You all stay away from me, and I will cer-tainly not speak to any of you, ask no favors of you, and write you no more letters—but I still say and will 'till the end of the chapter that I was in-nocent of wanting to distress Mrs Williamson (your pet) as you Dr's Searcy and Partlow were, and Mary Buck would not have had Lillie to tell you—but for what I had said about the whiskey, just what every one talks.

A. M. Sheffield.

***

Ward No. 14

Ca. late 1907

SHEFFIELD TO LANFORD[53]

Sheffield unleashes at Lanford a level of bitterness earlier reserved only for Searcy and Buck. Behind the vitriol is a wealth of detail about Sheffield's own self-awareness and the asylum's routine.

***

"Dr" Lanford.

"Dr" Partlow told me several days ago, that you had inquired into my health, and how I was getting on? Will say that I am getting on as any woman would, with even *one drop* of *proud blood* in her body, after being *"blessed out,"* and put under punishment on account of a *lie* told on her by an unfeeling unprincipled, heartless ignorant woman.[54] I do not appre-ciate your making any inquiry as to my self—but would appreciate your not giving me a moments thought. No one to blame in this matter but "Dr" John Lanford. I think I know a little of "Dr" Partlow but, he had nothing to do with it—so far as I know, [*sic*] It is not my nature to blame one, for what another is guilty of, but, to place the blame exactly where it should be. "Hew the line, let the chips fall where they may"", no [*sic*] this, the chips fall heavily upon your shoulders, for you alone mistreated me,

---

53. Sheffield probably wrote this letter soon after being sent there November 3, 1907.
54. A reference to nurse Lil Curry.

and through your mistreatment I was put under what you call punishment. True, "Dr" Partlow is said to have charge of the "East side,"[55] but I was in your ward, under your treatment, in your charge, and received worse treatment, and was more neglected when sick, (unable to do for myself) by the so-called nurse than ever before. Had you treated Lil Currys report as you did mine there would have been nothing of this. When I told you she was not giving my medicine according to your directions, you laughed in my face and said nothing to her; but when she told you that I was worrying your *private* pet patient, you were only too glad to come into my room, "stepping as high as a blind horse", your face as red as a beet to bless me out; and gave me orders that I must not give a nurse the *lie,* as much as to say, "she is too good to be given the lie, but you are not too good to be lied on", when I said that I would ask Williamson about it, oh: no you must not, for it would worry her, as much to say, "*she* is too good to be worried but you are not." You were not willing to give the friendless prostitute and criminal the chance of a "good yard dog". Think you, that I can ever forget this,? never, never. As soon as you were off the ward I went to Williamsons room and asked her about it, she denied it to me. I gave her orders that she must never speak to me again—much less come into my room. After you had "blessed me out" you went into her room and "patted her and talked your usual baby talk to her, so the nurse, (Roycroft) said. You have done less for Williamsons good than any of the Dr's, others would have her made to stay off the bed, go out in sunshine and air, and have the nurses *swab* out her rotten mouth to help keep down the terrible order [sic]. Now the nurses and patients have to contend with the terrible odor, only because she is a private patient, I heard Lil Curry read Mrs Williamsons history, and it was nice of course compared with my fathers trial, for that is what you all are governed by, but I'm human same as she is. And according to what she says I was reared in more ease and luxury than she was. This "blessing out" of indigents on account of private patients has come up here in the past three years. You all don't seem to realize that there are many poverty stricken weomen here who have known "ease and plenty", there are, and I'm sorry to say, I'm one of them. I'm between two private patients now, no fears of Roper having me "blessed out" for Dr's Searcy and Partlow don't seem to like her any more than they do me, but seem to have quite a preference for Fowls.[56] I reported Curry last spring to Mary Buck for not doing any thing for me when sick,

---

55. Women's wards were located on the east side of the large hospital. Partlow was Lanford's immediate supervisor.
56. Roper and Fowls were the private patients on Ward No. 14.

it made Lil mad, and she told nurses and patients that she would "get even with me", and so she did by telling a lie on me. I would not have been mistreated and put under punishment on account of Lil Curry not for any amount of money. I know her, you do not, you have only seen her before the scenes, while I have seen before and behind the scenes, was with her day and night for eleven months. Had I been well I would not have stayed on the hall with her three months, but was sick, and low spirited, and thought I could not give my room up on 4, but after all I had to give it up. I was cruely treated my first year here, but had rather had that cruel treatment again, than this. I can see no good that has come from that "blessing out" except Lillie Curry has the pleasure of knowing that it came about through her. It made enemies of Williamson and myself—enemies of Lil and myself, enemies of you and myself (Buck and myself were already enemies)[.] Had you done your duty, had her given me kind treatment when sick, no doubt she and myself would have been on speaking terms. True, Mrs Burton[57] suffered more from neglect of Currys duties than I, for she was in a more helpless condition than I, and she was a better, more worthy, and less deserving such treatment than I. (I was glad when the breath left her, for I as well as many others, was an eye witness to her inhumane treatment.) No don't you think for a moment that I will ever forgive. I had rather been mistreated on account of Aunt Laura, Sue or Clara[58] than on account of Curry. I would not have had it gone through the building that her *lies* sent me to 14, not for any amount, more especialy as she is known to be the woman she is, among nurses and patients. Had I been in the least guilty, it would be quite different. I had been nice and pleasant with you, gave you no trouble, made no complaints to you of her treatment, bore it all in silence except complained to Mary Buck and Miss Mattie once, and told you that she did not give medicine. True Dr's Searcy and Partlow had me sent to 14, but your "blessing me out["] was the foundation of that, so, no one to blame but "Dr" John Lanford. I had been fighting, quarreling or fussing, true I had sit in my room and cried several weeks as any woman would have, with one drop of *proud blood* in her body after being blessed out on account of such a woman as I know Curry

---

57. A patient.
58. These were black women who worked in the Hospital and who in their spare time accompanied women patients to town. Aunt Laura is probably Laura Cole or Laura Dodson, both ward attendants in the early twentieth century. Sue is probably the woman identified as Susie Perkins on the manuscript census for 1910 who was then thirty-five years old and is described as a laundress. Clara is probably Clara Hamilton, described in the 1900 census as a ward attendant, but in 1910 as a cook. She was twenty-seven in 1900.

to be. Had rather lain in cross hall twelve months, for I don't dread cross halls, I never asked to come out of one, except when put in on account of Tom Taylors impudence, and then only because I was suffering with dysentery.[59] When well I told Tom I was willing to go back to cross hall and serve out a twelve months term. No, do not think I fear a cross hall, neither am I afraid of the "pretty girl nurses" pulling my hair or beating me over the head. It has been done here in 1890—but will not do it again while I have my right mind and strength. I can't say that it is such a punishment to me to be on a violent ward, so far as my own part is concerned, but the horrible sights. I was so unjustly sent to 14 that I have no desire to leave it. No one to blame but you. "Dr" Partlow would not have had me sent to 14 unless Dr Searcy had agreed, and he agreed only because Buck told them that I wanted to go, she never heard me say that I wanted to go to 14, was mad because of the whiskey matter. I hope you will make no more inquiry about me, saving me the trouble of writing long letters. You go on and pat and talk baby talk to your pet, (as the nurses say you do) and give me not a moments thought. My sense of right and wrong is very *accute,* too much so to ever forgive you, for I was as innocent as you were. You said I had talked about Williamson on upper floors. I asked every patient and nurse on 2 and 5—and all denied it, I also asked Miss Connely[60] and she denied having told you any thing of the kind. No one told you but Curry, and her motive was to have me sent off the ward, and she succeeded. I was so unjustly sent to 14, I have no desire to leave it, although it is, as you all say "a place of punishment" more especialy is it, for sane weomen. For the past three years nurses have not only been allowed to mistreat the patients, but upheld in doing so, and I have tried to avoid the low class, knowing that I cannot submit quietly to their abuse—but I could not shun Lil Curry and she in the ward with me, and me in the bed sick. I hope you will get a little good out of my being under punishment, but I hope you will not give me a moments thought hereafter, but give all your pleasant thought to your pet.

(Miss) A. M. Sheffield.
"Bedlam".
Ala.

---

59. Her case history for May 6, 1906, refers to this event: "A few days ago this patient became very disrespectful to her physicians and talked very profanely. She created quite a scene on the ward so was sent to #7 [from No. 4] and slept the day and night in cross hall. She is very meek now and promises to conduct herself differently in the future." The note continues that she was allowed to return to No. 4, where she preferred to sit alone in her room so that no one could bother her. See *Case History Book #6*, p. 234.
60. A nurse.

෯

Ward No. 14

Late 1907

SHEFFIELD TO LANFORD[61]

Prompted by her recent bad experiences with nurse Curry, Sheffield vents her anger at the "pretty girl" nurses.

෯ ෯

Dr Lanford.

I was quietly seated on 4 hall[62] last Thursday night on my way to the "Negro Minstrel;" instead of you passing me by unnoticed, spoke to me as pleasantly as though you had done nothing to gain my ill will. I will not speak to you; for you had my good will, and could have kept it. You could come as near checking the sun in its onward course as to gain my good will. Tom Taylor had me in good "shape and trim" for the "bone yard", for he was giving me medicine for the purpose of putting me out of the way, and but for you I certainly would have gone there.[63] You treated me better, in way of giving me medicine, and relieving me of pain than all the Dr's. No, I cannot speak to you, for you have made a wide stream between us that can never be bridged, all on account of the willful and malicious lie told on me by Lillie Curry. ("the beautiful Lilly of the valley".) Not one of you need make any inquiry as to my wanting to go back to No 4. If I wanted to go, I could not stay there, for Mary Buck would not let me, so long as Dr Partlow is here, I suppose he will spend the remaining years of his life here; succeed Dr Searcy.[64] It is a well known and undeniable fact that she rules him, is only a tool within her hands, and no doubt that accounts for her not likeing him, (weomen never like men, who allow themselves ruled by them)[.] After she failed to get me on 14 through you, she took advantage of your absence knowing that she could work her plans through Dr's Searcy and Partlow. She wanted me on 14, she seems to think 14 a place of great punishment. It is not a place of punishment and Miss

---

61. Dated approximately by Sheffield's ward assignment.
62. Sheffield was only sitting in the hall of this ward before an evening amusement. Her ward assignment was still No. 14 at the time she wrote this letter.
63. This is a reference to her belief that Dr. Thomas Taylor had tried to poison her a few years before. See Sheffield to Lanford, ca. 1910, in chapter 3.
64. Partlow did succeed Searcy in 1919 and spent his entire career associated with the institution.

Saxon in charge. I was surprised that she did not have me sent to 14 when Dr Leach left here,[65] for she would have done so, for she could have *lied* me on it then, the same as now. She never heard me say that "I wanted to go to 14." She had only heard me say that I wished you would put me on 7 or 10 as I thought it very necessary that Lil Curry and myself be separated. I did want to leave No 4 but did not say that I wanted to go to 14. I knew far better than any of you, that it was best that Lil Curry and myself by separated. I had been treated so mean by her, until I entertained the greatest hatred for her, and she so very exasperating, I feared she would force me to do in a few moments what I would regret a life-time, for she had me wrought up to fighting point—and but one nurse on the ward. I say yet, she told a *lie* when she told you that I was intentionaly worrying Mrs Williamson.[66] She did *not*, tell a *lie* when she told her, that she heard me tell you that I never saw a drunk woman until I came here. I say that yet, and would if my life depended on it, for the "Recording Angel" does not book the truth *against* us. The first time I saw the sight was two years ago in the dining room, while putting breakfast on the tables, have seen the sight three times since, and heard of it many times, and there is not man force on the grounds sufficient to force me to take it back. It has been the impression, for several years, more especialy among the employes that the authorities know this. Mary Buck was furiously mad with Mrs Barnwell,[67] why did she not have Dr Partlow to send her to 14? because she knew Dr Searcy would not allow it. Why the difference in Mrs Barnwell and myself? the difference is this, she (Mrs Barnwell) unlike myself is a well educated, intilligent, refined dainty creature, a private patient, a family interested in her, is not a criminal, and not a prostitute so far as Dr Searcy knows, consequently she escaped punishment for telling the truth. Mary Buck treated me with freezing politeness from the time the committee left until she got me on 14. Mary Buck knew that I liked you, and knew that if you come on me about Currys *lies* that I would get mad with you. She does not want the patients to like the Dr's, never encourages their likeing them, does not like to hear patients speak well of, or give Sup't or Dr's any praise. She wants all praise herself, credit for all the *good* done but never willing to shoulder any of the *bad*. She told me while the committee[68] was here, that I had no right to give Dr Searcy any praise for

---

65. 1903.
66. Discussed in several earlier letters as one of Lanford's "pets." See, for example, Sheffield to Lanford, ca. late 1907.
67. Barnwell accused Buck of drinking in her testimony before the Commission in 1907.
68. The Investigative Commission, which visited the Hospital in August 1907.

any priviliges granted me, that but for *her* I would never have been allowed any privilege. No she does not like to here [*sic*] the patients, speak well of Dr Searcy, her best friend. I told you that Lil was not giving me my medicine, you laughed in my face, in Dr Tisdells[69] presence. If you and Dr Partlow want to do a good deed assist me in getting in the Pen—I had rather by a *trusty* convict at work—than here seated on any ward, to be treated according to lies told on me by weomen employes. It is certainly grinding to my feelings to be mistreated by and dictated to, and directed by the more common class nurses, unable to write legable, or read a paragraph in a newspaper correctly. You all will get rid of me before a great while. There is no chance for one to escape consumption, having asthma. God forbid that I should linger, and suffer for the want of attention from nurses, as other poor consumptives,[70] Mrs Burton who was in a more helpless condition than I received no attention from Curry except to take temperature and give medicine sent on waiter,[71] did not get her bottle medicine according to directions no more than I did. There has been but two nurses on No 4 since Dr Leach left here who would give the sick any attention, Park, and Bagwell, and Mary Buck and Miss Mattie know it. At one time last spring, my bed was not changed or made, for two weeks, because Mrs Mason[72] was sick, and not another one of the patients had sense to do it, but for all this you took Currys part and upheld her in telling the lie on me, did not reprove her, or tell her the importance of telling the truth. For all that you seem to think I ought to be nice and pleasant with you. I know it is natural for men to like pretty girls, but it is not right that their beauty should controle here among all of this suffering humanity. [T]he nurses are pretty—no reason why they should not be, they are (the majority) cotton patch and wash tub weomen—raised out doors in sunshine and fresh air, and are verry pretty, but we do not like to be *lied* on or mistreated by even a pretty girl. Hope you will not worry me by speaking to me again. Favor me by passing me by.

A. M. Sheffield.

---

69. M. L. Tisdale, not Tisdell, an assistant physician from 1907 to 1911.
70. Patients with pulmonary tuberculosis, an ailment quite common in institutions of all kinds in the early twentieth century.
71. A dumbwaiter.
72. A fellow patient whose duty it was to change the bedding on Ward No. 14.

Chapter 3

"THEY SURELY NEED ANOTHER DOROTHY DIX"

1908–1909

During the summer of 1907, a flurry of rumors about alleged abuses at Bryce Hospital resulted in a formal legislative investigation in August and September. Sheffield, however, did not participate. When the Commission came to Tuscaloosa in August, she offered no testimony. The nature of her complaints had largely been personal. She had never lobbied against the institution per se, only its role in what she considered her unique victimization. The letters in this chapter indicate that this long-held position changed in the aftermath of the investigation. Written after the Commission vindicated Searcy's administration, the letters suggest that conditions of life in the institution worsened rather than improved following 1907. Taken together, they offer a rare portrait of an asylum *after* an exposé.

Sheffield wrote these letters after being sent to the back wards for the first protracted period since the 1890s. Even though she had privileges seldom allowed on back wards (more furniture, including her own trunk, for example), she chafed under this reassignment, which she describes as a "punishment." Conditions on these wards were bad enough, she tells Dr. Lanford in 1909, "to make a sane patient . . . go insane." Perhaps because her perspective on the Hospital had shifted from the front wards to the back wards, she paints its portrait in increasingly malign tones.

Her last known letter to a governor—to Braxton Bragg Comer in 1908—epitomizes this altered viewpoint. All earlier letters to state executives narrowly plead her own case for removal to the penitentiary. This one makes no personal pleadings. Instead, it is an attack on the institution and a call for relief, not only for herself but for all the women patients. It is her only effort, albeit unconscious, to emulate "Dorothy Dix." Superintendent Searcy, however, foiled the attempt. He never mailed Comer the letter.

❧

January 7, 1908

EMMA STAUGH TO SHEFFIELD

Staugh, a former nurse, had accompanied Sheffield to an eye doctor in Tuscaloosa, George R. Rau, while still employed at the Hospital. Sheffield had written Staugh to ask for corroboration of the fact that she had indeed paid Rau for his services. Apart from its content, the letter is revealing in its affectionate tone toward Sheffield.

❧ ❧

Maares Bridge Ala.
Jan. 7 1908.

Miss A. M. Sheffield
     Tuscaloosa Ala.

my Dear Friend

I received your letter this A. M. Asking me about you Paying Dr. Rau, indeed you sure payed him for I was sure Present and know you did Pay him and are so sorry you have lost your receit[.] I would tell Dr Rau are any one else that you sure Payed him and you can let Dr Rau are any one read this letter that you want to. I am sure you Payed him. I remember it just as well as if it were only yesterday.

Write me at any time you wish

I am your
Loving
Friend
Emma Staugh

P. S. Excuse this letter as it is mail time and I want to get it off on time. Emma.

January 15, 1908

SHEFFIELD TO DR. GEORGE R. RAU

After getting Staugh's note, Sheffield wrote this angry letter to Dr. Rau. Because this letter, as well as Staugh's, remains in Sheffield's file, it is likely that Rau never received it.

Hospital.
Jan 15. 1908

Dr. Rau.

I send you a written statement from the ex nurse who was with me at your office and saw me pay you $15.00 for the glasses, and saw you give me a script.[1] You are now in my debt, will make out my account, hope you will settle at once and save farther trouble. You disturbed my rest and peace of mind which I value highly. A failure on your part to settle the bill will throw it in the hands of the sheriff of Tuscaloosa Co for collection, a failure on his part to collect it will result in your arrest, on a charge of forgery and false accusation, falsely accusing me of not paying a debt.

Nervous prostration	$5.00
Loss of sleep—five nights	$5.00
Failure to eat—8 meals	$2.00
	$12.00

A. M. Sheffield.

January 1908

SHEFFIELD TO LANFORD[2]

Sheffield here involves Lanford in the Rau affair. To this asylum inmate, the matter of a pair of glasses bore great emotional meaning.

---

1. A receipt.
2. Dated by reference to the preceding letter, which Sheffield dates January 15, 1908.

🙚 🙚

Dr. Lanford.

Dr. Rau did not give me a prescription to bring you—he said he would order glasses for me, and when he gets the glasses he can send them out, for I will certainly not go to his office to get them—I will not give him an opportunity of talking to me again as he did this morning—for he did not treat me with the courtesy that was due a good negro.

A. M. Sheffield.

🙚

Ward No. 14

Ca. 1908

SHEFFIELD TO SEARCY[3]

Sheffield discusses here the privilege of letter writing itself. She explains with considerable insight what she calls her "mania for writing letters" and the way in which letter writing has always served to vent her pent-up emotion.

🙚 🙚

Dr Searcy.

Ex Gov Johnston wrote me while in office that it was the duty of the Gov to send a commission of lunacy here to interview me in person if I wished it.[4] I am the deepest dyed, the most prominent criminal in the South, yet not a cent has been paid out by the State in my case, has not even cost Marshall Co a cent, for Judge Street paid from beginning to end.[5] As I am so very prominent I think it but right and just that I should cost the State enough to pay a commission of lunacy to interview me, don't you? I have been thinking for more than a year asking this of the

---

3. Dated by references to Partlow's discussion of Crump's testimony as being "last year." It was August 1907, when the former nurse, Freda Crump, testified before the legislature's Investigative Commission.
4. Probably a reference to Johnston's letter of July 19, 1897, in chapter 1.
5. There is no evidence that Street paid for her care as a private patient. Sheffield was always listed as an "indigent" or "criminal" patient.

Gov, provided he would compel you, Dr's Somerville, Bondurant, Wright and Leach[6] to appear and testify in my presence. I could have written and "slipped the letter out," but as it was a buisness matter I did not think it right to take advantage of you. So if you will promise not to allow Dr Partlow to place the letter on "file with my bond" I will write the Gov.
Dr's Bondurant and Leach sent my letters out, regardless as to whom they were to, or as to the contents. Never until Dr Partlow came, did I ever fail to get answers to my letters. According to what he says he should not object to sending out any thing that I might write. I'm a prostitute; and he said to Miss Rutherford[7] in speaking of Miss Crump last year, (so the nurses said) that "she need have no fears, that a prostitutes word was never taken, that they were not allowed an oath, and that it was unlawful to credit any statement made by them."[8] Col John[9] told me that he was mistaken, that he had "known some cases gained through their evidence[.]" If you all think that I am the only patient who has "sliped letters out," you are mistaken, take my word for it, that I am not alone, not by several, and theirs have gone out through the *same hands* that mine have. I'm the only one caught up with, so far as I know. I've known for more than a year, that my "slipped out letters" were falling into your hands, but I did not care. As for my part I wish you knew who this very accomodating employe was, I wish you could get up with them and put a stop to it, not because it is against "the rules," for no rule has been carried out for several years that was for the good of the patients, but simply no good comes from "slipping out letters," at least no good has come to *me*. I have all through my life, had a *mania* for writing, and all the trouble I've ever had, came from my pen. (My name would not today be Sheffield but for my *pen*[.]) So far as I know all the trouble I've had here came from my pen, except this trouble came from Lil Currys lies. I'm by writing as Darby[10] is by stealing—when she sees any thing she wants she is miserable, wretched and nervous until she gets it—so am I wretched until I write the letter—an indescribable feeling and one over which I've had no controle. After writing the letter I feel relieved as though a great burden had been lifted off me. Sometimes after the letters are gone I'd give my life to have them back, and feel miserable and wretched on account of hav-

6. Sydney Leach, a former assistant physician.
7. A nurse.
8. The Hospital's lawyers produced witnesses to testify that Crump was a prostitute and that her testimony was therefore presumably unreliable. See "Official Report" of the Commission, 40–46.
9. Trustee Samuel Will John.
10. A patient.

ing written the letter, as was before writing it. Yes, I wish you could catch
the guilty one and put a stop to it. If you could catch up with some of the
other patients, perhaps you could frighten them into betraying them. I
don't like to betray—but I wish you could know who this "loyal employe
was", not because it is against the rules, but no good comes from it—Mrs
Ivey[11] took letters out to envelope stamp and mail, but I did not send out
any by her. Although I do not like to betray—yet I no doubt would have
told it, when Hassell gave Mary Buck that note but Tom Taylor demanded
in a very authoritative tone that I tell him who mailed it,[12] as though he
thought he could force me to tell it. Mary Buck came on me saying she
knew that Miss Burks[13] had mailed it, in fact "blessed out" Miss Burks,
when she was innocent. Had Tom Taylor or Mary Buck approached me in
the right way no doubt I would have told it, although to betray is the meanest thing one can be guilty of. I'm satisfied that Miss Mattie and Mary
Buck would not believe this person guilty if every patient on the east side
should say she was, for their confidence in her knows no bounds. Should
any patient tell either of them that this person was the one, I do not doubt
that they would give it the lie. I've heard this person say that she would
never be suspicioned and if accused she would deny it to the last. I told her
last week that she would never mail any more for me that I intended to quit
writing if it took my life. She knows that some of my letters have fallen
into your hands, and have known it for a year. If she continues to mail for
others you will have to catch up at town, for the others are not so risky as
I was, to have them put in here.[14] I wrote each one of my relatives, (who
had been in the habit writing me—and mailed them the last time I went to
town) telling them not to write me except in answer to a letter, that I could
not get all the letters written me, and my letters were not sent out. So Dr
Partlow will not have the pleasure of holding back many if any letters written me. No indeed Miss Mattie and Mary Buck would not believe this person guilty if every patient on the east side should swear to it, for their
confidence in her, could not be the least shaken—at least I don't think
they could be convinced of her guilt—although she has been mailing letters not only for me but for several others occasionaly for two years—and
has not only mailed them here and at town, but has sent them to

11. A former nurse.
12. The local dentist. Sheffield evidently had sent a scurrilous letter to the dentist and
    signed Buck's name. Dr. Taylor evidently had tried to find out how Sheffield slipped
    her letters out.
13. A nurse.
14. In other words, to have the letters mailed in the mailbox in the central administrative
    hall.

Northport[15] and other offices. Well proof of the matter is, that some of my letters have fallen into your hands, and I did not put them in the letter boxes myself, and only one person has handled them. I've no idea that one of you men could be convinced of her guilt—for if told on she would of course deny it—and you would think it someone else. She does not seem to be scared up—although she knows some of my letters have fallen into your hands. She will never mail any more for me, but I cannot answer for the other patients. We patients are not to blame, this "loyal employe" is altogether to blame—for we could not have forced her to do this. No she will not mail any more for me—I would not object so much to telling who this accomodating person is, but I know how abusive Mary Buck is, if the Dr would go quietly on this accomodating person and reprove her himself I might tell it, although as have said, I doubt that you would believe it, for you would certainly be astonished—at least the Supervisors[16] would be for they have so much confidence in her. I find that the very ones that they have most confidence in, are the ones who do the meanness. Had Tom Taylor and Mary Buck approached me right I would have told them then. I may conclude to tell, although it would be mean to betray her, but I cannot see that I have gotten any good out of her accomodation

A. M. Sheffield.

Ward No. 14

March 5, 1908

SHEFFIELD TO GOV. BRAXTON BRAGG COMER

This letter, which Searcy never forwarded to Comer, differs from Sheffield's earlier letters to governors. She does not plead her own case, but attempts instead to speak for all the women patients. She suggests that matters have not improved, but worsened, since the legislature's investigation of the previous year.

---

15.   A town directly across the Black Warrior River from Tuscaloosa.
16.   Buck and Parr.

Tuskaloosa. Ala.
March 5. 1908.

Gov. Comer.

Dear Sir:—

As the only person who possibly can help in the matter, the patients in this, the Bryce Hospital must appeal to you to protect [t]hem against such things as are going on here still, there not having been the slightest change or improvement in the management since last year.[17]

The few patients who then dared to give testimony before the investigating committee, reflecting on the place have been punished in various ways—I did not testify nevertheless have for four months been under what is said to be punishment.[18] I was very wrongfully accused of advising one of the patients to expose, or rather report to the committee some of the woman supervisors bad habits, chief among them drinking liquor. We the patients ask that a change be made, that she be sent away from her place. The Institution, that is, the female department has been ruled altogether by woman supervisor for several years past. You holding the governmental reins within your own hands, will answer it to God, so we, the patients, beg of you to protect us, and remove the woman supervisor who is responsible for the most of the wrong things that go on here.

Her habits are far from good. That she occasionally takes too much *liquor* is testified to by many employes as well as patients, although she restrains herself in it, and is able generaly to keep up appearances. As there were over a hundred salaried officials, interested in keeping up the system, and playing into each others hands, it was perhaps not surprising that they were able to deceive the gentlemen[19] appointed to look into the matter. Those who were capable of cruelties, were certainly capable of lying to conceal them, their actions. There were many anxious to testify who were kept from doing so, while tales were told upon those who were able to testify to neutralize their statements, such tales having no foundation in facts. My seventeen years experience is, that the woman supervisor of the Institution is a Fiend, devil, monster in human form, and totally

---

17. A reference to the investigation in 1907.
18. It was almost precisely four months earlier that Sheffield went to Ward No. 14 from No. 4.
19. The Investigative Commission.

unfit to assume the position of supervisor, more, she pollutes a noble calling by daring to pass as a representative of it, and in justice to the afflicted
and unfortunate of this State she should be revealed to the public, not as
a human woman, whose mission is to serve the afflicted but as a *fiend*
incarnate[.] It is sinful in the eyes of God that she be allowed to do such
awful things and remain concealed or go unpunished. That she has been
seen in an intoxicated state numbers of times, could be testified to by
many employes as well as by patients.

Remove her, and you do the best deed of your life. Her habits, be assured,
are not by any means good. By removing her you will right the wrong.

Respectfully.
Andrew. M. Sheffield.

Ward No. 14

March 12, 1908

SHEFFIELD TO SEARCY[20]

*In keeping with an emerging pattern, Sheffield reacts here to one of
the Superintendent's small reachings-out with an outpouring of anger and
self-pity. The letter also provides a fuller sense of the Hospital's function-
ing in the aftermath of the 1907 investigation.*

Dr Searcy.

I hope you sent my letter to the Gov,[21] when I wrote it I did not know
that Mary Buck intended leaving so soon,[22] although I, as well as others
heard her say last fall that you would not serve another term, and that she
would leave rather than work under Dr Partlow.

---

20. Dated by a note on the envelope: "3910 [Sheffield's patient number] March 12th,
    1908."
21. Searcy did not send the letter.
22. According to a letter by a patient on Ward No. 5, Buck did in fact leave the Hospital
    in the spring of 1908. In a letter of June 18, 1908, patient #3318 said, "Miss Mary
    Buck has left this Hospital & is no longer employed here." The patient goes on to say
    that Mattie Parr and Nurse Kimbro were the new Supervisors on the women's side of
    the institution (see patient #3318, in letter to no one in particular, June 18, 1908, pa-

You said something about my going back to No 4, I did not ask to come to 14 neither will I ask to leave it. No 14 is as you all think, a terrible place but I prefer to stay in 14 where I can only see the sky above,[23] rather than go to one of Lanfords wards, for I can truthfully say that I was never neglected or mistreated by a nurse when sick except when in his charge. He knew she[24] was neglecting me, for I told him she was only giving me one and two doses of medicine a day while the directions was four a day. He laughed in my face, which was encouragement to her to treat me worse, and she did. No I do not want to go back to 4 or any other ward in Lanfords charge, to be "blessed out" on account of a lie told on me by any of the "pretty girl nurses."

Dr Partlow has not mistreated me so far, has given me medicine when sick, and I prefer to remain where I will not see Lanford or hear his voice. All the kind treatment he gave me when sick, relieving me of pain, was destroyed by blessing me out and supporting her in lying on me. You had me sent to 14 because Mary Buck told you that I wanted to go to 14, she *never* heard me say I wanted to go to 14, any more than you did. Had she told you that any of the "*nice* ladies", Lamar, Vassar, Darby, Northam, or Orm[25] wanted to go to 14 would you have sent them? No, you would have waited and asked them why they wanted to go. I knew, at least I believed when I heard that Lil Curry had told Mary Buck that I advised Mrs Barnwell to report the whiskey matter that she would take spite out on me, knowing that you would not allow Barnwell put under punishment, for she was not punished farther than kept locked in her room from the time the report was made, until the men[26] left. Mrs. Barnwell knows the injustice of my being on 14 for she knows I did not advise her. Ask Miss Fowls[27] what advice I gave her, she brought her statement to me to read before the men came, she asked me what I thought of it, and I told her this, that while I knew her statement to be true that it would amount to nothing, that the employes would out lie the patients, ex nurses and patients, that the matter would be settled in favor of the Hospital, and that all who testified against

---

tient's file, Medical Records Office). Buck evidently returned at least by the next spring. Dated letters show that by 1909, she was again in charge of the women's side. The manuscript census for 1910 also lists Buck as a Supervisor.

23. The Annex (in which Ward No. 14 was located) was separate and behind the main building, and had a wall that separated it from the rest of the grounds. When she went outdoors, Sheffield could therefore see above, but not beyond, the wall.

24. A reference to nurse Lil Curry on Ward No. 4.

25. Fellow patients on Ward No. 4.

26. Members of the Investigative Commission.

27. A patient.

the house would be punished in some way, and now, as she says, I was right, for it put her on 14. But little did I think that I would be torn up and mooved to 14 on Sunday on account of some other womans statement, for that was why Mary Buck had me sent here, for if she can't take spite out on the guilty she will take the innocent. I am prejudiced towards 4 for good reason—was sick all the year, so unkindly treated by Lil Curry, blessed out by Lanford on account of her, torn up and sent to 14 on Sunday no indeed I do not want to go to 4 under Lanford. I have never thought it a good idea for me to stay on 4, for this reason, you all try to collect all the stupid and dull, lifeless weomen there, what I call the "dead head" set, and of course these new Dr's seeing me there and me so quiet—so little to say, they of course mistake me for a "dead head" destitute of temper and resentment. Not a woman here with more temper than I, but I work to try to control mine not because I fear the punishment, but more because I am of a revengeful nature.

Lanford had not the least idea that I would take any offense at his blessing me out, but now, that it is too late, he knows. Even if I was good enough to stay on middle floor[28] I could not walk up and down the steps, on account of my hip as often as I would have to. I'm glad now, that the men did not receive my statement, for I did pick out what little good can be said of it. Yes, I'm glad they did not receive it, as I've had to suffer on account of Barnwells statement. Had I wanted the men to have known it, I had rather told them myself for I've been here longer and know more about than Barnwell. I hope you will not come to my door any more asking me "what's the matter": for the "matter" is that I have been unjustly and wrongfully treated, sick all last year, shamefully neglected and mistreated by so-called nurse, blessed out by Lanford, and sent to 14 by you on account of Barnwells statement. I don't say that you know why Mary Buck wanted me on 14, in fact I know you did not, for I know she did not tell you, but you should not have had me sent here on Sunday, unless I had been fighting or giving trouble in some way, should have waited and asked me as you would have most weomen, why I wanted to go.[29] I could have told you that I did not want to go to 14 neither had I said that I did. I certainly did not want to leave Lillie Curry and I knew that a change was

---

28. Partlow, not Lanford, usually had charge of the middle and upper floors on the women's side.

29. Sheffield's anger over being moved on Sunday probably was not directly related to its being the Sabbath, although that may have been part of her displeasure. More than likely, she was upset because Searcy authorized the move over the weekend. The doctors made no formal rounds on Sunday. There was, therefore, no official available to hear her story and balance it with Buck's.

necessary, only she [illegible] on the ward, and she so exasperating and me so full of hatred for her. I knew if I commented on her it would be a bad matter. Now that I have been put here for punishment let me alone, for I will never ask to leave it, neither will I go to a middle floor. I guess you all think as I do, that 14 is good enough for me. Dr Lanford need not ask what kind of a name I'm giving him, I'm not saying much about him here. Jerry C. King, Gunter and Rusk[30] would tell him. Don't come to my door any more asking me what is the matter: it keeps me worried for of course you know: No 14 is as you all say the worst place here, and as I'm the meanest woman here I say I should stay in it.

A. M. Sheffield.

Ward No. 14

June 10, 1908

SHEFFIELD TO GOV. COMER

In this letter, which Searcy never mailed to the Governor, Sheffield explains how matters have worsened in recent years at the Hospital, especially since the investigation vindicated Searcy's administration in 1907.

Hospital.

June 10. 1908.

Gov. B. B Comer.

Dear Sir—

The object of this letter is to give you information as to the present condition of things at the Bryce Hospital, and, to protest most solemnly against the physicians in charge of the female department, in particular Dr. W. D. Partlow, since the Sup't has left the management more and more to him during his frequent absences, and because of the rapid failure of his strength during the past year. Things have been going from

---

30. King and Gunter were members of the legislative investigation of 1907; it is not clear who Rusk was.

bad to worse since last summer. Since the pretended investigation many of
the better sort of weomen nurses, have decided to leave, on account of
their not wishing to be any longer identified with the Institution[31] and
those of the nurses who will remain, for those who were guilty of course
feel free to remain and go on with their practices of cruelty to their unfortunate victims, being cleared by the "whitewashing" reports of the
committee of investigation and by the grand jury[32]—while the Dr's have
shown themselves utterly deaf (more since the investigation) to any rep-
resentations or appeals against the nurses. I was thrown under punishment
near eight months ago on account of being willfully and maliciously lied
on by an ignorant unprincipled young girl nurse, the Sup't and Dr's turning a deaf ear to my denials. Was thrown into what is called the "ward of
punishment," (an appropriate name for the whole thing) a ward off from
the main building, entirely surrounded by a high brick wall, adjoining the
dissecting house and negro quarters, can only see the sky above, not a
breath of pure fresh air, and is so situated that the inmates of this ward, get
the benefit of all the hideous and horid yells of these poor friendless and
God forsaken people—the punishment is indescribable for those not insane, as many are, and you holding the governmental reins within your
own hands will answer this to God; You should awaken to your duty and
appoint certain christian weomen to come here and investigate this thing
thoroughly—interview the patients privately—I say privately because the
patients would fear to make any complaints in the presence of any employe. The most needed thing here is a little religion—christian, charatable feeling on the part of the authorities, not a particle of either has been
displayed for three or four years; they labor under the impression that they
are christians, but their "light is under a bushel." The patients are not
given a religious christian burial, and at the death of one while preparing
for burial, the nurses laugh as if the circumstance were an amusing thing.
No attention is given any complaint made by a patient, farther than the Dr
to dispute their word, and take sides with the nurses, and the nurses almost
go into fits of laughter while telling each other of positive falsehoods reported on patients. Will say that the majority of nurses are a coarse com-

31. One of the female ex-nurses (Freda Crump referred to above) who testified against the
    Hospital was discredited by the institution's lawyers as being a prostitute. It is possible
    that some nurses feared for their reputations after the highly publicized investigation of
    the preceding summer.
32. In addition to the legislative investigation, a specific charge of abuse (relating to an
    incident on the men's side of the Hospital) was turned over to a Tuscaloosa County
    grand jury, which returned no bill of indictment. See the Tuscaloosa *Times-Gazette*,
    September 15, 1907, p. 3, col. 3.

Regular meetings of the medical staff during Sheffield's years at Bryce Hospital included Superintendent Searcy (seated at the center of the photo), his assistant physicians, all male, and a female clerk who recorded the proceedings. Judging from her letters, Sheffield never attended such a formal staff meeting as this one with the male patient, photographed in 1916.

Near the end of her years at Bryce Sheffield ate her meals in this large dining hall on the women's side of the Hospital. Photographed in 1916, this view probably represents the dining hall's appearance on a special occasion such as the visit of the Trustees or the Governor.

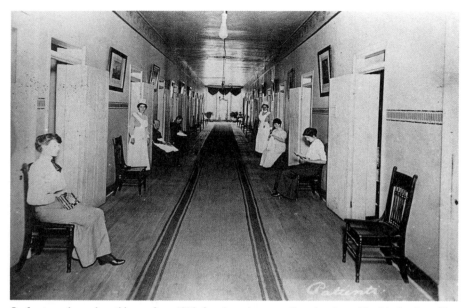

On front wards, such as this one from 1916, female patients usually enjoyed considerable freedom. Notice, however, that the doors all open to the outside so that the nurses rather than the patients controlled the degree and duration of privacy. By this time Sheffield had lived on the back wards for about ten years and only saw such placid surroundings as she passed through, as on her way to chapel services.

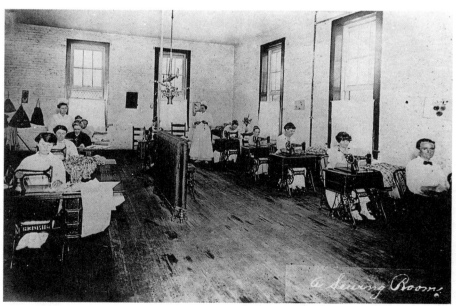

Most able-bodied patients worked during their stay at the Hospital. Sheffield probably never worked in this room, however; her sewing skills were such that she usually did fancy work by hand.

Sitting rooms such as this one allowed for a more homelike atmosphere away from the wards, if not away from the nurses, where the patients could relax and visit with one another. The enjoyment of such sitting rooms was one of the deprivations that Sheffield felt during her long stays on the back wards.

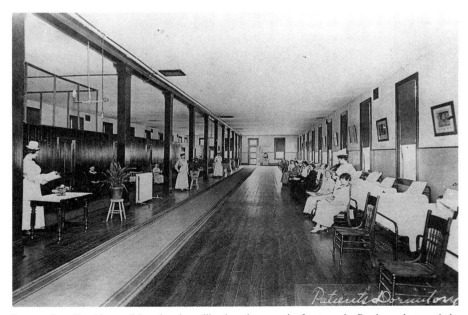

Some patients lived in conditions less homelike than those on the front wards. By the early twentieth century crowding had become such a pressing problem that some patients lost virtually all vestiges of privacy. Sheffield, it should be noted, never resided in one of these dormitories.

As this photo from 1916 shows, most of the assistant physicians were rather young. Sheffield occasionally called them ''mere lads.'' Searcy is the older man on the front row. The older man at the far right is unidentified.

The Hospital frequently offered various amusements for the patients in the large recreation hall at the rear of the center building. Notice that in this photograph from 1916 men sat on one side and women on the other, and the dancing partners are all of the same sex, one a patient and the other an attendant.

Occasionally on her walks across the outside airing courts Sheffield notes that she could see male patients playing billiards inside a room located near the rear of their wards.

In the nicer rooms of the front wards female patients enjoyed a considerable degree of domesticity provided by the use of many items brought from home. Early in her stay, Sheffield probably occupied a room much like this one. But during the second half of her thirty-year stay she usually had a private room on one of the back wards where, she says, she had only her own trunk to accompany the Hospital's furniture.

In this photograph of a teeth-brushing demonstration from 1916 something of the conditions of the lavatories on Sheffield's wards is revealed.

By the late 1890s the Hospital operated a training school for nurses. Most of the attendants during Sheffield's years did not attend this school, however, and most who graduated soon left the asylum's employ for more lucrative work.

From this photograph of one of the training school classes one gets a sense of the relative youthfulness of the nursing corps, whom Sheffield often called ''country girls'' or ''pretty girls.'' The older woman at the head of the table is probably Nurse Creagh, Supervisor on the women's side, whom Sheffield much despised.

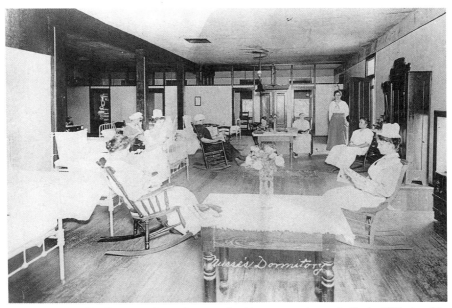

During most of Sheffield's years at Bryce the nurses lived in rooms on the wards. But by 1916 when this photograph was taken many lived in a separate dormitory removed from constant association with their charges.

Photographed in 1916, Assistant Superintendent W. D. Partlow dictates letters to a secretary. Perhaps even more than Searcy, Partlow received the brunt of unflagging anger in Sheffield's many letters.

During her periods of good behavior Sheffield probably enjoyed the library located in the central administrative hall. Ironically perhaps from Sheffield's perspective, a portrait of Dorothea Dix hung on the wall to the right. Dix had donated items to the library in the 1860s and 1870s.

mon uneducated lot of weomen; education does not make one good, but you will admit that it is mostly in uneducated natures where injustice prevails. The neglect, and unkind treatment, sick patients get at the hands of nurses, is indescribable. I was in almost a helpless condition four months of last year, did not get the attention from her that a brute should have received, and this same nurse *lied* me under punishment. I am of a very nervous temperament, suffered of insomnia all through my life, difficult matter to get sleep even when the surroundings are pleasant, and this the Sup't and Dr's know, and for this reason they threw me in this ward for life. I was accused of advising a private pet patient to report to the committee some of the Supervisors bad habits, was also accused of intentionaly distressing a private, pet, hysterically affected patient, who was, and yet is, a pet of Dr John Lanfords, all of which I was innocent of, but the Sup't and Dr's turned a deaf ear to my denials, consequently had to go under punishment. You would do me no greater favor than have my sentence commuted to Penitentiary for life, had rather be a trusty at work than here a prostitute and criminal, in fact had rather be there than here under any circumstances—under the present management. I was assigned to the Hospital seventeen years ago, will say that up to the past three or four years, the patients were as well treated as could be in an Insane Hospital, for the Dr's kept up with every thing, were interested in the patients, listened to their complaints, took their word occasionaly, so, but few acts of *cruelty.* Now the patient is given no chance, they are never questioned, or listened to. The Dr's never question a nurse in the presence of the patient, (a new rule of four years) but out of hearing of the patient, giving the nurse all the advantage of the patient. Not a nurse has been discharged for more than three years, for good reasons, the patients are given no protection. I have had no cruel treatment since 1890 and 1891—but have been very unjustly treated, in fact have had the worst treatment within the past year that have had since my imprisonment here, the cruelties of 90 and 91[33] not excepted. Is there any thing you can do for me in way of assisting me in the Penitentiary? If the Sup'ts evidence had Bob Watts—the Marshall Co criminals neck broken, why should his evidence not do the same for me? Is there no law to force him to make a public statement as to my sanity when sent here in 1890—and that I have remained perfectly rational all these many years, and that my conduct has been of a sane sensible person? Robert Watts was an innocent man, but had to give up his life because of the Superintendent's saying that he was not insane. I only want and ask for justice, life imprisonment in the Penitentiary. Is there no crazy

---

33. The year from 1890 to 1891, her first in the Hospital.

or half crazy convict you could exchange for me? Will you please write me
at your earliest convenience? and very much oblige

(Miss) A. M. Sheffield.

Tuskaloosa.

Box 268.} Ala.

Ward No. 14

Ca. July 1908

SHEFFIELD TO SEARCY[34]

*In the following, which discusses ward assignments, Sheffield holds
doggedly to a tone of victimization.*

Dr. Searcy.

Miss Hughes[35] told me you said something about my mooving. I'm
willing to admit that it is perfectly awful, terrible, and beyond all description in 14 a bedlam in day time, and but little if any rest and sleep at night;
the most depressing ward in the Hospital—and a home of *blank despair* it
is not only a shame but sinful to force any woman not insane to remain in
it, unless a fit subject for it. I am the same woman today that I was the 3
of Nov last;[36] the punishment has brought about no change, my disposition
the same. If I deserved the punishment of 14 ward last Nov. I deserve it
yet. If guilty then of the charges brought against me by Curry I'm guilty
yet. Had you not thought me guilty, (believed just what Curry said) you
would not have had me torn up and mooved to 14 for punishment. (Partlow
and Lanford would have, for they would punish the innocent, same as the
guilty[.]) I still say that I never did say any thing to Mrs Williamson with
the hope of distressing her, and did not advise Mrs Barnwell to report any
thing to those men.[37] I can see no good that has come from Currys *lies*
except it gave Curry, Buck, and Williamson pleasure to know that I was

---

34. Dated by Sheffield's reference to her having been on Ward No. 14 for eight months.
35. A nurse.
36. The date on which she was sent to Ward No. 14.
37. The legislators who investigated the Hospital in 1907.

put under punishment. Being "blessed out" and put under punishment, on account of lies told on me by an ignorant woman has crushed and grieved me more than would have thought for; I had long since come to the conclusion that I felt too low down to take any offense at any thing, but there are yet a few drops of proud blood coursing its way through my body. Coming to 14 was not the trouble—but the cause, to think that I was so unkindly treated by her, and so much neglected the four months I was on the bed sick, then to think that a *lie* of hers could have me "blessed out" by Lanford and thrown under punishment by you, and she knows that her *lies* did it all, as well as I know it. Many others have been treated as badly, but it is no consolation to me to know that others have been treated in like manner. This is the second time I've been mistreated on account of *private* patients. When Partlow came over here Virginia Powell[38] told him that I was trying to get out at No 1 door to negro men, instead his giving it no attention, he gave all kinds of orders concerning myself—and tried to deprive me of the few privileges granted by Dr Bondurant, while he, Partlow was in St Clair Co following behind a plow and a mule,[39] yet, he says, "he does not know why I dislike him". Yes, Dr Searcy No 14 gets the name it justly deserves—"ward of punishment." I have been out here eight months, have seen outside the walls twice—went to town last Dec—and to the kitchen last week with the nurse. Buck gave Miss Saxon[40] orders when I came out here, that she must not let me go to walk or outside the gate, and the order was never countermanded, consequently I have seen outside the walls twice. Miss Saxon told me that Lanford said I "quarrelled and fussed all the time with No 4 patients". During the ten years I was in 4, I had two disturbances with patients, and that was years ago. There are patients in 4 who have been there for years that I have never spoken to. I never speak to any patient except in answer—and then in as few words as possible. Mrs Mason was the only patient in 4 that I ever spoke to—I was dependant on her to do for me—when sick—as I was afraid to call on Curry (the twenty five dollar month nurse)[41] [(]for a drink of water.) Why jail is a pleasant place compaired with 14, that is, the part of the jail I was in while in Guntersville, for I could see from the windows all over town, and get fresh air. But with all its horrors, I'll never humble to ("Dr") Partlow to ask to leave it—neither will I ever appologize to

---

38. A patient.
39. Partlow was the son of a small farmer in St. Clair County, Alabama. In other words, Partlow was decidedly younger than she and lower in social station.
40. The nurse in charge of Ward No. 14.
41. Most female nurses were paid less than this amount. Sheffield was being sarcastic, insinuating that Curry was not worth the premium wage.

Lanford for giving Curry the lie, for I "stick to my text" she *lied* on me, and she knows it.

Mrs Williamson was in 4 two years before we spoke—and it would have been best for me had I never spoke to her. She would boast of her income, her nice home and farm at Mt Meigs[,] nice home at Birmingham, and her son Bens prominence; and ask me, as she did many others, if I thought she could stay at home, or if she would die before she could get to Birmingham? and I would tell her what every one else would, and I thought I was doing the woman a favor, *encouraging* her. Partlow and Lanford need not be mistreating me on account of the private patients, for if the majority of nurses and patients are cotton patch, and wash tub weomen I'm not though I'm none the better, or better off by it. If Mrs Williamson tells the truth I was reared in more ease and luxury than she was. Manny [*sic*], very many people of Marshall could and would testify to the fact that I was not brought up in *poverty*. No indeed I was not I'm glad for poor Miss Fowls[42] that you thought nine months sufficient punishment on account of her report to the committee[.] I think I got even with Lanford 23 last Dec. I am not Mrs Ivey[43] to beg plead and fight to get out of 14. I did not ask to come to it—did nothing to justify you sending me here—and will never ask to leave it although it is terrible.

A. M. Sheffield.

Ward No. 14

Ca. 1908

SHEFFIELD TO SEARCY[44]

The following begins a series of letters centering on Sheffield's mounting difficulty with a fellow inmate on Ward No. 14, Mrs. Roper, a private patient.

---

42. A patient.
43. A patient.
44. Dated by a reference to trouble with fellow patient Roper. This letter suggests that the difficulty was just beginning. Subsequent letters show that the trouble got worse and ended with Sheffield's being moved to a different ward.

Dr. T. J. [sic] Searcy

I'm not speaking to you, neither do I want to speak to you, but you are the propper one to look to, from the fact, you told me years ago, that "you were the boss". Will say in the beginning that I'm not asking to leave 14. I did not ask to come here, did nothing to justify you in sending me here, except that I did not take stand against you and the Hospital. My object in writing this is to ask that you allow the nurses to try to controle Mrs Roper, enough so to keep down a fight between me and her, as she will not find me a Miss Fowls,[45] who has had nothing but abuse from Roper from morning until bedtime, for seven months past. Roper and myself have not gotten on very well, on account of my being on pleasant and speaking terms with Fowls, Saxon and White,[46] but she has not given me any abuse until a few days since. I can't quarrel and fuss, but I can fight, and will do it rather than allow Roper to abuse me as she does others. There is no controle taken of Roper, she can sit on the ward and abuse people from morn until bed time, while others go into cross halls and on back yard for trivial things. Will sit on the ward, and in hearing of all, rejoice over negro men assaulting southern white weomen and little girls, and said six weeks ago, that a "negro ought to rape Fowls cut her open from throat to regina[47] and throw her body in a briar patch", now all such as that we have to listen at from morn until bed time, and not a word said to her—never reproved or told to hush—she really has worse talk than that but too hard to put on paper. I'll take abuse in the bounds of reason from any patient except Roper, have often said that I would never let her abuse me, and I mean it. I'll fight her, go in the cross-hall, and when I come out I'll fight her again if she gives me cause to do so. Mary Buck has told me that Roper had weak heart, for that reason I would hate to fight her—but if it has to come, it will come. I don't hate Roper and have nothing particularly against her, but she is one patient that shall never abuse me to my face. She has made a dog of some patient ever since she has been here, but she will not make one of me, I had rather stay all the time in cross-hall, than out on the ward and take the abuse that poor Miss Fowls has. Ropers abuse was cause of Fowls having this last crazy spell, she abused her and kept her so confused, until she got nervous over it. I'm surprised that Fowls has any sense after being under Ropers domineering and abusive

---

45. Roper and Fowls were both private patients on Ward No. 14.
46. Saxon and White were both nurses on Ward No. 14.
47. Vagina.

tongue seven months. The nurses excuse for not controlling Roper is that Partlow does not allow her put in cross hall. I must say that Miss White has, locked her in her room twice, and taken a little controle of her. I don't see why any of you should not allow her controlled same as other patients, she is worst enemy any of you have; but that is not here nor there with me, so long as she let me alone. Fowls is not the only patient that Roper abuses, she is abusive to most of them. John Lanford reproved me for saying Tom Taylor, told me that I must give the ''Dr's['']] the title of M. D. when talking to him, I notice that he does not reprove ''Lady Roper''—but stand for an hour and listen to her abuse of ''Searcy and Partlow,'' he has never corrected her, he knows, she will clash him—afraid of her tongue. Yes, she can ''old Searcy and Partlow,'' and he dare not reprove her. Roper abused Fowls Tuesday evening from two o clock until five—Fowls was punished, locked in her room yesterday evening and Roper on the ward, escaped punishment as usual. I take no stand for or against others in their fussing, but I will stand up to Roper in my own case if it keeps me in cross hall all the time. She only got mad with me because I would not quit speaking to Fowls, and join in with her, in her abuse to Fowls and Miss White. Of course you will say that Roper is crazy and I should pay no attention to her—If I'm not crazy you should not keep me here. Not an employe on the grounds who take one word from a patient, if one of them say one word to any of you, that you do not like[,] that patient is put in cross hall—but Roper can abuse the patients from morn until bed time and it is all right, nurses not allowed to controle her. I take sides for nor against no one, and Ropers abuse to others is no concern of mine, but I say she shall not abuse me from morn until bed time in my hearing. She never knows when to stop—but one endless and never ending strain of abuse.

A. M. Sheffield.

Ward No. 14

Ca. October 1908

SHEFFIELD TO SEARCY[48]

According to the following, Sheffield's relations with Roper quickly deteriorated. The letter suggests much about Sheffield's daily life and her relations with fellow patients and nurses.

---

48.   Dated by a reference to her having been on Ward No. 14 for eleven months.

ॐ ॐ

Dr Searcy.

Now that Mrs Roper has written me up to Lanford it is but right that
I tell my side whether believed or not. She and I got on very well until
convinced that she could not controle me, have me mistreat and quit
speaking to Miss Fowls, as she made some other patients do. Three weeks
before Miss Fowls left 14, Roper told me that I could no longer be on
pleasant and speaking terms with both—that I had to drop one or the
other. So I told her that I would drop her, as Miss Fowls was the best
woman of the two, besides there was a great deal to be learned from Miss
Fowls as she was a woman of unusual talent, cultivated to the utmost, her
education thorough, the best educated, most intelligent and intellectual
woman in the Hospital, and it was but just to class her mind as *great*. So
while this is true, it was crushing to Roper as she thinks no one here has
any education but herself. I told Roper then that she must remember that
I was not Fowls to very quietly submit to her abuse from morn until bed
time, so she has not as yet called my name in my hearing. I did not know
the other morning that I was the "Hospital Pass" until after inspection,
Miss Hughes told me that I was the "Hospital Pass" as Fowls was the
"Episcopal church".[49] (It amused Lanford very much as any thing would
coming from a private patient[.]) I've had enough of private patients—
already served eleven month in 14 on account of Williamson and Barnwell. Partlow told Miss White that if "I resented any of Ropers abuse to
lock me in the cross hall that she was crazy but I was not," I give him
credit for that one truth—but if I'm not crazy I'll not submit to Ropers
abuse. He resents every thing from a patient, but the patients must take no
offense. I'll show him whether I submit to her abuse or not. He can have
me locked in, and give orders for cruelty as he did in Mrs Iveys case, and
he can keep me in cross hall but I will not quietly submit to Ropers abuse,
if she unlike myself is an educated and private patient. Mrs Ropers insanity comes from *jealousy,* she hates all patients of any education who have
their own clothes, or get a morsel of any thing to eat outside the hall food.
She knew Miss Fowls was her superior intelligently so she hates her. Roper
gets on very well with the ignorant class, and all who are dependant on the
Hospital for clothes, such as "Snap", Whitlow, Haden, Pelham, Kilgore

---

49. These are evidently the nicknames that Roper assigned to Sheffield and Fowls. Mrs.
   Fowls was the wife of an Episcopal bishop. It is unclear why Roper called Sheffield
   "Hospital Pass."

and Barrett.[50] She did not speak to Mrs Ivey or Gonzalis all the time they were in the hall—except to abuse Ivey until she resented it, after that Roper let her alone. She has great influence over the ignorant class, she leads them. She does'nt [sic] want any thing to say to or do with patients that she can't controle except to abuse them, but she will never abuse me to my face, I would not try to kill—cripple, or beak any of her limbs, but she shall not handle me in my hearing if there is a thousand men on the hall. I'm sorry I did not know the other morning that I was the "Hospital Pass."

She told you and Lanford a lie—that "I got all the cream[.]" I don't drink sweet milk, never drank a pint in all my life.

Miss Mattie has favored me some in my eating for the past year from the fact I have not been able to eat the regular hall food. Mrs Roper fusses about the food, at the same time she eats ravenously of any and every thing put before her and eats more in one day than I ever did in two—is the "biggest" eater in 14 except Deloney. Roper is realy a gormand. The melons she wrote about, Miss Mattie gave me several whole ones last summer to divide with Mrs Barnes, Haden and others, and Miss Mattie has for a year had my best dresses ironed, just as Ropers is ironed, and I am allowed to eat my meals in my room, because I could not use my teeth at the table with others, as I have to clean them several times before I can eat a meal. She *fusses* when Miss Mattie sends any of the sick any nourishment— "they are State patients[51] and are not entitled to favors." You men need not think Roper is abusing me as she did Fowls—no indeed she is not. I have to stay in the hall with her and I'll take my own part and go in cross hall—which of course I'd have to do as she is a private patient, and me an indigent, prostitute and criminal. Partlow told me a week before he crosshalled Ivey that "every one had to take abuse" but we all saw how he took her abuse—gave orders that "she only be given water twice a day— no nurse must speak to her, cross hall all patients who were seen speaking to her, and given only a quilt to lie on at night[.]" "Roper tells the nurse that if any patient should strike her she would die of heart failure". She has no heart trouble, if so, she could not live through her "*tantrums*". I'd rather be in cross hall at times, than out in 14 hall. You and Miss Mattie are the only employes who take abuse from the patients. The Dr's and the nurses resent every thing with cross halls. If you would do your duty by me Dr Searcy as you thought you did by Robert Watts I'd not be here to be

---

50. Indigent patients on the back wards.
51. The indigent patients were generally referred to as "state patients" within the Hospital because the state paid for their upkeep.

abused mistreated and punished on account of "pretty girls" and private patients. I am under the impression that Miss Hughes has charge of 14— so please ask her if I abuse the patients, Mrs Pelham[52] takes pride in telling it that "Dr Searcy asked her if Miss Sheffield abused the patients". I'm here as have been in other wards—my room is private. Sometimes Miss Brown and Alice Nelson[53] come in my room—I never order them out. What pleasure do you think it would be to me to have my room crowded with crazy weomen, talking all kinds of talk? John Lanford wrote on my history that I was very abusive to the other patients. Do not know if it was a lie of his own make or one of Currys lies. I want you to tell me some time what are my Delusions, as every Dr except Bondurant has me charged with delusions. Miss Saxon read my history to me—no harm to tell as she will never be back here. There was more truth in Joe Lelands[54] part of my history than any other, *Lanfords was no truth in it—except one sentence.* Even poor Dr Killebrew who I thought was my best friend had me charged with delusions, and also Dr McCafferty. I must say that Tom Taylors account was some better than others. Yes, Miss Saxon read my history to me, for she did not uphold any of you in mistreating me on account of Currys lie—for she knew Curry. After all of you agreeing with me, that I "was not insane, sent here to keep me out of Penitentiary" have me charged with delusions. Will you some time tell me what are my delusions? I'm astonished, did not know I was in the least deluded.

A. M. Sheffield.

<hr>

Ward No. 7

Late 1908

SHEFFIELD TO SEARCY[55]

After she had spent eleven months on Ward No. 14, Searcy moved Sheffield to No. 7, another back ward. The cause of the move, she sus-

<hr>

52. A patient from Ward No. 14.
53. Patients.
54. Dr. Joseph Leland, an assistant physician from 1904 to 1913.
55. Dated by references to Sheffield's ward assignments and number of years in the Hospital. She had just moved from Ward No. 14 to No. 7, another of the back wards. She refers to her "eleven months" on No. 14, which would date the move to No. 7 as the fall of 1908, probably October. The letter also refers to Sheffield's "18 years" in the Hospital.

pects, is the fact that she became so angry with Roper that she had finally "knocked" her.

ટ♦ ટ♦

Dr. Searcy

I can truly say that you were mistaken when you told Partlow in Miss Hughes[56] presence that I asked you to let me leave 14. I must say that I did not, and I never intended to ask. Miss Hughes did not tell me yours and Partlows conversation until we were almost to No 7, or I would not have come. I did not want to come, but let her influence me: I knew that 7 and 10 were more violent wards than 14 and I also knew that Miss Farris who has charge of 7 did not like me when in 4 hall—and I thought she influenced Lil Curry, so of course I hated to come under her. For when a hall nurse[57] dislikes a patient, the other nurses in the ward are afraid to treat that patient nicely. I did not know that I was put in 7 for a punishment for taking my part with Roper until I was in 7 ward. Had I known it I would not have come, unless dragged here. Roper would not have given me any more cause to knock her, she said not a word to me or about me in my hearing after I knocked her. I intend to take my part with all *private* patients hereafter, not that I'm prejudiced or jealous of them, but because I have been punished on account of them. Indigents can abuse me to their hearts content, I'll not resent. I'm a subject for abuse, and I don't expect any thing but to be abused by the patients, if mistreated by the bosses—patients like patients who are kindly treated by the "bosses". For instance Miss Darby, she is here for crime and disgrace—at least I was taught that stealing was a crime and disgrace, all the patients know her history as well as they know mine, but she is kindly treated by the bosses, consequently the patients like her, and she gets no abuse. It is an undeniable fact that patients and most nurses treat patients just as the "bosses" treat them. All patients know all about my troubles of the past year, for I kept the cause of my punishment no secret. I thought like Hughes said that it did seem hard that after spending eleven months on 14 and giving no trouble getting on with the nurses that there was no where for me to go but to No 7. I often hear No 5 patients complaining, and I tell them if they could exchange places with me for a few weeks—have a taste of what I've had for 18 years

---

56. A nurse.
57. The "hall nurse" had charge of the ward and directed the other nurses.

they would appreciate being in No 5 where they are comfortably situated, kindly treated, and respected. But of course I do not expect any thing but the back wards. It did seem that you might have let me gone to 12—true it is a noisy ward but nothing compared with 7 and 10. I perhaps could have pulled up and down the steps. I know that Dr Lanford has no sympathy for me, but I do hope that my trouble will teach him to live up more with the "golden rule," "do by others as he would like to be done by," and that there is nothing lost by kind words, and never approach one as he did me, but give every one hereafter in his charge the chance of a "good yard dog.["] Several patients have been sent from 14 this year, all but myself were sent to middle floors—no one sent from 14 to 7 except the criminal. I am sorry now that I let Miss Hughes influence me, but my weak point is to allow myself influenced by one that I like. I can't say that I thought so much of Miss Hughes, but, she did not mistreat me while in 14, so I let her influence me to come to 7. I don't know how Miss Farris will treat me, but I do know that she disliked me when in 4 ward. If you would give me my bed, make me comfortable in cross hall,[58] I'd rather be behind two closed doors than out in 7 ward, not because I'm afraid of the patients, but to get out of hearing of the noise and confusion. I wish some one of them would knock me in the head and put me out of the way. I try to think that I deserve the punishment whether guilty or not. I can't see why it is that God spares me and takes others, when I've nothing to live for, no one to care for me, no one to give me a pleasant look or kind word, much less to sympathize with me. No one on earth to give me even a kind thought, nothing but abuse and punishment. (I've one consolation—"The heavier the cross, the brighter the crown.") If God would only take me out of it all. Under the circumstances I feel it my duty to take my own part as far as I can with the private patients, and I intend to do so.

Unlike most patients I am not jealous of the private patients—I'm not jealous hearted, but I have been mistreated on account of them. I tried to get on with Roper, and did until she wanted to rule me, and force me to do a wrong. Had I let her rule me as most of them do in 14 we could have gotten on. If I do wrong, it must be of my own will.

I wrote this letter to Col. John[59] But did not get to see him, will you please send it? and oblige.

A. M. Sheffield

---

58. Cross halls did not typically have beds, only in some cases a mattress on the floor.
59. The following letter.

Ward No. 7

Late 1908

SHEFFIELD TO SAMUEL WILL JOHN[60]

Searcy never forwarded this letter to Trustee John as Sheffield requested.

Hospital.

Col John

You will remember that while the "Legislative Committee" was here I called you in my room, told you that I had a written statement that I wished to give in, but felt backward in doing so, as Dr Partlow had been heard to say, in speaking of Miss Crump "the star witness", that the "nurses need have no fears of her testimony" as a "prostitutes word was never taken". You contradicted his statement, so sent my statement in, but for some cause unknown to myself it was not received. You will remember that I expressed myself as being in sympathy with the Sup't, that I thought the Hospital had been somewhat misrepresented, and that it was a reflection upon him.
(I was very much in sympathy with him, is my nature to sympathize with one in trouble—even if it be of their own make[.])
I did not speak to any one of the committee, did not want to, but for all that, my punishment has been far greater than that given any one of the patients who testified against the Hospital. The 3rd of last Nov I was sent to ward 14 the most violent of wards, for having been wrongfully accused of having advised one of the patients Mrs Barnwell to report to the committee some of the Supervisors (Miss Bucks) bad habits, chief among them liquor drinking. I was innocent of having done so, but Sup't and Dr's turned a deaf ear to my denials, so Miss Buck had them put me under what

---

60. Sheffield wrote this letter while still on Ward No. 14, just before being moved to Ward No. 7. The previous letter notes that she did not see Trustee John on his visit and therefore kept the letter until after the move, which likely occurred in October 1908, the time of the Trustees' annual visit. Searcy never forwarded the letter. The envelope, addressed in Sheffield's hand to Col. John, is still in her file. The stamp is not postmarked.

they call punishment, for what Mrs Barnwell did of her own will.

(Mrs Barnwell is a favorite of Sup't so no punishment was given her.) I do not mean to say that she should have been punished for telling the truth, but very unjust that I be punished for what she did of *her own will.* Had I gone before the Committee I would not have told them any thing about her drinking, for I supposed they knew that before they came to the Hospital. It is reasonable to suppose that it is known throughout the state, as nurses and patients are going from the Institution to all parts of the state from year to year, and under no obligations to keep it a secret. Her drinking had not interfered with me, so had not muddled with it. That she took too much liquor could have been testified to by many employes as well as patients if not *afraid* to have done so. She restrains herself somewhat in it, and is able generaly to keep up appearances. Have written this only because I talked with you, and expressed myself as thinking that the Hospital had been somewhat misrepresented, and to show to you the unjust treatment given the *friendless* and *disgraced,* and to prove to you the influence Miss Buck has over the Sup't with that class. Have not written it with the hope of arousing your sympathy in my behalf, for well do I know that every one of the Trustees would agree with the Dr's that No 14 was far too good for me, and no punishment too severe. If the Trustees would do their duty they would force the Sup't to clean the Institution out of Criminal patients, send them out as he gladly sent Robert Watts the said-to-be criminal of Marshall Co—either to go to Pen—or gallows. I prefer the latter.

A. M. Sheffield.

I intended giving this to you while here, but did not get to see you, so send it.

Ca. 1909

SHEFFIELD TO LANFORD AND DR. W. D. PARTLOW[61]

Sheffield complains in the following that a fellow patient has spread false rumors about her.

---

61. Dated only approximately by the style of handwriting and tone of its content.

Dr's Lanford and Partlow.

You know what I was sent here for, the full particulars, so I would like that you relate the matter to your friend Mrs. Lamar.[62] Dr Leach straightened her out, and quieted on the subject years ago; it seems that she has broken out afresh. I am tiard of the patients throwing it up to me that "Mrs Lamar said that I was sent here for stabbing three weomen and killing two men". She has all these many years talked that to the patients, and years ago I had disturbances with crazy patients on account of them throwing it up to me that "Mrs Lamar said that I was sent here for stabbing three weomen, and killing two men". She talking this to the patients would amount to nothing if the patients did not throw it up to me. If she would throw it up to me her self and give me a chance to "fan *her* out," but she will not do that. My case needs no exageration, it is bad enough without her exageration. Have had many disturbances with patients, on account of patients throwing it up to me that "Mrs Lamar said that I was sent here for stabbing three weomen and killing two men". I am far from wanting to make any complaint of Mrs Lamar—for it seems that she is a great favorite—she *boasts* that she can ["]say and do as she pleases—write any kind of letters—and stay in No 5—never punished[.]" My case is bad enough without her exageration. I have written her that Mrs Howls[63] was the only woman here from Marshall Co who knew me personally, and the only one who has been here, and that she would give her the full particulars—the truth—and inform her of her mistake that I had "stabbed three weomen and killed two men.["] I have had many disturbances with patients on account of Mrs Lamars exageration—but not of late years, for Dr Leach settled her on the subject. She as broken out afresh so I'd like that you have her confine herself to the truth, as my case calls for no lies, as the truth is bad enough.

Yes, indeed she boasts of "doing saying and writing, as she likes and still stay in No 5"—boasts that if "she wants any patient out of No 5—all she has to do is to complain to Miss Buck and the patient is sent out of the ward". I am tiard of patients throwing it up to me what Mrs Lamar says, so I'd like that you tell her of her mistake, that I "stabbed three weomen and killed two men.["]

                                                    A. M. Sheffield.

---

62. A patient.
63. A patient.

Ca. 1909

SHEFFIELD TO PARTLOW AND LANFORD[64]

Continuing her complaints about vicious gossip, Sheffield relates rich details about friction among the patients in the following.

Dr's Partlow and Lanford.

You will please pardon my worrying you as matters of more importance demand your attention. As I have put in my complaint as to Mrs Lamars exagerating my case I feel it but right in justice to Miss Lucy Watkins[65] to inform you as to how Mrs Lamar has been slandering her for some time. I say slandering, because I believe it to be slander. It is not impossible that Mrs Lamars statements could be true and Miss Watkins the woman that Mrs Lamar says she is, but I do not believe it as coming from Mrs Lamar. For some cause unknown to myself Mrs Lamar seems to entertain the greatest dislike for Miss Watkins. Mrs Lamar was berating Miss Watkins, to me several weeks ago on the yard, and got far enough to say that she was a "loose character," when I checked her, and told her instead of her talking so badly about her she should take an interest in her. I never did see or hear tell of Miss Watkins until I saw her here, and I know nothing of her, but if she is not what Mrs Lamar says she is, you should not allow her to slander her. Mrs Lamar is jealous hearted—and Miss Watkins is pretty, intelligent and very nice looking—and you Dr's take some notice of her, as is right that you should, and for that reason Mrs Lamar dislikes her—at least I think that is the cause of it. If one of you were to tell me that Miss Watkins was the woman that Mrs Lamar says she is, I would believe it—for you are in a position to know the character of the weomen, you have their histories. Mrs Lamar has had this talk to many here about Miss Watkins—not only to me, but to many others, but I don't know that it has reached Miss Watkins ears. Mrs Lamar has had a good deal to say about her, with Dr Partlow, "following him down the ward and as she says holding long and private conversations"—trying to impress it on every one the nature of their conversation—something bad. It is bad enough for Mrs Lamar to exagerate my case—but is a great deal worse for her to talk

---

64. The content of this letter shows that it follows the preceding one, which also complains of the behavior of Sheffield's fellow patient Lamar.
65. A patient.

about a nice young lady as she has talked about Miss Watkins, that is, if she is a nice young lady—I have no cause to think her otherwise as I have never heard any one except Mrs Lamar say any thing to the contrary. She handles her with Dr Partlow and not with kid gloves either.

A. M. Sheffield.

The evening that Mrs Lamar said to me on the yard that she knew Miss Watkins to be a "lewd woman", it made me mad, and I thought I would write it to you, her conversation, but concluded not to do so, as you all seem to have such a preference for her, according to what she says—that she can "say and do what she pleases and write any thing to any of you— and still stay in No 5." She boasts of being a "privileged character.["] If she is, she should not be allowed to slander virtuous weomen.

Ward No. 7

March 14, 1909

SHEFFIELD TO PARTLOW AND LANFORD

Still hurt over the privileged treatment that private patients received, Sheffield writes here to tell her doctors the proud history of her own family.

March 14. 1909.

Dr's Partlow and Lanford

Under Dr Partlows administration[66] I have not only been unkindly and very unjustly treated but tongue clashed, abused and *lied* into violent wards on account of *private patients,* and only because they were *private* and thought to be *prominently related.* Dr Partlow was the first to mistreat me on account of a private patient, it seems that he has not recollection of mistreating me on account of *lies* told on me by Virginia Powell.[67] Dr.

---

66. Partlow's Assistant Superintendency began in 1908. At that time, he took over much of the daily operation of the Hospital from Searcy.

67. A patient. In an earlier letter (Sheffield to Searcy, ca. July 1908), Sheffield claims that Powell had said that she was "trying to get out at No. 1 door to negro men."

Lanford gave way to his *temper* and abused me on account of *lies* told on me, not because he thought me guilty, but, because Mrs Williamson was a *private* patient and as *he* thought very *prominently* related. Dr Searcy on account of *lies* told on me by so-called Supervisor,[68] (I say she *lied* because she *did not* tell the truth) sent me to 14 ward to suffer for what Mrs Barnwell was responsible for—not because she is private, like myself "poverty stricken", but, *unlike* myself, well educated, very intelligent and the widow of a very widely known Episcopal Bishop. Now that I have been so unkindly and unjustly treated, and had to suffer on account of your *educated, private* and *prominently* related weomen, I think it but right that I give you a sketch of my family history—enough for you to know that I'm not far behind your private, and educated weomen, so far as *prominent,* and *wealthy* relatives are concerned. I do not doubt that I'm as prominently related as any woman under the roof of the Hospital, and feel less *proud* of it, feel very much *ashamed* to owne that I am of *respectable parentage.* Would be only too glad to exchange places with the lowest.

I have rich, prominent, and poor kin, money does'nt "grow on trees" for all my kin. *Have no low down, trifling*—shiftless, *worthless, ignorant kin.*

Can tell you many things about my family that you don't know, the newspaper so carefully handled and well cared for is not a "*nut shell*" it does'nt contain it all—only gives a partly *untruthful* account of my Father and myself.[69] My father was *prominent,* said to have been one of the most prominent, best informed politicians,—and political speakers in the State. Had *great* influence, *never* failed to carry his home county for himself or for his friend by a very large majority[.]

Was said to have been the best buisness man in Marshall—was the leading merchant of the county for many years, until financially wrecked in 1880. Was as near a good man, as any man, even the best, his motto was "Do right", and he did do right, did not "preach one thing and practice another[.]" His charity knew no bounds, was charatable almost to a fault. Was conscientious, just, and honest. Had he faults, they were no more than the best of men have. Was remarkably handsome, said to have been the handsomest man in Laws Brigade.[70] Like Carnegie was a *book worm.* Like yourselves was "*poor raised*" and "*self made*" (Unlike most self made men he never did get to where he imagined he had "harnessed and buckled" the world")[.] Born in a little one room "log cabin"—

---

68. Mary Buck.
69. Reference to a newspaper clipping about her own case and her father's trial that Sheffield believed was kept in her file. No such clipping now exists.
70. A Confederate brigade that fought at Gettsyburg in 1863.

"stick and dirt chimney" "puncheon" floor—at Huntsville Ala,—then a village,—never went to school but one month,—too poor,—his mother was educated—taught him at night,—at twelve years of age, went on the streets and into the boarding houses to polish shoes, and boots, swept store floors, made fires, brought water—and was a "lacky boy" for the merchants to help to support a widowed mother and younger children. At 14 years of age took hold of the plow and followed a mule, until in his seventeenth year,—his mother had advanced him far enough to enable him to clerk,—at twenty two years of age was elected Sheriff of Marshall Co,— from then on went up—prospered—and when the war came was a large land and slave owner. Was a member of the Legislature when the state seceded, the last to sign the ordinance of secession—from the fact he did not favor the war,—was Col of 48 Ala Reg't—raised and equiped the Reg't at his own expense, sixty thousand dollars—the *mistake* of his life.[71]

My mother was the only child of a wealthy planter—said to have been the third largest land and slave owner in the State of Ala. She was educated—not only was she educated—but well posted well informed, and of high social standing. First husband was a presbyterian minister.

My half brother Judge Street was prominent—well blessed with this "worlds goods"—was for many years the largest planter in Marshall Co, and Judge of Probate, I think, twenty seven years—a graduate of the Lebanon Tenn Institute. Have two own brothers—were educated and could have been men in the higher walks of life—but sorry to say—for their love of *whiskey* (unlike Dr Searcy I tell the bad as well as good. I picked out the good from the bad two years ago,[72] and you know what it did for me, give me a cell in a violent ward)[.]

I have a widowed sister in Marshall—who is neither rich nor "poverty stricken,["] comfortable circumstances, of high social standing—a graduate of the Winchester Tenn Female College. Have two nieces in Marshall—wives of Merchants, one Dr Partlow says is worth a hundred thousand, (a neat little sum) both graduates of Wards Female Seminary, Nashville Tenn, are of high social standing.

Have four nephews in Marshall, one a lawyer and district attorney, prominent, (all professional men are prominent) educated at State University Ala. One a clerk in the largest Mercantile house in Guntersville—good common school education. One, I'm sorry to say a drunkard, good com-

---

71. Sheffield's account of her father's history is accurate. According to one brief biographical sketch, he did in fact spend fifty-seven thousand dollars of his own money to raise a regiment in Marshall County. See Owen, *History of Alabama and Dictionary of Alabama Biography,* 4:1540. This account also verifies the main points of her father's biography as she presents it here.

72. Sheffield was sent to Ward No. 14 about two years before.

mon school education.

One a planter—making his living by the "sweat of his brow", "following behind a plow and mule"—an honest and honorable occupation—at least *I* think so, and one no man need be ashamed of.

Have a nephew who is Proff of Law at the state University of Mo—educated at the State University Ala.

One who was Proff of Law at the State University of Texas—recently resigned to practice his profession in the city of Waco—educated state University Ala[.]

Have a sister in Texas who is neither rich nor poor—comfortable circumstances, wife of a planter—educated, graduate of the Winchester Tenn Female College. Have a nephew a lawyer at Ft Worth—educated I suppose at the State University of Texas.

Have one a druggist at Dallas Texas.

Have two, Dr's, in Johnston Co Texas—medical education St Louis Mo.

Have one a stationed Presbyterian minister at Malvern Ark—ministerial education—Lebanon Tenn.

Have one at this time attending the Theological School at Lebanon Tenn preparing himself for the presbyterian ministry. One a traveling sales man for a new York house.

Have two nieces in Texas—educated—graduates of the Dallas Texas Female College—one the widow of a prominent well to do Dr—the other the wife of a planter—poor—.

Have two nieces in Ark common school education, wives of poor men, planters.

As for cousins some of the most prominent and wealthiest men in the States of Texas and Ark are cousins of mine.

Have lost sight of them since I came here—but when I came here, in fact when I visited them last, the largest land owner and wealthiest planter in Lamar Co Texas was my uncle—the Probate Judge of Lamar Co was my cousin. Two of the most prominent lawyers at Waco were cousins of mine. Had a cousin, Dr, at Little Rock—one a Dr at Palestine—two who were very wealthy cattle ranchmen. Had a number of cousins who were poor men—had to "follow the plow and mule['']—but were honest honorable citizens and very genteel.

Dr. S. H. Lowry (a cousin) who died at Huntsville two years ago, was a very prominent physician, a large planter, and the second largest tax payer in Madison Co.

Mr. John Cross, a cousin, who died at Huntsville Ala last year, was both wealthy and prominent, had the U. S. Government Land Office fifteen or twenty years.

Mr. Jeff Cross, a cousin, who died at Talladega last Oct, was a prominent wealthy retired merchant[.] The Rev E. W. Crisman, a cousin, who died of old age at St Louis Mo last Oct was widely known as one of the most eloquent ministers, and foremost lecturers in the presbyterian church.

To go back,—away back—to *ante-bellum,* days. Some the wealthiest most prominent and arristocratic families of Tenn, Miss, and Ky, were my mothers relatives. The two wealthiest men in the city of Memphis Tenn when the war came were my mothers uncles. Abner, and Mack Tate— counted their acres by the thousands, and counted their negroes by the hundreds.

Today some of the prominent, wealthy—arristocrats—of Memphis Tenn, Iuka, Corinth, Holly Springs Miss—and St Louis Mo, are distant relatives of my mothers, *descendants of the old time blue blood arristocracy.* Only three drunkards in my family—two brothers and one nephew. I am the only disgraced woman in the family—throughout the whole connection. My nephews—except O. D. Street are poor men, they are young, just started out have'nt had time to make a fortune. Now I've told you enough to let you know that if I am, as Tom Taylor said, the worst disgraced woman in the State, I'm not far behind your private pets—in way of *professional, prominent wealthy relatives* All this is no good to me and will never be, and is right that it should never benefit me in any way and as for my own part I would not give a penny for it all. For after all I'm the same friendless—poverty stricken uncared for, thrown away disgraced outcast. I'm sorry you "self-made"—"poor raised" men have mistreated me—for I've always had a great preference for the *nice,* "poor raised", "self made men", *"plow boys and rail splitters".* Have your private, prominently related weomen to write up a sketch of their family history— so you will know how far they are ahead of me, in way of rich prominent & professional kin[.]

A. M. Sheffield.

Ward No. 7

April 19, 1909

SHEFFIELD TO PARTLOW[73]

73. The back of this letter was addressed to "Dr's Partlow. and Lanford." The letter itself, however, is to Partlow only. There is a date, not in Sheffield's hand, on the letter: "April 19—1909." Sheffield probably handed it to Lanford on his rounds.

Sheffield defiantly reminds the Assistant Superintendent in the follow-ing that she has been in the Hospital far longer than he or any other doctor on the staff.

ə̀ə ə̀ə

Dr. Partlow.

Whether you are "boss" or not we are under the impression that you are,[74] so I'd like that you have Miss Mary Louise Buck to let me alone. I have *nothing* to say to her, and I'd like that she have nothing to say to me. If there is any more punishment that any of you want to give, give it, but have her let me alone. Now that she has carried her point, had full satis-faction out of me for what Barnwell did,[75] she would be more willing to get on speaking and very pleasant terms with me, because she is now sat-isfied with the punishment given, but I'm not pleased to know that she *lied* me into the violent wards, only because she could not get satisfaction out of a favorite patient. You and Dr Lanford have only been here a few years, while I've been her eighteen, you are not posted as to the cause of my dislike for Mary Buck.
I came here June 1890—Dr Bondurant in Europe—Dr Somerville "*hen pecked*," and Bryce allowing her to have the patients treated as she liked. No *convict* was ever more *cruelly* treated than I was by nurses my first year here, at Mary Bucks orders, and only because I was sent here, as she said, only for *crime*. I have'nt forgotten it, I never forget any thing, it is fresh in my memory—although I've allowed her to be on speaking and somewhat pleasant terms with me a good part of the time, but have all these many years, acted in a way to let her know that I had not forgotten the past. In 1890 Dr Searcy was at Tuskaloosa doing town and county practice, you in St Clair Co—and Dr Lanford in Sumpter Co—and not knowing any thing about the cruel treatment she had me given. It was me here, not you, I was the sufferer, the punished one. When Curry told Buck that I had advised Barnwell, could she have come on me and "tongue clashed" and abused me, as she could have any other woman here, she would not have *lied* me into 14. She can't get satisfaction out of me by abusing and "tongue clash-ing" me.
She "tongue clashed" and abused me my first year here until she got me

---

74. The patients were aware that Searcy had handed over the daily operation of the Hos-pital to Partlow.
75. In her testimony before the Investigative Commission, Barnwell had accused Buck of drinking.

completely *wrought* up, so much so that I attacked her, I told her then that
she must *never* come on me in a rage, that my disposition and my temperament would not admit of it, so she never has since, in fact she has
never spoken an unpleasant, unkind word to me since. She can't "tongue
clash" and abuse me, so she has to get satisfaction out of me through Dr's
and Sup't. This is not the only time she has *lied* me into violent wards. Dr
Bondurant let me go to No 8 against her will and in a little while she had
the Sup't to send me to 14—told him that "I would not scrub or allow any
one to scrub my floor," when I had given Ella Reed,[76] this negro woman
a nickle to scrub my floor on Monday before she had me sent to 14 on
Wednesday. When I was sent to 14 Buck gave Miss Saxon order, that I
must "not be allowed to go out of 14 ward, except on back yard, without
special orders from Dr Partlow.['] It did go hard with me at first never to
be allowed to go to dances, chappel, walk but I've gotten use to it, and
never think of even going on the yard. Of course I know it is worse for me
that I never get sunshine or fresh air, but the sooner I die out the better.
You are more than welcome to deprive me of the few priviliges allowed me
by Dr's Bondurant and Leach. I have no favors to ask of you, except that
Buck pass me by as I do her. Heretofore after lying on me, and stealing
from me, I have allowed her to get in with me, but she will never do so
again. I don't want her to come about me, or have any thing to say to me.
I've never been able to see wherein I was any the better off by being on
speaking terms with her. She has done me every mean, shabby trick, that
could be done one. Dr Searcy told you that I asked to leave 14—I did not
and would not have had you and Buck to have thought that I had asked to
leave 14—not for any thing—I never intended to ask to leave it. I will
admit that it is perfectly awful in violent wards, but for all that I'll never
humble to any of you to beg to leave them—no indeed. I'll never acknowledge that I advised Barnwell, or that I worried Williamson intentionaly.
I'm different by patients now, when they ask me *now* if I "think they will
ever get well, I give them no comfort" I tell them no, that ["]they are
incurable and will die here," I tell them the truth insted of trying to comfort them. There was never any foolishness over Mrs Williamson until after her children began coming to see her and spending sunday evenings
with her behind closed doors. (Pity that all the patients relatives could not
spend sunday evenings with them[.])
I have no favors to ask of any of you, have no apology to make; but I still
stick to my text that I did not advise Barnwell to report Mary Bucks bad
habit—but *I did* tell Dr Lanford that I never saw a drunk woman until I

---

76.   It is unknown whether Reed was a patient or an employee of the Hospital.

come here, never did, I went to bed when I got drunk—so did not see myself—I did not go staggering round as she does. I don't object to spending my time hereafter in cross hall had as soon be in one as out. I never asked to come out of cross hall but one time, and only because I was sick then. Not one of you need think I'm scared of cross halls, for I'm willing to go in and stay in.

Mary Buck knows that I don't want her to speak to me, and I would like that she let me alone. I have no favors to ask of any one of you. If you want to give any more punishment give it.

A. M. Sheffield

Ward No. 7

May 1, 1909

SHEFFIELD TO GOV. COMER

In this last known letter to a governor, Sheffield pleads with Comer to improve the quality of care-givers at the asylum. She also reveals her class consciousness as she insists that the quality of doctors and nurses has, if anything, declined since the investigation in 1907. Hospital authorities never forwarded the letter to the Governor.

Insane Hospital
Tuskaloosa. Ala
May 1st 1909.

Gov B. B. Comer.

Dear Sir—;

I know you are encumbered with many cares, and you knowing so little of the situation, and I knowing so much of it, may cause you to think that I am intruding upon your time an unimportant matter, while to me it is all important, demanding the most serious attention given to any question in Gods kingdom. You cannot realize the need of a help, a protection, and a hearing for the Insane of the Bryce Hospital. (They surely need another Dorothy Dix.) If you could only be one factor, as far as your power

goes. If you are a personal friend of Dr. J. T. Searcys we do not ask you
to like him less, but to leave individuality out and deal with it as a question. He is no worse than some Superintendents—to a great extent they
are all creatures of circumstances. You may be assured that things need to
be revised, *greatly* revised, different laws made and them enforced. With
the *same* system, rules, and laws, with even men and weomen of different
classes abuses could exist. The most needed thing is a better woman as
supervisor—the next is Drs of a high degree of culture, conscientious,
just, *truthful* and honest, men who would denounce, instead of *aiding* and
abeting in these cruelties. While you are living among the gentle mercies
of Christianity, Humanity, and Heaven—the Insane are suffering, perse-
cuted, struggling, and defenseless—"in prison and ye visited me not, hun-
gry and ye fed me not, thirsty and ye gave not drink, naked and ye clothed
me not"—they are looking, longing, and grappling beyond for the shadow
of "Those Wings."

I do not decry that "Honor and shame from no condition rise, and
that acting well your part there all the honor lies"—but the wearing and
the privileges of reputation without character, of honors without merit—
the penalties in sufferings paid by Gods helpless unfortunates, by these
missplaced powers. The great pity is, the lack of *honest worth*—The Dr's
living and rising on the performance of duties *well done*. They come here
with the idea of duty—but very soon catching the spirit of false inflation,
absolute power, and the credulity of the public as *successive* Dr's. Coming
very often from the very *coarse* or stinted walks of life,—with only the
title of M. D. and very little else,—"arrive" here, are feasted and toasted
the best of the kitchen, the bakery, the dairy, the laundry, the vineyard, the
orchard, the house are placed at *his* feet—the patients themselves body
and soul—wielding the sceptre as a Lord of this "Little Russia" if he
chooses. A whistle and the stable boy hastens with the horse and buggy, a
nod, and a dash, and he *is feted* by the credulity of the Tuskaloosa elite, in
the empty distinction, (how empty the world does not know) of being a
physician in the Bryce Hospital—their importance increasing (to them)
the patients decreasing until in regard to their first aim in coming here,
administering to the patients and protecting them, they become *pampered*
"Lethargies of Conscience", and going back into the world with their
"*high sailing colors,*" knowing less, and much less worthy of respect,
than an *honest, earnest,* villege Dr. This is a place of many contradictions,
that the world on the outside unsophisticated, would never come near un-
fathoming—but, the *truth* is here, and while to mortals the *perfect* truth is
never given, the hope of the Insane lies in its search by competent persons
in a competent way.

Send men and weomen of intelligence, refinement, gentle breeding, sympathies, sensibilities, and of a social standing—behind the scenes—to give the Insane a hearing. What is greater than Right? More honorable than justice? and more far reaching to human souls and hearts than Humanity? The Committee came here, and there was never a more ridiculous farce enacted,—so very ridiculous that the *untruth* of it would weight them down if they knew it. Fooled by the superficial appearances. The committee suggested a rise in the wages—to enable the authorities to procure the services of a better class of nurses,[77]—the same class or a generaly lower class are still getting the increased salary, and, *patients* really less to eat than ever. How *fresh* from hard labor in *corn fields* they get in here,—sit up as "grand ladies," and soon get to complaining of their salary "being too small," when there are many refined weomen outside working hard all day for less. Come in not only unrefined, but unable to either read or write,—soon get to brandishing their keys, dressing in silks, satins, laces, ribbons, jewels, and flowers, playing the "grand lady", calling "temperature", "thermometer"—"laboratory" "library"—knocking, slapping, and pulling the hair of the patients,—and instead of them waiting on the patients, the patients waiting on them, often leaving the care of the sick patients to other insane patients—a rare sight—and one that I have never seen a nurse to condescende (her attitude) to remove and cleanse a vessel from a sick patients bed,—and how many sick patients are given water or any means by nurse to bathe face and hands in the nursing before eating?—even *laughing* over, and jostling the patients corpse as they shroud it for the dead house and the grave—Such is their graduation into "Lords and grand Ladies." Gov Comer, there is *nothing* in all the annals of history of nature like it.

Behind all this, behind the scenes are the neglected, sick, and dying patients, tho bruised and bleeding from nurses hands, calling to the Dr to receive his refusal of protection or aid, tho distressed, mistreated, ill used in any form, with no hope, no chance of reaching a genuine honest, human heart, while the Dr's and nurses play on into each others hands—one does not counteract or check the other—both are reaping mutual benefits, and the *patients* in their graves. Only allow the Insane to enter their plea, and something can surely be done,—out of the chaos and wreckage from these *long standing* cruel systems, *you* in good faith and honest effort could bring forth a peaceful and restful alleviation, if not a perfect cure of the Insane. You will remember that Dr. W. D. Partlow (the physician in

---

77. One of the key recommendations of the Investigative Commission in 1907 was an increase in the nurses' wages.

charge) testified before the committee, that "nothing was ever done for the purpose of punishing a patient[.]" Not a day passes that some patient is not given punishment in some form— (and no respect for age) in fact punish seems to be the height of ambition. At this time, there is an old eighty seven year old insane woman in the lock up[78]—only because she in a playful way gave the Dr a light wrap with a slender switch. The Supervisor and Dr's make no allowance for mental irresponsibility—but resent every thing by administering punishment in some form to the insane. I was put under punishment eighteen months ago—was accused of having advised one of the patients to report to the committee, some of the "Supervisors *bad habits.*" Was innocent, but, have had to suffer all the same, powerless to help myself and have had to endure the conditions imposed, same as had I been guilty. Have been deprived *fresh air* and *sunshine* until it is interfering with my physical well being. Hoping that this will (although I have written you before) be *received kindly* and with thought.

A. M. Sheffield.
Tuskaloosa.
Box 268.} Ala.

ᘒᕒ

Ward No. 7

May 28, 1909

SHEFFIELD TO LANFORD[79]

The following, somewhat rambling, letter fleshes out some details of Sheffield's interaction with doctors and fellow patients.

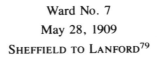

Dr Lanford.

I have not spoken to Dr Searcy this year, and I'm none the worse off. I have concluded that under the circumstances it would be but right that you all quit speaking to me, and me to you. No good comes to me from these "good mornings", and "how do you do." With you all, there is only *one side* to any thing, and that is *your* side, you always in the right, and the defenseless patient in the *wrong.*

---

78.   The cross hall.
79.   Dated by a notation on the envelope: "Miss Sheffield   May 28, 1909."

I know the ill feeling you all have for me, and I will never live down the prejudice. If there is any more punishment you all wish to give I'm willing to accept it—if there is a more noisy ward—more disagreeable violent ward than No 7 I am willing to go to it. If you all think me more comfortably situated in my cell than I *deserve* to be, I'm willing that you have it stripped of everything except my bed.

(Am only indebted to Dr's Bondurant and Leach for the few comforts and conveniences of my cell[.]) If it suits you all to make a "cross hall" woman of me, I'm willing, and I'll promise to never ask to come out. One reason for my not speaking to Dr Searcy is, that I'm afraid he might tell Dr Partlow that I asked him to "let me leave No 7." Would not have had him told Dr Partlow that I "asked to leave No 14," not for a million dollars. I did not ask to leave it, and never intended to ask to leave it anymore than I intend to ask to leave No 7, not because there was any inducement for me—but because I did not ask to go there, neither did I do any thing to justify Dr Searcy in having me sent there. Why should I beg and plead to leave the violent wards? Where have I spend [*sic*] all these nineteen years?—in the violent wards, except ten years in No 4 the *filthiest* and most *undesirable* hall on the Hospital grounds. (Was only allowed to stay in No 4 because Dr Searcy had a little hope that I would agree to let a jury acquit me of a crime that I've been held responsible for all these many years. I'll never be acquitted, neither will my case be "nol pros;" I wrote O. D. Street and mailed the letter in town myself that if he ever allowed my case "nol pros" he would *suffer* for it, that I had as soon be acquitted as to have a "nol pros.") If any of the nurses have told any of you that I have expressed a wish or desire to leave No 7 they have *lied*. I have no where to go but from one violent ward to another, after staying in violent wards eight years No 4 was my only chance, there an epileptic and consumptive ward. Dr Partlow told me in No 14 that I "was not insane", but "*we*['] want to do what "we" think is for the best. There is no "*we*" in my case, that is, the law part, so he should have said Supt instead of "*we*". (You Dr's have *nothing* to do with my going or staying, I'm not here as most patients, snatched up and sent here by home folks,—the *State* sent me here, and there was good deal to be done before I could be sent.) There was no statement in the writings sent here with me authorizing the Sup't to do what he thought "for the best"—I read the bond[80]—even had I not read it, I would have supposed that I, as other criminals, was sent here to remain until cured or adjudged responsible and should a cure be effected sent out to face the charge, (I'd be only to [*sic*] glad that any of you handle my case if you would deal with me as you did Bob Watts, have

---

80. The judge's commitment order.

me sent to the pen—you could'nt have my neck broken)[.] Yes I think it best that I have no more to say to any of you. I know my *doom,* a violent ward,—I'll admit that it goes much harder with me to stay in them now, than heretofore, from the fact the patients are more noisy, and violent from the fact that they are treated worse, they have more to contend with, more to exasperate them. It is enough to cause a sane patient, of a sympathetic nature, to go insane to be forced to remain in violent wards now—but I stay close in my room and try to see as little of the cruelty as possible. The nurses have treated me well but I give them no praise for it, for if insane, and give the least trouble, I'd be treated as the insane are. You told me not long since that "you did not have me sent to 14," I'm aware that you did not, but I wish to remind you of the fact, that the abuse you gave me on account of Mrs Williamson was the cause of my being sent there. Had you not abused me on account of her I have no idea that Lil Curry would have told Mary Buck that I advised Mrs Barnwell to report her "bad habit." Abusing me on account of Williamson was encouragement to Lil to tell more. To tell the truth, my telling you that I never saw a drunk woman until I come here was the very *foundation* of it all, for Lil told Mary Buck, and Buck was mad with me, and treated me with freezing politeness, from then on—for she knew I had reference to her—why of course, she knew her guilt. You and Dr Partlow keeping me closely confined in No 7—not allowing me to go to dances, chappel, or to walk will make no change in me, for I say yet and will forever hereafter that I did not worry Mrs Williamson *intentionaly,* neither did I advise Barnwell, but I did say that I never saw a drunk woman until I came here, and, I say that yet, and will forever hereafter. I never will take it back, for if I should I would *lie.* Many, very many patients who are better than I, *lie* to escape punishment, or to get from under it, but I can very truthfully say that I *never* have. I'm not the only patient who has been punished on account of private patients, and lies told on them by Supervisor, and nurses—and I'll not be the last, but it is no comfort and consolation to me to know that others have been treated in like manner. I have been as it were, in *"hot water"* ever since Dr Partlow took charge of the East side, not only has he mistreated me, but every Dr has, who has been under him except McCafferty,[81] and he would have, had he allowed himself influenced, for I remember his telling me that Dr Partlow made some objection to his giving me medicine when sick. But I must say that I've had the *meanest,* and *best,* treatment from you, that I've had since my imprisonment here. I consider that your abuse

---

81. E. L. McCafferty, an assistant physician from 1902 to 1908. He then served at the Mount Vernon Hospital for blacks as Assistant Superintendent until 1945.

to me was not only the meanest, but, most unjust treatment I *ever* had. You have done more for me when sick, and given relief more than any Dr— (that is what you are here for, but it is more than some of them have done for me,) for I have many times been allowed to suffer intense pain for want of medicine—more especialy did I suffer for medicine under Dr's Partlow, Leland and Faulk.[82] Had you done as Dr Partlow, there would have been nothing of this—when Virginia Powell told him, (but he has forgotten all about it) that I was "talking to negro and white men through the windows of No 1 hall and trying to get out among them," he said not a word to me—gave the nurses orders, and went on Buck about it—I'm sure that was better than going in on me and abusing me; on account of a report made by as crazy a woman as she is, at least I think her crazy. She has had the delusion about me ("rattlesnake poison") ever since I've known her. What if all the Dr's had abused me every time she has abused me, or reported some lie on me?, no one except Dr Partlow ever give her reports any attention, but unlike yourself he said nothing to *me*. As I had to knock Mrs Roper I was sorry for that it did not happen in your presence instead of Dr Partlows, I would have willingly lain in "cross halls" six weeks— could you have seen it—you make more difference in indigents and private patients than he does, for he has misstreated *private* patients, at least I've heard of it. You all think I *hate* Tom Taylor—I don't dislike him as much as I do any of you—I have *contempt* for him, and will never speak to him again. He did not mistreat me and abuse me on account of private patients, or *lies* told on me—He told me the *truth* and I got mad at him for telling me the *truth*, just as you all get mad with me, for telling the truth. (The truth hurts us all—and ain't it a pity that it does?) True Tom Taylor gave me medicine with murderous intentions, but had he succeeded in taking my life—it might have been best. No I do not hate Tom Taylor—with all his faults—He did not hurt my feelings as you all have, he only made me mad, by telling me a *truth* as true as the Bible. You all have treated me so much worse than he that I realy feel hurt that I took any offense at him. I have spent all these years with the *weomen*, except one month in No 11 with the *ladies*, five months in No 8 with the *ladies*, and three weeks on No 3 with the ladies. (For some reasons I had as soon be with the *weomen*, as the *ladies*[.]) When Dr Partlow first took charge of East side, he sent a good number of the disgraced from middle floors, and had I been on a middle floor no doubt he would have sent me then to a violent ward. Had

---

82. W. M. Faulk, an assistant physician from 1897 to 1902. He left the Hospital and set up a private practice in Tuscaloosa and served as a Trustee from 1910 to 1919. In 1919 he returned to the Hospital as its Assistant Superintendent and remained until his retirement in 1945.

you known my disposition, as you now know it, I do not believe that you would have treated me so, you had not seen me except in a *weak* state, *low spirited* and *despondent*—you had no idea that I was so sensitive to wrong treatment—or that I would take offense at *any thing*—and for this reason I have tried to forgive but, I cannot. Yes I think it best that you all pass me by unnoticed. I am where Dr Partlow and Mary Buck want me, and where they can keep me as the Supt "never go behind any of you" except to protect and defend the private patients and better class indigents. I don't care what you all do with me, I feel indifferent, am willing to go to the annex, even to No 18. I have never come under but one time to get out of "cross hall", and that made against me. I was sick when Dr Searcy had me put in for resenting Tom Taylors impudence, besides I was some to blame for his impudence from the fact I allowed him to come in my room and take his seat, I asked him to stay out, but he would not—I should have "*cursed* him out" and forced him to stay away from me, and not given him an opportunity throwing my prominence into my face—I did not force him to stay out of my room—so I say I was some to blame, and when in *fault* I come under, but I'll *never* come under in this, will never "*bow* in humble submission," for was not guilty of worrying your pet, was not guilty of advising Barnwell. What will you all do with W. L. Halsey[83] of Huntsville who has murdered two men, in cold blood—have him hung? He is educated, of a nice, proud, respectable family—and a man of some means. Will it go the rounds of the press that the "authorities of the Bryce Hospital pronounced him sane when sent here"? Will Dr Searcy say with an *exultant* smile as he did of Bob Watts, "why they had to smoke him out of his cell like *twisting* a rat out of its den." (Halsey is not insane and should have been lynched as I should have been.)

A. M. Sheffield.

Ward No. 7

September 16, 1909

Sheffield to Lanford[84]

Sheffield's anger over the preferential treatment given private patients spills over in the following to include a catalogue of drug abuse among various nurses.

---

83. A patient on the men's side of the Hospital.
84. Dated by a notation on the envelope: "Miss Sheffield   Sept. 16—09."

੩੩

Dr Lanford and Missis Buck and Parr.

Dr Lanford.

I was talking with several patients yesterday, (on the yard) and the subject of my being in the violent wards, and the cause, came up. One of the patients asked me if I had not heard of the request that "Mrs William-son made of you" some time ago. I told her I had not, and insisted that she tell me, she refused to do so until I promised I'd not "give her away" (they all fear punishment.) She told me that it was talked while I was in No 14 that Mrs Williamson has asked you not to send me back to No 4 that she was "afraid of me." I'm as far from wanting to go in a ward with her as she is from wanting me. I hate her, and do not want to be in a ward with her. Why do I hate her? because you abused me on account of her, only because she was paying her board and her children looking after her. Do you pay your board? No, you get yours as I get mine—the difference is, you get the best that is on the market. If you ever abuse me on account of another private patient you will get to treat me as you did Mrs Ludus, in a cross hall with a "pillow and a blanket." When you Dr's conduct visitors through the wards you tell them that the "patients are never locked in for punishment," but to keep them from "hurting themselves or others". They are seldom locked in for any thing but punishment, more especialy are they punished for offending Dr's and Supervisors, and not one of you ever return kind words for abuse—and when attacked you are never calm, neither do you display a spirit of humanity—and when spat upon, and called harsh names it is never borne with evenness of temper, more espe-cialy do you give way to your temper. You give the patients medicine and relieve pain—with that exception you are not better to the patients than the other Dr's. You uphold and encourage unkind and cruel treatment, same as others. Mary Buck knew your temper, she knew what she was doing when she told Curry to report to you, she knew you would "blow" me up, and she knew what the result would be, she knows a lie will stir me, for she has practiced it on me enough to know what it does for me. After all the abuse and punishment I say the same, that I did not worry Williamson intentionaly, neither did I advise Barnwell—but I did tell you that I never saw a drunk woman until I came here, and I say it yet, and will down to my grave, and Dr. J. T. Searcy will never make me take it back. You took no offense at it, but Mary Buck did for she knew who I had ref-erence to, although she knows that I know, that she is not the only employe who has eaten morphine and drank whiskey. This whiskey and morphine

matter came up years ago, and the Sup't had a nice good nurse sent out for
telling Dr Leach of it. A Miss Archabald was discharged for getting drunk
in town, a Miss Austin drank, Miss Lindsey kept it no secret that she occasionaly bought whiskey—but, I never saw any of them *drunk*. A Mrs
Branch eat morphine—also a Miss Russell, and a Miss Parr[85] who had
charge of No 4 eat morphine—and at times so much under the influence
of it that she could not attend to her duties—and when she left No 4 there
was four empty morphine bottles in her bureau drawer. Miss Mattie[86] got
very mad with me, at the time, for speaking of it. No one, can sit and lie
round me under the influence of morphine and me not know it. I know all
about what morphine will do for one. If Mary Buck should ever tell any of
you (and call on "Mattie" for proof as she often does) that I asked her to
forgive me for telling you that I never saw a drunk woman until I came
here you may know they *lied* as they did when they told you all, that I
asked them to "forgive me for accusing them of stealing my money[.]"
True, I thought I would die, but I was rational, and did not think it necessary to ask them to forgive me for giving them credit for doing what God
himself knew they did do. There is not so much distress among the patients since Miss Mattie handles their money. I can't say that she is *strictly*
honest, as but few are who handle other peoples money, but it is not
wholesale robery as has been heretofore.

I *hesitate* in giving Miss Mattie the lie, and am sorry that I ever have cause
to do so, but when the occasion demands it, I have it to do. I like her, she
is in some ways good to me, and she is a kind good hearted woman, but
she can't do as she would like in every thing, and hold her position. She
has to agree with Mary Buck—if Mary Buck calls on "Mattie" for proof,
"Mattie" has to prove her statements true and often against her will. Had
Mary Buck told one thing and Miss Mattie another the Sup't and Dr's
could not have come to any conclusion—not know how to settle matters.
I know that Miss Mattie lies on me, as I've told you heretofore, when
called on by Mary Buck for proof, but I do not hold it against her, she has
it to do, she is under Mary Bucks rein, she could not have held her position
here had she not agreed with Mary Buck, she has it to do. Miss Mattie has
her living to make, but unlike the rest of you she has made hers by hard
work and under very trying circumstances. She could not have spent all
these many years here had she gone according to the dictates of her own
conscience. Mary Buck has had so much influence over the Sup't in way

---

85. Not a reference to Mattie Parr, the Assistant Supervisor. There were other Parrs who
    worked as nurses in the Hospital. In all likelihood, they were related to Mattie Parr and
    got their jobs through her influence.
86. Mattie Parr.

of having me punished, I wish she could influence him to have me sent to Wetumpka, she told me my first year here, that I was "no better having escaped the penitintiary than had I been sent there—" I agree with her, I would like that you say no more about my going on the front, for the next thing Mary Buck will be telling it that I'm begging to go on the front yard. I'm in a violent ward, and on the back yard for telling you the truth that I never saw a drunk woman until I came her [sic]. Prostitutes tell the truth sometimes—as little as Dr Partlow seems to think. I can't say that Miss Crump was, or was not a prostitute, but can say, after spending two years in violent wards that her statement was true from start to finish.

Suppose you and Dr Partlow influence Dr Searcy to have me sent to the Pen —you might succeed—Dr Partlow says you all want to do what you "think is for the best," I think that would be best. I am under punishment for telling you the truth—but I did not inform any of you—that is, I have'nt told you all of any think [sic] that you did not already know. It is bad enough for her to be guilty, but worse to punish patients on account of it. But "patients and nurses must not talk", "must not speak of what they see"—must be *mute,* like you told Mrs Colmer[87]—"if you are mistreated you must not speak of it, if you see others mistreated you must not speak of it," ["]you must never speak of any thing you see". My tongue has never been silenced, and never will be. When I know that it is right to use it I will do it regardless the punishment. Give this to Miss Mattie and Mary Buck for I want them to know that I am not wanting to go in a ward with Mrs Williamson.

A. M. Sheffield.

Ward No. 7

December 7, 1909

SHEFFIELD TO LANFORD[88]

The following letter suggests the immense emotional weight that asylum patients sometimes attached to such seemingly trivial affairs as a visit to the circus.

---

87. A patient.
88. Dated by a notation on the envelope: "Miss Sheffield   Dec. 7—1909."

ᥣ ᥣ

Dr Lanford.

You are in the "west side,"[89] but you have'nt given up all claim on
"the weomen,["] so I wrote you, as did to Dr Partlow to know if I could
go to the circus. You claim that I'm sensitive—too sensitive—If I'm sensitive, just such treatment as this has made me so. I'm given every cause
to be sensitive. I know right from wrong, have sense to know when I'm
treated right—or mistreated, and sorry that I have. I have the same right
to take offense at mean treatment as any other woman—more especialy
that I know that the law does not warrant any difference in treatment of
criminals and others, at least Ex Gov Johnston wrote me that it did not.
But as Dr Partlow says, you have a "law unto yourselves." As I wanted to
go to the circus, it was my right and privilege to ask to go. I wrote you and
Dr Partlow a note Thursday[90] (sent it by Dr Davie)[91] asking to go with
Miss Cork[92] as she had asked me to go, with her, and that Mary Buck had
told her she could take the day off. I wrote you that I would give no trouble, behave myself nicely, and speak to no man—I thought that sufficient.
I wrote you to let me know Thursday if I could go to the circus Friday. If
you sent any word I did not get it. I was not told that I could go to the
circus until 11–30 Friday—too late for me to get ready as Mary Buck said
"they would leave the Hospital at 12 o clock—Nannie Hargrove[93] came
through No 7 at 10 o clock, she asked me if I was going, I told her that I
had asked to go but had gotten no word that I could. When I wrote you to
know if I could go I did not know that any of the patients were going. I
thought that orders would have to come from "head quarters" as to
wheather I could go or not,—for Mary Buck gave Miss Saxon[94] order every day for a month in 14—that I must not be allowed any privilege, except to go on back yard, "without orders from Dr Partlow," and that "he
said so". When I came to No 7 she gave the same orders every day for a
month, that I was not allowed to go out of No 7 ward except to back yard
without orders from Dr Partlow that "he had said so"—so I thought I
would have to get permission from Dr Partlow. I did'nt think she could
give *me* permission to go, so wrote you. I did'nt do it to make her feel little

---

89. The west side was the wing of the Hospital which housed men.
90. This note has not survived.
91. N. T. Davie, an assistant physician from 1909 to 1914.
92. A nurse.
93. A nurse.
94. A nurse.

as she seemed to think. I have all these many years asked such of the Supervisors until she has given so many orders in Dr Partlows name. Some time ago I wanted to go to No 5 with the nurse and Kate Palmer[95] (to hear Kate play) the nurse told me that I could not go unless Dr Partlow said so—so I thought if I could not go to No 5 for a few moments without special permission from him I could not go to the circus without orders from him, so I wrote you. I know that Dr Partlow entertains the greatest enmity for me, at least I think so—and don't doubt that he has given orders—but I do not believe that he has given all the orders that she has given in his name. When you received my note, you and Dr Partlow should have sent word that I could or could not go—that would have been buisness. I told the nurses that if you did not let me go—that I would not get mad, that I doubted Dr Partlow allowing me to go, and told them the report that Virginia Powell made on me four years ago about the men.[96] (If you all were right yourselves you would not be suspicious of me—"evil to him who evil thinketh[.]''') Have you and Dr Partlow ever heard Virginia Powells delusions about you? I wish you could hear them just as she talked them in the presence of nurses and patients when in No 7 several weeks since—I could not write it to you much less talk it—Now, I say they are delusions—it is not *impossible* that it could be true, but, I do not believe it—not one word of it. If Dr Partlow could only hear her talk it—he would never mistreat another patient on account of her reports, he would give them no attention; I wish he knew—but I can't tell him—can't write it. I wanted to go to the circus, and would have been willing to pay my way, and I certainly did think it wrong that you treated my note with silent contempt. Had I gone I would not have been the only disgraced woman on the grounds, all kinds go to circuses. There were some of the weomen employes who went at States expense—who in some respects are meaner than I, and guilty of more sin and crime in the eyes of God and sight of Heaven than I. Not a meaner piece of flesh was under the circus tent than Annie Farris.[97] Did you go to the circus? Yes. Did Dr McDermot[98] go? Yes. Did Dr's Partlow and Davie go?—Yes, and went in time to see it all, street parade—animals—and even stayed to the negro minstrel—Yes you all saw it all, had a grand time as you usually have. I don't regret that I asked to go as I wanted to go—I think I did right, but I dont think I'll ever shed another tear over being refused to go to anything. But you would say that my being hurt over not getting to go was *sensitiveness,* you can call

95. A patient.
96. See Sheffield to Searcy, ca. July 1908.
97. A nurse.
98. Probably T. S. McDiarmid, an assistant physician in 1909 and 1910.

it that if you wish to, but I say it was a piece of unjust treatment. As soon as Miss Buck heard that I had asked you to let me go with Miss Cork—she came down and told Miss Cork that she could not take the day off—that she would have to go "with the crowd,["] but she said not a word to me about going. I was not told that I could go to the circus untill 11–30 Friday too late to get ready—and if any one says any thing to the contrary they *lie*. After Dr Partlow got my note Friday morning, and went to No 2— Miss Buck did come then and tell me that I could go—but it was too late to get ready—besides I had cried until my eyes and face were frightful to look at. I don't know where the fault was, but I do know that not a time was I told that I could go to the circus until 11–30—But I suppose it was *sensitiveness* of me that I took offense at not getting to go. I've had enough here to make me sensitive.

I'll tell you of a piece of your unjust treatment to me last Spring. In three weeks time I received \$10.^{00} from two of my sisters—one of them wrote me "you must get out and take a long carriage drive—it will do you good—do this for my sake". I told you of this but you give it no attention—Had it been Lamar—Cater, Northam,[99] or any of the nice ladies you would have had Miss Mattie to order a carriage and gone or sent a nurse with them. I told Miss Mattie of it—she treated it with silent indifference, but I did not blame her—you were to blame. I did not want to go for the good or pleasure it would have given me, but to carry out my sisters request—My sisters don't know how it is here for me, and they will never know—I don't suppose it would be of any good or pleasure to them to know my daily life. (But of course it was sensitiveness of me that I felt hurt at the way you treated it[.]) I can't say that I am sensitive, no more than is natural for every one to be but I can say that I know when I'm treated right or mistreated, and have a right to feel hurt over wrong treatment, same as any other woman. Crime, and disgrace, does'nt transform weomen into brutes. I'll never shed any more tears over not being allowed to go to a circus.

I don't know who of you were in fault, you or Miss Buck—I only know that I wrote you asking to go—but got no word, and was not told that I could go until 11–30 Friday. If any say any thing to the contrary—I must say they lie. Not a time was I told that I could go until 11–30— A. M. Sheffield.

---

99. Patients.

Chapter 4

"HAVE ALL MY LIFE HAD A MANIA FOR WRITING LETTERS"

1909–1911

Two years on the back wards elevated Sheffield's level of resignation, but failed to soften her character. "I'm not conquered," she told Searcy in early 1910. And indeed she was not. The letters in this chapter, all to persons within the Hospital, suggest the rigidly narrow parameters of her world. To readers unfamiliar with the confining world of the asylum, Sheffield's complaints twenty years after her admission may sometimes seem petty: unending squabbles over ward assignments, personality clashes, the use of her limited funds, or going to the circus. But to her, such concerns were absolutely vital. They defined the boundaries of her autonomy. And as such, they defined the very meaning of her self.

The letters in this chapter also suggest much about the quality of asylum relationships. Many of the letters, for example, are to John Lanford, Sheffield's ward physician and the doctor who probably came to know her as well as any except Searcy. To him she offers the most insightful explanation of what she calls her "mania for writing letters," the only madness to which she ever admitted. In addition to exploring the maturing relationship with Lanford, this chapter also tells much about the role of Mary Buck, the Supervisor of Nurses, whom Sheffield despised. In particular these letters provide a perspective on the sharing of power among various members of the staff: Lanford, Buck, Assistant Superintendent W. D. Partlow, and Searcy. It was, needless to say, a view unlike that found in the Superintendent's annual reports.

Many things changed over the twenty years of Sheffield's confinement. But her character was not among them. Her "contrary" quality remained. She even interpreted permission to go to the circus as an insult rather than a privilege, for example. But rebellion was, as we have seen, already blended with resignation. Now, near the end of her life, the rebellion and resignation sank into repetition. With the scope of her expe-

175

rience so narrowed for so long, her communication in these letters
increasingly centers on complaints that repeat a very familiar message over
and over.

Ward No. 7

December 22, 1909

SHEFFIELD TO LANFORD[1]

*Reacting to an institutional rumor, Sheffield tells Lanford that she
must be moved if a particular nurse gets charge of her ward.*

Dr. Lanford.

I am not Miss Darby,[2] to get just what I ask for and want—to get any
nurse that I might ask for—or to have any nurse sent out of the ward. Have
never asked that any nurse be given a ward, have never asked that any
nurse be removed, and never will; but I do ask that if Annie Farris is given
No 7 that you send me to No 10—14—or 15.—either would be preferable
to staying in a ward with her, knowing her as I do—and knowing yours
and Dr Partlows hatred for me. I'm not afraid of her or of the cross halls
as you may think, but I don't want to be with her—I know her—her spiti-
ful and cruel nature—her untruthfulness. I know her dislike for me and
mine for her, and there would be no getting along with her. She openly
states that she hates me just as I do her. The nurses and other patients in
No 7 would dread her as much as I do—even the insane hate her. She is
not physically able, having consumption[3] to run a violent ward—I must
say to her credit that unlike the majority of nurses these days, she works—
that is her only good quality—like all with her affliction she is irritable
and [it is] impossible for one she dislikes to please her—it use to be that
nurses had to learn the disposition of the patients and try to get on with
them, now the patients have to learn the nurses disposition and try to
please them, and knowing that she is one that I could not get on with—I
do not want to be thrown with her. If it suits you all to give her No 7 it suits

1. Dated by a notation on the envelope: "Miss Sheffield   Dec. 22—09."
2. A patient.
3. The common term for pulmonary tuberculosis.

me provided you send me out. Annie Farriss is not alone as to mean traits of character, there are very many others who would report more lies on me than she did—but I know her. Lucy Hughes[4] knew your dislike for me but she did not take any the advantage of it—she did not report even *one lie* on me while she has had charge of No 7. I am not wanting to dictate to your "Lordship" but I do know that there would be not getting along with her, so if she is given 7 I only ask that you change me.

A. M. Sheffield.

Ward No. 7

Ca. January 1910

SHEFFIELD TO SEARCY[5]

Ending a two-year hiatus in her correspondence with Searcy, Sheffield asks that she be given a change of back wards.

Dr Searcy.

In 1895 you told me that you were "the boss," so I address you— whether you are or not, you have never failed to handle my case in giving punishment, having me sent from one violent ward to another—keeping me in the back ground. I am willing to remain under what is said to be punishment, but there are as you know, different grades of punishment here, No 14—12—7—10—9—15 are considered the worst. I have served two years and two months in what is said to be the worst on account of *telling* the *truth*. Do you think you could afford to lessen the punishment by sending me to No 12?—as that is said to be a ward of punishment—but of course it is nothing to what 14—7—10—9 are. I am not humiliated, strange to say—for I say just what I did the morning I left No 4 and will down to my grave. I have no appology to make, I take nothing back that I have said—not one word. I don't think it asking a favor to let me go to No 12—from the fact it is a violent ward, but it is not the noisy ward that

---

4. A former nurse.
5. Dated by Sheffield's reference to her having been on violent wards for two years and two months. She went to Ward No. 14 November 3, 1907.

No 14—7—10—9—are. I have no favors to ask of you—I know my
doom, "the Hospital and a violent ward." It is perfectly awful to think of
having to spend the remaining years of my life in the violent wards, but if
it has to be, it can be, and will be, and I can but make the best of it, and
I have tried—and intend to hereafter make the best of it that I possibly
can, grieve, worry, and trouble over it as little as possible. (I saw Halsey[6]
the *double murderer* in No 5 or 8—playing billiards (yesterday morning)[.] Where did Bob Watts stay while imprisoned here? Where is Mrs
Pelham?[7] Where is Miss Sheffield?) I have lost sleep, and been in this confusion day and night until I am so nervous that I never go to sleep until one
o clock and often not until 3 o clock. It is wonderful that I have held up as
well as have. I am only asking to go to 12—I'm not asking to go to 11—
8—or 13. I don't know that I could hold out to go up and down the
steps—but I could try it. I'm not *conquered,* for I don't consider that my
asking to go to 12 is taking back any thing that I've said. I take back *nothing,* from the fact I've said nothing but the *truth.* True, many very many
weomen, far better than I, in some respects, have *lied* to get from under,
and escape punishment, I *never* have, and *never* will. I've spent all the
nineteen years in the back ground, was only allowed to even stay in 4 ten
years because you had hope that I would come under to an acquittal—had
you known that I would have held out stubborn you would have had me in
the violent wards the 10 years I was in 4.
I have stayed in 12—more than a year—I know it is bad. Don't think that
I'm asking for a change because I fear the patients as many would. I'm not
afraid of any, my hands are not tied any more than others are. No, I'm not
afraid of any of the patients. I do not dread or fear any of them in the least.
Many of them of course could whip me, and kill me, but for all that I'm
not afraid of them—neither do I fear the cross halls. Have never asked to
come out of a cross hall but one time, and only then because I was more
in fault than Tom Taylor was. I have regretted that I did ask to come out
on account of the impression it made on you all, that I dreaded and feared
the cross halls. I was to blame for getting mâd with Taylor for telling me
of the truth, just as you all get mad at being told of the truth. I'm not
expecting any thing but a violent ward, neither am I asking for any thing
else. No 12 is a violent ward—but if we *poverty stricken criminals* have to
stay in violent wards why not give us a change from one to another? Why
not give poor Mrs Pelham a change from 14 to 7—or 10? Mrs Pelham was

---

6. A male patient. There was a billiard room off the "airing court," or recreation yard.
7. A female patient who, like Sheffield, was listed as a "criminal" patient by the
    institution.

right in doing what she did. You, put me off on Dr's and supervisors, but you take care to act yourself when it come to giving *punishment*. *You* had me sent to 14—*You* had me sent to 7—but only because Roper, the private patient demanded it. Mrs Barnwell was sent to 14—where Miss Buck would keep her if she could—but, that was a case for Dr Searcy. So Barnwell through you, is in 8. I don't ask for anything except what I've had [,] a violent ward, but as my conduct does not make me a subject for the worst, I'd like to change from one to another occasionally. Understand I am not asking for 11—8—or 13.

A. M. Sheffield.

Ca. 1909/10

SHEFFIELD TO LANFORD[8]

Money troubles prompted the following note to Lanford.

Dr Lanford.

On last Thursday I sent Miss Buck a $2.00 post office order to cash. She sent me word that she "was not going to town but would send it by Mr Harris."[9] I suppose he went to town yesterday or the day before but she has not sent or given me the money. Had Miss Mattie been here I would have had it cashed soon after receiving it.[10] The post master at Tuskaloosa wrote me to send the order at once so, I did not know what to do but give it to her—did it reluctantly—for "a burnt child dreads the fire." I knew that if I gave it to you or Dr Partlow that you would have Mr Harris to give her the money for me—so knowing that it would fall into her hands in the end, I thought I had as well send it to her. It is a small amount, but it is mine, and I want it, don't want her to beat me out of it. She could keep it if she wanted to, and tell you that "she gave it to me," and you would take her word. If Mr Harris has not given her the money, will you please receive it from him and give it to me yourself? I fear no one on the Hos-

---

8. Dated only approximately by the style of handwriting and the type of stationery.
9. W. C. Harris was the Hospital's steward and, as such, was responsible for the patients' money.
10. Parr was probably away on her annual vacation.

pital grounds in money matters except her, have no cause to doubt the honesty of any one except herself—my fear does not come from a "suspicious" nature, it come ~~by~~ from having been *severely burned* by her. Will you please see that she does not "beat" me out of it? Not so much for the *money* but because I do not want to be *"torn up in mind,"* worried and troubled—for I've had enough worry of late.

    and oblige.

A. M. Sheffield.

January 2, 1910

SHEFFIELD TO LANFORD[11]

    The following brief note glimpses a rare playful mood. The letter to Searcy which follows it, however, makes clear that the mood did not last.

Dr. Lanford.

    Now that I've had you a little worried, I'll relieve your mind. I was jesting this morning as to what I said to the visitors. The ladies from Mobile were at my window—but I told them that they were on private ground, that visitors were not allowed on the inside of the inclosure[12]—so they left at once. I only wanted to worry you a little—but after you left I felt bad that I did not correct it. They questioned me as they did others—but I did not handle you all roughly—but with kid gloves—So as I felt bad that I left you under the wrong impression I thought I'd correct it.

A. M. Sheffield.

Early January 1910

SHEFFIELD TO SEARCY[13]

11. Dated by a notation on the envelope: "Miss Sheffield   Jan 2—1910."
12. A wall surrounded the back wards.
13. Dated by its reference to the preceding letter to Lanford, dated January 2, 1910, in which she also discusses the encounter with the "ladies from Mobile."

This stream-of-consciousness letter is quite long and moves from one subject to another fairly abruptly. In doing so, it connects threads of many concerns voiced in earlier letters.

≥≥ ≥≥

Dr Searcy.

I told you that I would write you my conversation with the ladies from Mobile. I think it will prove to you that your "pets," "favorites", and "show patients," are more anxious to do you harm than I am, although I have more cause to want to harm you. The ladies passed my window going towards No 10, when they came back they stopped at my window—they were talking to each other—pittying the "poor woman in the dark room". I supposed that they had been to Miss Zellnors[14] window as she was that day on the South side.

They asked me where I was from? how long I had been here?—and asked me how I was treated? I told them that I tried to think that I was treated as well as I deserved to be: (Should have told them that I was cruelly treated)[.] They asked me how the patients were treated generally? I told them they were treated here as were in all public institutions (Insane Hospitals) that it was no better or worse *here,* than was in all others. (Should have told them that they were cruelly and very unmercifully treated.) They asked me if we were warm and comfortable? I told them that for the most of the time the ward comfortably warm. (Should have told them that we suffered of cold and that our feet were frost bitten[.]) I was seated at my window eating my dinner, when they came—they asked me if I got enough to eat?—I told them that I got enough of such as it was, coarse, rough, substantial food, such as was served in all prisons. (Should have told them that we suffered of hunger that the allowance was not sufficient to satisfy the hunger of a sickly kitten.) They seemed to be surprised when I told them what I had eaten for my dinner, I think they expected me to tell them that I had bread and water. Had Bessie Davie, Miss Fowls, Barnwell or many others of your pets had the chance at those weomen that I had, they would have gone back to Mobile with quite a different tale to tell—that they had talked to a woman patient at the Hospital, who seemed to be of sound mind, perfectly rational, and that she gave a terrible account of the cruelty and starvation at the Hospital. I'm under punishment on account of willful *lies,* and on account of Dr Lanfords abuse to me—but for

---

14. A patient.

all that I failed to handle any one of you, not because I was afraid—but just because I did not do it. I should have treated you all as you have me— for my religion is, treat others as they treat me, let it be good or bad, right or wrong. I should have handled Dr Lanford more especially, for he gave me the meanest treatment I've ever had, not excepting the cruelty my first year here. I should have told them that he was cruel, and encouraged and upheld the nurses in their cruelty to the patients, that he was high tempered—no controle of his temper, abusive and domineering to all the friendless indigents, and the criminals, but made himself foolish over private patients. Yes, I should have handled him in pay back for his abuse to me. He tells me that "he did not send me to violent wards"; it is very true that he did not but his abuse to me on account of Mrs Williamson being a private patient was partly the cause of it all; had she been an indigent there would have been nothing of it. I have never thought any the less of Mary Buck for telling Lil Curry to tell Lanford that I was "worrying Williamson", for Mary Buck was mad and not speaking to me on account of what Curry had told her that I had said to Lanford about the whiskey, and Buck wanted satisfaction, and the only way she could get it was through the Sup't and Dr's, she knew how foolish he was about Williamson and I suppose she knew of his temper—and I'm sure she knew how it would end if he abused me. I have all these many years had a good deal to say against having young boy Dr's here, but I hope Dr Lanford will be the last old batchelor. Dr Partlow mistreated me by paying attention to Powells report, but unlike Dr Lanford he did not come in my room and tongue clash and abuse me. I should have told those ladies of Miss Bucks bad habits, (it is likely that they knew them) and how much harm came from them. If many of your favorites had been in my place they would have told it all. I had time to tell it all, for they came to my window as the nurses and patients were going to dinner, so I had them all to my self. They did not leave my window until I told them that it was against rules for them to be there. Yes, indeed had some of your pets had my chance they would have handled "this thing".

There is Miss Davie[15] that you have stood by, protected and defended, all these many years—who can say as many hard things about you and the Hospital as she can? not one—for she is a woman of natural intelligence and does not (like myself) lack for words to express herself. I'm glad that you do protect her, (for the most of what she says is true) for if Miss Buck could have her own way with Bessie Davie, and had the influence over you with her (Davie) as she has in my case, Davie would spend all of her time

---

15. A patient.

in *violent wards.* Mary Buck has never liked Davie any more than she likes me, and I heard her say years ago that Davie was "not insane, but lazy". She is insane—has the most confused and unsettled mind of any one I've ever known, but there is a great deal of truth in what she says, yes, there is truth in it, and if I abused you, as she and many of you pets do, you would like me. You have been the worst enemy that I've ever had, yet I have never abused you—cannot account for why I have not, for I have had more cause to do so, than many who do abuse you. But for you I would have been free, for Oates or Johnston would have pardoned me, and could I have done no better I perhaps could have gotten a situation, as a "chamber maid" in Booker Washingtons Institute,[16] for my food and clothes. Do you suppose that he would have taken in a "house burner" and prostitute? I have no idea that he would, he is too high minded. Yes, I'm glad you protect some if you don't protect me, I'm glad that Miss Buck can't influence you in all cases. I'm glad that you "go behind Dr's and supervisors" in some cases. I expect to spend the remaining years of my life in 7—10—14—and 15 and die in 18 but there is one thing sure I'll stick to my text, that I did not worry Williamson intentionally—did not advise Barnwell—but I did say that I never saw a drunk woman until I came here—and if Miss Buck should ever tell you that I asked her to forgive me for saying that I never saw a drunk woman until I came here, you may know that I did not, any more than I asked her to forgive me in the money matter. True I thought I would die, and felt very much concerned, but was perfectly rational and did not think it necessary to ask her forgiveness— from the fact I had never wronged her.

You came in No 2 one day as I was leaving, you said to me that you "had a better opinion of me than ever before". I did not know what you meant, and could not think of any thing that I had said or done to raise me in your estimation, and not being in the habit of multiplying words with you I did not ask for an explination, so after I heard that she had told you that I had asked her to forgive me in the money matter my mind went back to what you had said to me and supposed that my asking "her forgiveness" had raised me in your estimation. I did not ask her to forgive me—and she knows it—and more I never will. I know that I have never wronged her— and I give her credit for what good she has done, as well as bad. She has done some good here and I give her credit for it—and that is more than the most of patients and nurses do. But her unjust treatment to me will far out balance the good. Miss Buck is *naturaly very jealous hearted,* and is very jealous of my love for Miss Mattie. All patients have a preference for Miss

16. Tuskegee Institute.

Mattie just as I have, but all except myself are afraid to express themselves. I openly, boldly, and independantly say that I love Miss Mattie Parr—and but for her sympathy and kind feeling for me I would have been dead or crazy. She has several times mistreated me, but she had it to do, She has misrepresented me to Sup't and Dr's but she had it to do—she has to agree with Miss Buck, so I hold nothing against her, she has been my friend so far as she could be in safety to herself, and I'm her friend as all other patients are. She has earned every dime that she has gotten here— she unlike the rest of you has made hers by hard work, and under very trying circumstances; has done a lot of good here, and would have done more had she been allowed too. It matters not what her physical condition may be she should be given her place back—paid the same money and every thing done for her good and comfort that can be done, she justly derserves it. I'm not the only patient who love her—and I'm not the only one who dislike Miss Buck—It has been said that Darby loved Miss Buck—so I asked Darby several years ago if she did really love Miss Buck? She said no, I "fear her, I'm afraid of her." Miss Buck is somewhat like Dr Lanford as to the private patients, she is as a rule pleasant and very respectful to private patients—unless they do or say something to give them her ill will. Not so with Miss Mattie, she tries to treat all right and is pleasant with all who will let her be, does not harbor ill will for any— seldom takes offense at any thing the patients say to her—if they abuse and "bless her out" today she is pleasant with them tomorrow. She doesn't seem to want to "get even" with them by having them punished, as Miss Buck does. Had Miss Buck not had me so cruelly treated my first year here, she and I could never have gotten on well, for she expects too much of others—my rule is, to treat others as they treat me, and that does'nt suit her. I treat her just as she treats me—if she speaks to me pleasantly I speak to her pleasantly—if she speaks to me with a grunt I speak to her the same way—if she passes me by unnoticed I pass her by the same way, I treat her just as she does me, and that does'nt suit her—it does not matter what she *says* or *does,* the poor patient must meet her with a smile and show her the greatest respect—regardless as to how she may have treated them—how much wrong she may have done them, how much punishment she may have had them given, the patient must greet her with a smile and show her the *greatest* respect. I am not sorry that I did not handle you all as I should have to the Mobile ladies, have long since gotten to where I feel it useless to try to contend with people who are so much meaner than I. I know that I will not live much longer for any of you to abuse and punish on account of my telling the truth. If any of you are so fortunate as to get to Heaven I hope the good Lord will not punish you for telling the truth—that is—if you happen to tell it. While I did tell the truth, I've no idea that I would have said what I did to Dr Lanford about the whiskey—but that we were talking about voting the whiskey out of the county. I'm not sorry that I said what I did—and never will call it back. All the harm came from Lil Curry repeating my conversation, for it sent me to No 14.

I love whiskey—the taste, and effects—have drank it, but could I have had my way I would have fined or imprisoned every man who voted against the amendment.[17]

A. M. Sheffield

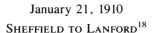

January 21, 1910
SHEFFIELD TO LANFORD[18]

Sheffield's tone in the following reveals her low spirits, the results of two years on the "violent halls."

Dr Lanford

I am not speaking to any of you, but it is not because I am "mad" as you will say. I am hurt, and feel grieved, over unjust treatment as have felt for more than two years. I have been in an excitement and confusion from one day to another for more than two years—have had my rest broken at night—until I am nervous. I feel completely "let down", but not enough so to tell a lie, for I still say that I never saw a drunk woman until I came here, and will say down to my grave, let come what may. I little knew at the time what those few words would do for me—spoke them on the "spur of the moment" just as you and many others have said things—Lil Curry repeated my conversation with you, to Mary Buck, for the purpose of making trouble, and she did make it for me, for I do not doubt that she put me under punishment for life, from the fact, I will never "take it back," will never say that I lied, for I did not lie. I advise other patients

---

17. A constitutional amendment that allowed Alabama's counties to prohibit alcohol by local option.
18. Dated by a notation on the outside of the folded letter: "Miss A. M. Sheffield   Jan.
21—1910."

to lie to escape, and get from under punishment, but I will not do so myself. Last fall there was a patient sent from upper floor to No 7—for making some truthful remark about Mary Buck, it was reported, so Buck abused her and sent her to No 7. The patient vowed that she would not take it back, I advised her to lie rather than be punished with No 7—that under the circumstances God would not hold her responsible for lying—but would hold Mary Buck responsible for forcing her to *lie*. So she did lie, took it all back and Buck sent her back to middle floor—Yes, indeed I advise patients to lie rather than be punished with the violent patients, God will not hold them responsible, I cannot do myself, what I advise them to do—my disposition will not admit of it, but I wish that it did. No, I am not mad as you will all say—I'm low spirited, (not crazy in the least) and I can't see any thing ahead of me but violent wards. I think I have held up well, being of a nervous temperament and in an excitement for day and night for more than two years. Many patients more especialy nurses have advised me to lie rather than remain in violent wards. Miss Hughes repeatedly advised me to lie, told me the day before she left that I "had better *lie* than remain in violent halls,["] and no one knew better than she of Miss Bucks bad habits. Her bad habits never did interfere with me, and but for what I said to you no doubt I never would have suffered on account of them. Lillie Curry knew I had refference to Miss Buck, for she had seen the same sight—No I am not as you say, mad, but under the circumstances I don't feel that it is my duty to greet you men with a smile and talk pleasantly with you—Had I been guilty of worrying Williamson *intentionally*— advising Barnwell—or had I *lied* about the drunk woman I could perhaps "come under." I have'nt asked to leave violent wards, for I know that it would amount to nothing. I did not ask to leave 14—although Dr Searcy told Dr Partlow that I did. I asked to go to 12—but that is any thing but a quiet place—and it is very well that you all refused for I could not go up and down steps. I'm sick, have been for a week, nervous, and low spirited—have held up under it all just as long as I can. I can see nothing ahead of me but the noise and confusion of violent wards, so all that I have to ask of you Dr's Searcy and Partlow is to stay away from me, for I do not under the circumstances feel that I can talk to you.

A. M. Sheffield.

My mind is all right—is not "weak" as you wrote on my history two years ago.

❧

Early 1910
SHEFFIELD TO PARTLOW[19]

As before, Sheffield turns the granting of a favor into an occasion of persecution.

❧ ❧

Dr. Partlow.

Last fall after being defeated in going to the circus you approached me in a very nice way, and explained to me in a very nice way that I should have gone had you known that I wanted to go—so that was encouragement to me to ask to go to this Fair. I knew that you are here for life, and am sorry to say that I am—and if you ever know me to ask to go to a Fair-Circus or any place of amusement I hope you will have me put in cross hall and given the cruel treatment given me my first year here. I wanted to go to the Fair and so I asked Dr Lanford if I could go—he very reluctantly with a nod of the head told me I could go—at the very same time asked me if I did'nt want to "go by myself"?—As much as to say that a disgraced woman would prefer going from under guard. He told me not long since that I was "suspicious of every thing and every body" he has the advantage of me, for I'm sure that I would never feel suspicious of a *sixty one year old woman,* head almost snow white but few natural teeth and face more wrinkled than most weomen at seventy years of age. Yes indeed he is more suspicious than I am. He said what he did to hurt me and it did hurt me for of course I knew why he said it—would he have asked Mrs Hass—the Missis Watkins or any of those nice ladies[20] if they "wanted to go to the Fair by themselves?"—no—for he has respect for them as ladies, and so he respects their feelings. I don't ask to be respected as a lady, for I am not one, but I am not destitute of feeling—I wish he had told me no that I could not go, rather than hurt my feelings—for I have a little feeling as little as he seemed to think. If I was suspicious of a sixty one year old woman I'm sure I'd never tell one as he did me, "You are suspicious of every thing and every body". He was judging me by himself. I don't say that I will never ask Dr Searcy to let me go to town to do a little

---

19. Dated by Sheffield's description of herself as being sixty-one years old.
20. Other patients.

shopping, but I do know that I will never ask to go to another Fair-Circus or to any place of Amusement. I wish he had told me no—that I could not go and saved my feelings but little does he care for the feelings of a friendless disgraced woman. I asked Miss McGhauy[21] to go with me, I have many reasons for not wanting to go in the crowd of nice ladies, one reason is I feel it an injustice to them—for I am not allowed to mix and mingle with them in the building, and they of course know why, so I feel that they (the ladies) feel it an injustice to throw me on a level with them on the outside. If I ever ask to go to any place of amusement again I hope you will have me punished.

A. M. Sheffield.

Ward No. 7

Ca. 1910

SHEFFIELD TO LANFORD[22]

The following letter approaches a surreal quality as Sheffield recounts a dream that warned her of a former doctor's plan to poison her.

Dr Lanford.

I cannot prevent your coming into my room and inquiring after my health when sick, but you will get no answer. I'll make no complaint to you neither will I take medicine prescribed by you if I know it. I've been sick a month—cold and rheumatism; I'm very much a primative babtist in my belief, when my "time come I will go", no Dr can save my life. My time had not come three years ago when Tom Taylor gave me *poison* in a very small quantity for three months, with *murderous intentions,* so, you saved me. It was not Gods will that I go then but Tom would have taken my life had he remained here, and I continued taking his medicine.
As for giving me *poison* with *murderous* intentions, you all know to be a fact—but not one of you gave me warning. God alone warned me through

---

21. A nurse.
22. Dated by reference to Dr. Thomas Taylor's alleged attempt to poison her, probably in 1907.

a dream. Three weeks before Tom left here, I dreamed that I died—was dead —had been taken to the "dead house", and Tom Taylor was standing over me with that *cock crowing fiendish* smile of his making ready to dissect my body, the next morning I discovered arsenic in my medicine, that was the last dose that I swallowed until you came. Had you not known that he had given me poison, you would not have known to have given me medicine to counteract the poison, for it was all through my system. (I've taken arsenic given by our family physician,[23] I know the effects.) I told Mrs Williamson—Mason[24]—and Miss Mattie of my dream—they gave it no attention farther than to tell me "there was nothing in dreams." I told Miss Fowls of my dream—asked her if she believed in dreams,? yes, she was a firm believer in dreams, that "God often times, through dreams, gave us warning of trouble or danger ahead". Had he given me a sufficient quantity to have taken my life almost instantly, that would have been a good deed—but no, heartless creature he did not want to favor me with a quick and painless death, his fiendish nature would not admit of that, he must give in a small quantity worry—aggrevate—torture—nag—and jag my life slowly, slowly, out of me by degrees. Soon after I went to No 14 I dreamed again of dying—and strange to say, although Tom had gone, he appeared in my dream with that same cock crowing fiendish smile. I have no hope of being buried should I die here. I was told soon after I came here that a great many of the bodies—not claimed by relatives, were shipped to "Mobile and Birmingham Medical Colleges to save the students the expense of buying subjects."[25] That is why I have such a horror of dying here through the winter months—while those schools are in session. If my body was dissected in either of those colleges the fragments would be thrown into a waste pool and washed out into the gulf. I would like to know that the fragments of my body would be put in the Hospital grave yard, who do I? because in *looks*, it corresponds with my feelings—

---

23. Arsenic was common in prescriptions of the nineteenth century. It was used specifically in the treatment for addiction to chloral hydrate. Once the addiction had been broken, physicians often prescribed arsenic, sometimes in combination with strychnine, as a tonic. Since Sheffield had once been broken of the chloral habit prior to resuming it, it is quite possible that she had personal knowledge of arsenic. See T. D. Crothers, *The Drug Habits and Their Treatment* (Chicago: G. P. Engelhard, 1902), 88.
24. A patient.
25. It is possible that the bodies of indigents were occasionally made available to medical students, but there is no corroborative evidence for this rumor that Sheffield no doubt heard on the wards. Bodies were sometimes dissected in autopsies conducted at the Hospital. It should also be noted that the two state medical schools did have a number of former Bryce staff doctors on their faculties. In fact, the schools' deans were both former assistant physicians.

is the most desolate, gloomy, lonely, neglected, uncared for and forsaken
looking place that I've ever seen—no one visit there—no one go there
except the negroes who put the dead away. My body would be at your dis-
posal—let you dispose of it as you may—I intend to make lawful arrange-
ment as to my head, that is, my brain. I intend to request it of the next
Legislature that they appoint Dr. Leach[26] to remove and examine my brain
at my death, and make a public statement as to its condition, it of course
would be found to be in a healthy condition—and no sign of ever having
been diseased. He would make a truthful statement, he is not connected in
any way with the Hospital—it is no reflection on him that I was detained
here, while he was here—could he have done as he liked, he would have
given me choice of prisons. He told me that my "mind was all right"—
that my "disposition was my trouble." (My disposition is all right—but
unsuited for the Hospital[.]) Dr Leach would do my brain justice, he is a
high toned, honest, conscientious, truthful gentleman; the best friend the
patients have ever had, and had he remained here the state would not have
paid out eight thousand dollars investigating the *"rotten rules* of the
Bryce", the employes would not have gone before a committee with a
"trunk full" of lies. He was the best friend I've ever had here, among the
men. Dr's Bondurant, Huey,[27] McCafferty, Killebrew and Rudolph[28] were
pleasant with me, and never did mistreat me, much less abuse me, but Dr
Leach more than all others, was at all times and on all occasions willing
to do *me*, even *me*, the friendless criminal justice and he did do it. He was
the patients friend, and he discharged his duty by this suffering humanity.
As for Dr. W. G. Somerville (who received me into the Hospital and allowed me so unmercifully treated my first year here,) I do not like to
speak—but could his wife and children have been saved, I would have
shed no tears had he gone down with the sunken vessel—he deserves to be
at the bottom of the Atlantic Ocean. I consider that my trouble com-
menced when you took charge of the weomen, for up to that time I had
gotten on with the nurses, had only had a few disturbances, no nurse ever
neglected or refused to do for me when sick except under you, no nurse
ever reported a lie on me to a Dr except to you, my history is proof of
that—(your part of my history, is like Dr Partlows statement to the committee, only *one* sentence of truth in it)[.] Up to this time you have given
me medicine when sick, but I'm under no obligations, nor due you no
thanks for that—for you are here for that purpose—paid a yearly salary to

---

26.   Sydney Leach, an assistant physician from 1896 to 1903.
27.   T. F. Huey, an assistant physician in 1901.
28.   C. M. Rudulph, not Rudolph, an assistant physician from 1900 to 1908.

do for the patients, criminals as well as others. If you or Dr Partlow will tell me of one thing you have done for my comfort or pleasure I'll give you credit for it—"credit to whom credit is due". I know of nothing you have done for me except to mistreat me on account of *private patients,* and deprive me the few privileges granted by Dr's Bondurant and Leach. I'm not the only one you mistreated on account of Mrs Williamson—you had Miss Raymond a nice lady, and a worthy patient sent from 4 to 1 because you saw her in Williamsons room—when she had been invited in. I'm not the only criminal you have mistreated, you abused Mrs Pelham while I was in 14 for "killing her husband." Mrs Pelham and myself are *prisoners*— no *man*[29] will mistreat a prisoner in his care, even though an enemy. I have had a good deal to say about "boy Dr's" having charge of all this affliction and suffering humanity—I hope you are the last old Batchelor who will have charge of "the weomen" while I live. You forever bear in mind that I blame no one for this punishment but you—I know you did not know that Mary Buck was mad and not speaking to me on account of what I had said to you about the drunk woman—but that is no excuse for you—your abuse did it all—for that "upset" and got me all "stired up"—had you gone on, attended to your own buisness instead of coming in my room abusing me there would have been nothing of this. I do not blame Mary Buck for telling Lil to tell you that I was worrying Williamson, for she was mad and wanting satisfaction out of me, and no way to get it except through Supt and Dr's. Annie Farrish [Farris] told me the day she left here, that her sister Lee was sent away for "meddling with the Supervisors bad habits." Mary Buck was as much opposed to Lee Farrish [*sic*] having that position as any of the nurses were, she knew that Lee would expose her. Her discharge may be warning to her, but the punishment has been no warning to me, for I yet say that I never saw a drunk woman until I came here.

I have not been well all winter. I'm on the down grade—but little sleep and no appetite—no sunshine or fresh air. Why did not Miss Buck keep the pretty "show patient" in No 7?—because the Supt would not allow it I'm satisfied that Mary Buck makes daily reports on me—when she has only spoken to me four times since I've been in No 7—but it is all right with me, if she never speaks to me. I'll not beg you for medicine, death is preferable. I owe you no appology—I gave you no cause to mistreat me—but your mistreatment to me has taught me a dear lesson, to never to allow myself to like another Dr, or to speak a kind word of one, or to allow myself to think that one think kindly of me. I wish that I was

29. The word "man" is actually triple underlined.

dead, and out of your sight. You told me last week that you had never mistreated me—why no, you don't think that abuse any more than I deserved.
I wish Dr Partlow would tell me what he had seen in my conduct, or heard
in my conversation to have confirmed Virginia Powells report, that I was
"trying to get out to negro and white men." Davie came to my door this
morning and instead of speaking to me as though I was a white woman,
asked me if I was "mad". He shows a disposition to want to pick at me—I
don't give Davie any cause to pick at me—and if he keeps on I'll get out
on the Hall and give him what I gave Tom Taylor in the presence of these
"pretty girls." (He should have gone to Mount Vernon[30]—and Dr Ivey[31]
who was a nice man remained here.) He is already feeling his importance,
and only been in his state home a few months—I've never liked his
looks—and his showing a disposition to pick at me has caused me to dislike him very much. Dr Ivey treated me as though he was aware that I was
a white woman. The best thing Davie can do for himself is to let the "old
criminal["] alone. Yes, I intend writing the next Legislature, making lawful arrangements as to my brain, that Dr Leach be appointed to examine it
at my death, which I do not think will be long off.

A. M. Sheffield.

Ca. 1910

SHEFFIELD TO LANFORD[32]

Sheffield wrote an offensive note to Lanford which has not survived.
The following is her apology, along with a revealing explanation of her
"mania for writing letters."

Dr Lanford.

When I went to town I did not buy any stationary, and will not get any
hereafter. This is the last of my Tablet—have given away my ink and
pens—will not keep any thing in way of writing material except a lead

---

30. Mount Vernon was the site of a second state hospital, solely for blacks, which opened
     in 1901, just to the north of Mobile.
31. R. R. Ivey, an assistant physician from 1909 to 1914.
32. Dated only approximately by the style of handwriting and the stationery.

pencil. I bought some "post cards" so that if I get a letter I can send a card in answer. If I keep stationary in my room I will use it when I should not do so.

I have fully determined that I will not write any more letters to any of you —*I will not.* The last letter I wrote you was the worst letter I've ever written, and no good cause for writing it—But then, as heretofore acted on the "spur of the moment". I handled your private affairs which was none of my buisness, no concern of mine—made you all kinds of bad wishes—the day after I gave you the letter would have given any thing had I not written it. (I hope you did not let Dr Searcy read it).

You all think it meanness of me—inate meanness that cause me to write such letters. I don't attribute it altogether to inate meanness—I hardly know how to account for it—my crave for writing such letters—unless it comes from my sensitive nature I'll admit that I am and have always been very sensitive, and when any little thing worries me, I want to write. I am also revengeful, and when ~~any~~ any thing goes wrong or not to please me I feel that I must avenge it. I think that things are done for the purpose of worrying me, just because it was *me.* Now you told Miss Buck about my going to town—you thought that sufficient, and was, had she told me of it—but at that time, no one could have convinced me but that you had planned it in order to deprive me of going to town—when you had no objection to my going—no doubt wanted me to go.—but while in a mad fit—and thinking these things I wrote that letter meddling with your private affairs and making you all kinds of bad wishes—sinful wishes. I am sorry I wrote it—hope you care nothing for it. I have fully determined that I will quit writing letters to you all if I die in the attempt—it grows on me, the more I write the more I want to write. I don't say that the contents of all my letters are untrue—no indeed—I write many truthful things but, it is not right that I should do that—for the truth hurts everybody. The contents of my last letter to you was not true, thought while writing it that it was—I do not wish you any such luck as I wished you in that letter. At the time I could not have been convinced that I was not justifiable writing it. It was certainly a very bad letter—*sinful wishes.*

I think you are to blame for taking my letters.

Have all my life had a mania for writing letters—when any of the family or neighbors would offend me in the least—not a word would I say—but would write them a letter. I will quit it—I can do it if I set a determination to do so. No I do not wish you all that harm, in fact I do not wish you any harm for I like you as a man and Dr. Tom[33] may be assured that I will write

---

33. Thomas F. Taylor.

no more letters—and I regret writing you the last letter more than any I ever wrote. You have proven yourself to be the best of the two—for had I been in you place and you had written me the letter that I wrote you, I would have seen that you did not go to town.

A. M. Sheffield

Ward No. 7

June 8, 1910

SHEFFIELD TO SEARCY[34]

The following reveals the static quality that had come to characterize Sheffield and Searcy's interaction twenty years following her confinement.

ɸ ɸ

Dr Searcy,

I have been thinking for some time that I would ask you to have the furniture taken out of my room.
I would not ask Miss Buck to have it mooved out from the fact, I knew she would tell you and the Dr's that I was "mad", "had it done in a *passion*". I am not mad, am in a perfect good humor, but under the circumstances I think it would be best. As I have to stay in the violent wards the low down set, and crazy class, I think that it would be best for me to be more on a level with the low and crazy. My room is the only one in No 7 that is furnished, and the patients can't understand, why my room is furnished and theirs not, and I have been cursed, abused, hounded, and doged around by this low down set on account of my room being furnished until I have long since been tiard of it.
While in No 14 it was Burrett, Lawton, Deloney, Miles and Petty to fuss and complain about my room being furnished, and "why I was any more entitled to comforts than they were"? In No 7 it was Mrs McRay, Brooks, Ludus, Owens, Burton, Hughes, Miles, and many others that you would not think had mind enough to take any offense at my having a "furnished room." Now, I don't suppose any of you would think that Miss

---

34.   Dated by a note on the envelope: "Miss Sheffield File June 8, 1910."

Black had mind enough to take notice of *any thing,* but she came to my door not long since and asked me if I was a "boarder", I told her no, she says, why is it then that you are so comfortably "situated in your room? *"I"* have no comforts." (No one is ever too crazy to show jealousy.) I had nothing in my room for ten years except my bed, am under no obligations to any of you that I've had a furnished room for the past ten years; Dr Leach had the furniture put in my room, am only due him thanks. I am as much entitled to a furnished room as any one here, (if I am the *meanest,* and *worst disgraced*) for my kin are tax payers, and some of them heavy ones; but I had rather do without the few pieces of cheap furniture than contend with so much jealousy. Having my own clothes is enough for this low down set to worry over, and keep me worried. I am satisfied that Dr Lanford would approve of putting me more on a level with the *lowest,* as he told me last winter that I "must do as other patients did". The patients in 14 had fussed so much about my "furnished room," that I asked Miss Hughes not to bring the furniture to No 7, but, she did bring it, and I knew that if I did not let them put it in my room, that Miss Buck would tell you all that it was only because I was "mad[.]"

As I have to stay in the violent wards with the lowest down and craziest class I think it would be best to do away with the furniture, have nothing, but bed and trunk in my room. As I have my clothes in my possission it is a convenience to have the furniture, but I am tiard of so much complaint from others on account of having it. I am the only patient in No 7 with mind enough to appreciate a furnished room—yet all take notice of my having it.

I am not mad, can only give you my word for it that I am not mad, but I think it would be best, as I have to stay with this class to have as little attraction about my room as possible, and I realy think as I have to stay with this class, that it would be best to be more on a level with them.

As you mentioned my going out of the Hospital (few days since) will say, *Yes I'm willing* and *ready* at any time *you* do your duty, but never until then, so help me God, I'm ready, willing and waiting to go at any time that you "dance to *my* music,["] not me to yours.

Punishment of the violent wards will *never* reconcile me to an acquittal or to a "nol pros," it only strengthens my determination that a jury shall never acquit me—never—no—never. I am more determined against an acquittal today than was the day you had me sent to 14—am more determined today than was yesterday and have the consolation of knowing that should I live until tomorrow I will be more determined than am today. No your punishment of the violent wards will never bring me under in that, not even the cross halls. Punishment of the violent wards, did the work, pinned me hard and fast to the Hospital. Punishment did it all.

A. M. Sheffield.

Ward No. 7

June 15, 1910

SHEFFIELD TO SEARCY[35]

Sheffield had an intense dislike for a nurse, Annie Campbell, who "influenced" the other attendants. As a result of this situation, Sheffield feared that her own penchant for physical violence might resurface.

Dr. Searcy.

I have asked you several times to let me leave No 7 ward. There are other violent wards, and I am willing to go back to No 14 rather than remain in 7 under the circumstances. I asked some time ago to leave No 7 only because I was fearful that some nurse would get No 7 who would allow themselves influenced by Annie Campbell, but fortunately for all patients, all the nurses—Hughes, Hannah, Archabald and Vest kept her down, and did not allow themselves controled by her. Annie Campbell has been in the ward a year, she has from the first disliked me so have I disliked her as all patients do, and will here after as no patient could like her. Miss Lewis[36] has several times mistreated me, in fact she mistreated me less than a week after she came to No 7, and I knew that Campbell was the cause of it, that it was through her influence that Lewis mistreated me[.] Campbell unlike Lewis, is an educated and intelligent woman, and has more common sense in an hour than Lewis would have in a year, for that reason Lewis "looks up" to her, allow her to dictate to, and direct her in every thing, never does any thing without first consulting Campbell. The ward is run and the patients managed altogether through Campbells directions. I have made no complaint because the nurses heretofore have not allowed themselves influenced by her, so she has let me alone, until now.

35. Dated by a note on the envelope: "Miss Sheffield File June 15, 1910."
36. A nurse, probably the woman identified in the 1910 manuscript census as Burta Lewis.

I have so far, quietly submitted to Lewis mistreatment through Campbells influence, not through fear of cross halls, but because I did not want a fuss, and I knew they would lie out of it all as they usualy do—and Lanford and Partlow throw all the blame on the "old criminal[.]" There is a limit, or should be to every thing and I feel that I cannot controle myself any longer. I have had so much to contend with in the past three years, unkind and unjust treatment from you and Partlow, abuse from Lanford and lied on by Mary Buck, and several nurses—and been worried, aggrevated, and tormented—kept nervous, loss of sleep in violent wards, until I feel like that I don't care if I do something *desperate,* and don't feel that I can controle myself any longer. I have often known nurses to mistreat patients through the influence of other nurses but Lewis is the first to mistreat me through the influence of another nurse. I had rather leave 7 than for Annie Campbell to leave it, for I as [illegible] Lewis, for she is one of the kind to take advantage of Mary Bucks disliking a patients, and I *think* she is one of the nurses who was heard to say last winter, that if "Miss Buck should order them to stick fire to the building they would feel it their duty to carry out her orders." Mary Buck has known all the while of my and Campbells dislike for each other—for I told her of it in the beginning, but as have before said, I made no complaint for there was not need of it, as all the hall nurses kept her under until Lewis came, I don't see why Dr Partlow should object to my going to 14—(his ward,) I gave him no trouble out there, except to knock Lanfords pet.[37] I got on better under him than have under Lanford, besides I don't believe that any of the nurses reported a lie on me while in 14—that is more than I can say of 7. It was only through my liking Miss Hughes—*her influence,* over me, that I came to No 7 without being *dragged.* There is no inducement in 14—none whatever—but I had rather go there than remain in 7 under the present circumstances. We can be driven to do desperate things, and it is strange why patients don't do more desperate things, being treated as they are. I don't believe that I can stay in 7 with Lewis and Campbell much longer and controle myself, because I am satisfied that Lewis will let her controle her. If Lewis had mistreated me of her own will it would have been bad enough— but it has all been through Campbell. I believe I could have gotten on with Lewis but for Campbell. If Annie Campbell should agrevate me into striking her, (as Underwood was agrevated into striking the nurse at the Annex) *then* you would separate us, why not do it before? I have spent the best part of my time in my room behind a closed door for three weeks, to keep from coming in contact with her. As have said I had rather go to 14 than

37. Mrs. Roper.

for Campbell to be changed for I do not want to stay with Lewis—for she carries out all of Mary Bucks orders as to mistreating the patients, but nothing for the good of the patient[.] I hope you will act by me as you would a favorite, change me, I say to 14 because there is no where for me to go except to 10 or 14—and I had rather go to 14. I am almost as nervous and worried as was over Lanfords abuse to me. I am sorry that Miss Lewis let Campbell influence her.

The nurses in 7 are all mad because you sent Pelham to 7—they I suppose think you are imposing on them by giving them both of the noted friendless criminals, and I think so.

A. M. Sheffield.

Ca. 1910/11

SHEFFIELD TO SEARCY, PARTLOW, AND LANFORD[38]

In a letter which has not survived, Sheffield asked for the privilege of keeping her door open at night (the nurses locked most of the patients' rooms at night). In this letter, directed to all of her doctors, she is angry because not one of them even acknowledged the request.

Dr's Searcy, Partlow and Lanford

Had you not treated my request with silent contempt I would not have had to have written this. I have sworn off writing letters, but I wanted you to know that I knew why you refused me of an open door—; it was not because you thought I wanted to fire the house as you would like for me to think; not one of you thought that—not even did Dr Lanford think it although he is so "very suspicious." You refused because you thought it would be doing me too great a favor, to allow me an open door—plenty of air and sleep well all night. Not one of you thought that I wanted to do any meanness, but you want me to think you did. Because I threaten to burn in Marshall Co is no reason why that I would do the same here—I owe the State of Ala no ill will. I don't blame the State for what a few men have

---

38. Dated only approximately. Since Lanford was still in the Hospital, Sheffield would have written it prior to the end of 1911.

done. I openly, boldly, and independantly say that if placed before a grand jury and acquitted, the foreman of the jury would suffer at my hands—would not only *threaten,* but would carry my threats into execution, it would be my duty, my unbounden duty to seek vengeance on him and I would do it. I know that you only refused me an open door because you thought you would give me pleasure—but you did not "set me back" any for I have not the least idea that I could have gone to sleep with my door open.

I have had many very many opportunities to have fired the house had I wanted to. I don't want to injure the States property one cent. The State did'nt send me here—Judge Street had me sent here, at least I've been under that impression all these many years. He told me—in the Marshall Co jail June 4–1890—that he "intended to have me sent to the Insane Hospital if it cost him all he was worth, and all his future prospects, and if I had to be handcuffed and twenty five men to bring me". So you see the State had nothing to do with it. No, not one of you thought that I wanted to fire the house, you refused because you thought you would be doing me too great a favor,

A. M. Sheffield.

Ca. 1910/11
SHEFFIELD TO SEARCY[39]

Sheffield expected her nephew, the U. S. Attorney for northern Alabama, to visit Tuscaloosa soon and wanted the Superintendent to make clear that her family had no voice in whether or not she stayed at the Hospital.

Dr Searcy.

I had a letter from O. D. Street, two weeks ago, stating that he would "be in Tuskaloosa soon and wanted to come to see me". I wrote him that he could come, that I would see him, and that I would not call it back this time.

---

39. Dated approximately by the style of handwriting.

When he comes I want you to go in the "sitting room" and let him, in my presence, read the law in my case that my "kin, my folks", have *nothing* to do with me—no "say-so" in the law part of my case, that I was not sent here with the understanding that my "kin my folks" take me out or have any "say-so" in the matter.

I have no buisness with him—and I'm sure he has'nt any with me farther than to see me, and the law part of my case will not be mentioned unless you are present.

I can't say as to when he will come but I hope you will put in your appearance when he does come.   And oblige

A. M. Sheffield

ॐ

Ca. 1910/11

SHEFFIELD TO SEARCY, PARTLOW, AND LANFORD[40]

Sheffield wrote the following letter at about the same time as the preceding one.

ॐ ॐ

Dr's Searcy—Partlow and Lanford

Dr. Searcy.

I have received another letter from O. D. Street—He wrote me that he would be in Tuskaloosa in a few weeks and would come to see me. I sent him a "post card" the day I was in town[41]—wrote him that he could come to see me as he had often written me that he "wanted to come". So now when he comes I want you to see him, as he is a "first class" lawyer he can tell you the law on my case—I'm sure he will not hesitate doing so. I don't expect to touch on the subject to him—will not mention Hospital Penitintiary or any thing in the subject—as he will not come on that buisness, at least I'm under the impression that his visit will only be to see me. It is him wanting to see me, not me wanting to see him—I think too much of him to want to see him. I will let him come, at the same time I feel that

---

40. Dated by the letter's content, which shows that it followed the previous one about her nephew's visit.
41. Mailing her card "in town" assured that the doctors could not intercept it.

I am doing him a great injustice to allow him to come here and call for me as his aunt—the "worst disgraced woman in the State of Ala[."]

If I were to tell him any thing I would tell him that life imprisonment here for a criminal in some respects was a more terrible punishment than hanging—that it was not correct to regard the death penalty as the most severe punishment that could be inflicted upon the friendless and disgraced. No, I will not mention my case to him in any way, but I want you to, so that he can tell you the law on it—that I was not sent here for my kin to take me out.

You have never seen any of my kin—but I'm going to give you the opportunity of talking to him—on the subject of my going out of the Hospital. As he is a well posted lawyer he will tell you as I often have that my kin have nothing to do with it—at least I hope he will.

A. M. Sheffield.

Ward No. 7

February 18, 1911

SHEFFIELD TO LANFORD[42]

Sheffield returns here to her complaints about neglect by the nurses, Porter Lewis in particular.

Dr Lanford.

Please read the letter to Miss Buck[43] before giving it to her. Then you will know just what I wrote. I don't want her telling you all that I have "demanded that Lewis or myself be changed" as she told you of Curry and myself. I don't demand that Lewis be changed—I don't demand that I be changed—but I want a change, rather than stay under Porter Lewis.[44] I did not want Miss Buck telling you all that I was "begging her to send me to a quiet ward," so for that reason I want you to read the letter. I don't

42. Dated by a notation on the envelope: "Miss Sheffield   Feb. 18 & 19—1911."
43. The following letter, which was included in this one to Lanford.
44. This is the same nurse identified in note 36, above. Her real name was Burta Lewis, which Sheffield had probably only heard spoken and had not seen spelled out.

ask for a quiet ward—for I know too well that I'd not get it. I've given my
reasons in her letter for asking to leave No 7—So long as I am kept in
No 7—I'll be low spirited. If there was no nurse that I could get on with,
I'd not want a change but I've been here 20 years and have gotten on with
all hall nurses—except four—that speaks very well for the meanest
woman on the grounds, more especialy one that is always quarrelling and
fussing (as you have written on my history.) I never get a pleasant word
from Lewis unless I speak to her in the presence of one of the Supervisors.
I don't deny that I had rather stay in 7—than 14 but I'd gladly go to 14
rather than stay in 7 under Lewis.
She spends the most of her time reading yellow back novels—out of one
into another, and I think that is one reason why she is so irratable. I must
say that she is more irratable with Pelham and myself than any of the others, because you don't like Pelham and myself. But fortunately for Pelham
she got from you and Lewis both and I'm glad of it. It would be best for
all if Lewis never had a hall under you, she makes her brags that you, unlike Dr Partlow, "never believes any thing a patient says." That accounts
for the nurses thinking so much of you is because as they say, you never
believe any thing the patients say.
I have asked you all several times to change me since Lewis came to 7—
and you gave it no attention—so I thought I'd try Mary Buck, for if she
can't have a patient changed any other way she can lie them out of a ward.
She is so irratible and unpleasant with me that it keeps me low spirited, for
when I speak to her I get an abrupt answer—and if I return a word there
is a fuss, and says I'm "quarreling and fussing." Farrish [Farris] and
Lewis and Curry are the only nurses that I have not gotten on with under
you, from the fact they are the only ones who have taken advantage of your
not liking me. I know that Lewis will not be changed because Mary Buck
knows that we do not get on, but I certainly want to get away from her, and
rather than stay with her I'd be willing to go back to 14—and it had better
be that than have to lie in the cross hall, but if I have to stay with her, I'd
rather be in a cross hall. But if I liked her and she liked me I would not
want to stay in a violent ward with her, for she keeps no order—does but
little besides reading cheap "yellow back novels.["]
I have taken more abuse from Lewis, than any nurse I've ever been with
Curry not accepted—for she has given me more. I have never been able to
account for why she dislikes me so much unless it is because she knows
I'm a criminal and that you dislike me. She would speak of Mrs Pelham as
a "nasty dirty criminal," and I suppose she speaks of me the same way to
my back.

I often go to one of the other nurses—for soap pins or any thing, rather than speak to her—only to keep down a fuss. I want you to read the letter to Mary Buck for I want you to know that I'm not begging for a quiet ward—for I don't expect any thing but to spend the balance of my time in the violent wards. Porter Lewis is one woman that certainly take advantage of the Sup't, Dr's, and Supervisor not liking a patient.

A. M. Sheffield.

Ward No. 7

February 18, 1911

SHEFFIELD TO MARY BUCK

Sheffield sent the following letter through Lanford; in it, she discusses the same issues she does in the preceding one.

Miss. Buck—

You worked your plans to get me out of No 4—I wish you would work them to get me out of No 7—into some other violent ward—if back to 14—as it seems that Porter Lewis has been given a deed to No 7—I don't feel like that I can stay much longer under her outside the cross-halls. Had rather be in a cross hall all the time than out on the ward with her. She is one of the kind that does'nt like no patient—but those who drudge and delve—and never return a word or murmur can live in a little peace with her. She has never liked me—and I never get a pleasant word from her—and for that reason I never speak to her unless I am compelled to. She is by nature high-tempered, over bearing—domineering and abusive, but, more so with me. I think because she knows, that is, she is under the impression, that Dr Lanford does'nt like me—some nurses will take advantage of the "bosses" not liking a patient. Now that I know her I am not surprised that you charged her for "talking and lying" a year ago.[45] She makes her brags, (as many others do) that she "does'nt care what a

45. Nurses could be fined for violations of rules, and it is possible that Lewis was fined or reprimanded by Buck as Sheffield alleges.

patient tells Dr L he never believes any thing they say'', and he does'nt, and that helps to account for her manners.

Porter Lewis reads enough novels to impair her mind. The best part of her time is spent in reading novels, playing cards, embroirdering, and writing letters. If I'm ever changed I hope it will not be to a violent ward, where all the time of the nurses is taken up in card playing and reading novels. No nurses can do their duty by a violent ward and spend most their time novel reading and card playing. No patient dare to speak to her while reading a novel. She said a few days since that when she was ''interested in a novel she did'nt know any thing that was going on around her'', and she does'nt. I'd rather go back to 14 than stay another year under Porter Lewis. If I knew that there was no other nurse that I could get on with, I'd not want a change. I've been here 20 years and have gotten on with every hall nurse except Curry, Taylor, Farrish [Farris] and Lewis. (and one who says that I have'nt, tells a lie) That speaks well for the meanest woman on the Hospital grounds, who is always ''quarreling and fussing'' as Lanford wrote on my history. All the nurses through the house know that the nurses have spent the most of their time playing cards and reading ''yellow back'' novels—even in Hospital hours ever since Lewis has had charge of the ward, but they would be afraid to say so—one nurse is afraid to tell on another. And it is certainly bad to be in a violent ward and no charge or controle taken of the patients. She stays out of the ward a good part of the time, but when in it she is deeply absorbed in a novel or card playing. I have been sorry many times that I asked for the cards. It is certainly bad to be in No 7—and the nurses spend most of their time playing cards and reading novels, for they can't play cards and keep noise and confusion down—Miss Lewis allowed Miss Mead[46] and Mrs Pelham to play cards all day on Sunday and from supper until bed time Sunday night for weeks, until I told her if she did not stop it that I would tell Dr Partlow—that it was wrong, and that I did not think he would approve of it. True they played in a room in day time on Sunday but at night they played on the ward, Lewis would say that this ''was not true''—nevertheless Miss Mead has'nt spoken to me since ~~since~~ I told Lewis that if she did not put a stop to it that I would tell Dr Partlow. (I am not a good woman, lay no claims to being good, but I did not approve of card playing on Sunday.) Now don't tell the Supt and Dr's that I've ''demanded that Lewis or myself be changed'', I'm not wanting Lewis changed—and I don't demand that I be changed but I think it would be best to take me from under Lewis—unless she treated me half way right—and that she will never do for she does'nt have it to do. There

---

46. A patient.

is no one who had not rather stay in any ward than 14—but like Pelham I'd take 14 in preference to being under her.

A. M. Sheffield.

❧

Ward No. 7

Ca. February 1911

SHEFFIELD TO BUCK[47]

Mary Buck was upset over Sheffield's letter complaining of poor nursing. Sheffield says here that it precipitated a flurry of denials. The fact that Sheffield sent word through Lanford had also disturbed Buck—which was perhaps the desired effect. In any event, Sheffield also sent the following letter through an intermediary, Dr. Partlow.

❧ ❧

Miss Buck.

I heard of your orders to Missis Lewis and Campbelle [Campbell]—that Miss Campbelle must meet the Dr in No 1 or 4 and Miss Lewis must go to No 10 and make denials; you need not have put them to that trouble, for had they stood in front of my door I would not have put in one word—for words from a patient these days—in self defense does'nt amount to any thing. They carried out your orders, Miss Campbelle went to No 1 or 4 as directed, and Miss Lewis to No 10—and denied all of course. You seemed to be very angry; I sent your letter through Dr Lanford only because I've had so much told on me that was not true, that I wanted him to know just what I had written. I have no appology to make for sending it through him but I did'nt do it to make you so mad. I judged from the tone of your voice while in the ward this morning that you were very angry over the contents of my letter—Please give this to Miss Buck and I'll not trouble you any more.

A. M. Sheffield.

---

47. Included in an undated envelope addressed to Partlow. The letter also refers to the previous letter that Sheffield sent Buck through Lanford.

Ward No. 7

April or May 1911

SHEFFIELD TO LANFORD[48]

Sheffield's pleas evidently failed to get her moved from Porter Lewis's ward. As a result, she tried—unsuccessfully, it turned out—to avoid all contact with nurse Lewis.

Dr. Lanford.

When I wrote you yesterday evening[49] I was so nervous, (not so much so but that I wrote the truth) that I forgot to state the cause of mine and Porter Lewis fuss yesterday morning. A statement from a patient does'nt amount to any thing, but, I think it right that the patient write their side, as they are not allowed to talk it to any of you. Some three or four weeks ago I decided that as I could not get on with Porter Lewis that I would have nothing to say to her if I could possibly avoid it. So when I had cause to go to a nurse I went to one of the others, she and I had not spoken more than two or three words since, until yesterday morning she came from Mr Kilgores[50] shop with some newspapers—she put them in her room and started to the yard, so as I wanted something to read, I asked her to please let me read the papers while she was on the yard—she got mad and *threw* the papers at me, and muttered something. I did as you or any one else would have done, I did not pick them up, and we had a few short words. I have been in the violent wards three years and six months, have gotten on with every hall nurse except Farris and Lewis. Miss Hughes, Saxon, White, Hannah, Archabald, Nabors, Vest and myself got on without an unpleasant word, because they treated me right, and took no advantage of Sup't and Dr's and Miss Bucks dislike for me. Annie Farris and Porter Lewis did not like me and did'nt want to get on with me, so took

---

48. Dated by Sheffield's reference to her having been on the "violent wards" for three years and six months.

49. This letter has not survived.

50. James Kilgore was the Hospital's Outside Manager and was in charge of the property and grounds. He was also the Hospital's printer and in that capacity received newspapers in exchange for annual reports or articles written by Searcy that he had dispatched to the newspapers.

advantage of your dislike for me, at least that is the way I account for it. I do more to get on with these nurses than any of you think that I do, for I know that if any thing comes up that you take sides with her, just what the nurse and Miss Buck tells you is just what you believe, and being mistreated on account of false reports is more than "a notion,["] there is certainly no fun in it—I speak from experience. When she first came to the ward, I saw that she did not want me to speak to her or go about her, and I said to the nurses that I was afraid she would not let me get on with her. These "fusses," getting on badly with the nurses, makes me low spirited and nervous, I can't sleep—did not close my eyes for sleep last night— and no doubt will not tonight, so you see it is to my interest to try to get on with them—but when they don't want me to get on with them I can't do it—and Porter Lewis was one that did not want to get on with me. I had rather stay in 7 than in any of the violent wards, and was satisfied in 7 from the time Farris left until Lewis came.

Porter Lewis openly says, she tells the patients, that she "does'nt care what any one tells you, that you don't believe any thing the patients say". She says it this way, that "Jack does'nt believe any thing the patients say." I did not know that your name was Jack until she came to No 7.

I certainly have tried to get on with her, for as I have to stay in a violent ward I'd rather stay in No 7—and I thought that after awhile she might be changed. No indeed it is no pleasure to me to have falling outs with the nurses, I have enough trouble without that and all I can do to hold up under it—sometimes I give down and wish that I had some one to speak one kind word to me—just one comforting word, and then I think I'm not worthy *one* comforting word.

No indeed these fusses are not pleasant to me, but when I can't keep them down they have to come.

A. M. Sheffield.

Ward No. 7

Late 1911

SHEFFIELD TO LANFORD[51]

---

51. Dated by a reference to Sheffield's having been in the Hospital for twenty-one years.

During the months that nurse Lewis had charge of Ward No. 7, Shef-field took the opportunity to read and memorize her case history. In the following, she throws up to Lanford virtually everything he ever wrote about her. The material quoted from her case history cannot be precisely corroborated, but it is consistent with what is known from her existing file.

ə ə

Please give this to Dr. Lanford after you read it.[52]

Dr. J. A. Lanford.

During the thirteen months that Miss Lewis had charge of No 7 it was very seldom that all the histories were locked in, as a rule part were on her bed, trunk, table or bureau, scattered round in her room,[53]—so any patient who had sense and curiosity enough to want to read their history could do so—I read mine until I have it committed to memory. She either did not know that it was against orders for patients to read the——charged against them, or else she did not care. All of my history will do very well except your part of it—that is, there is a little truth in it. One to read my history would know who was my *enemy* among the "bosses." During the year in No 14 Dr Partlow did not write *even one*——against me, true he made me out all in fault, that I attacked Mrs Roper—but it was very reasonable to suppose that he would do that, as she is a *private patient.* You (since I've been in No 7) state that I do not "get on with, or like any of the nurses"—in the three years, there has been eighteen different nurses in No 7—I got on with and like all excet [sic] three of them. You state that I'm "never pleasant," can't you remember back that I smiled a few times? I can remember that I did smile a *few times,* for after you were gone I'd think of your treatment to me, and how wrong it was for me to smile upon you. You state that I am "continually writing *threatening* letters". I have never threatened the life of any one here, I could not kill any one if I wanted to—I am not *stout* and *strong enoug* [sic], most any patient could whip or kill me, while I could not even hurt one, that is, one that would fight at all.
You state that I am *"obtrusive"* "thrust in against the will". I ask less against your will than any one here—it is but little that I ask of any of you. There is not a woman in the house who could not have come under to you

---

52.   This letter was in an envelope addressed to Partlow, but, as the salutation shows, it was
       intended for Lanford.
53.   Those nurses who had charge of wards had rooms on the wards themselves.

all, rather than remained under punishment four years, yes they would have acknowledged that they lied when they said they never saw a drunk woman until they came here—that they did worry Williamson intentionaly was sorry of it—and that they lied when they said Curry was disreputable—while I have'nt taken any of it back—and never will, although the punishment is so *severe*.

You state that I say I am "not insane"—but you fail to state that Sup't and Dr's agree with me,—I think *you* maybe stated that I was a "*little* wrong mentally"—but you did that so that the nurses would allow for my handling you. You state that I say I "ought to be in the Penitentiary". I have *never* said it, and any one who says that I have, willfully prevaricates—I have said that I ought not to go there that my punishment here was sufficient for the crime, but rather than remain here under the punishment that I've had, would gladly exchange this for the Pen—and say it yet, and will forever hereafter—yes indeed I'd take the Pen—rather than the punishment of violent wards—had rather be there "digging up stumps["] and bossed by a negro guard—and he to lash my back; yes indeed I had, and would say so in any court house in the state of Ala.

You state that I am "stubborn", and why? only because I contend for the right—will not sanction all that you all say and do—and go back to Marshall as the Sup't wants me to do, and allow a jury to acquit me of a crime that I have been punished for twenty one years—yes, for that reason I'm stubborn[.]

"She is never pleasant with the nurses or patients—quarreling all the time with patients—doesn't like any one—never pleasant with any one, is stubborn—obtrusive—says she is not insane—she ought to be in the Pen["]—could'nt you think of more mean things to say of me?

You state that I am "dictatorial"—any one who says that I have ever given an order or countermanded one in the ward willfully prevaricates. You may have cause to handle my history again, if so get some one to help you do me justice—that I'm lazy—no-account—filthy—untruthful—deceitful—hypocritical—vulgar obscene, cruel—brutal—by nature—sneaking—mean, the meanest woman in the house—the worst disgraced one—is "despisable —detestible"—You state that I am "opinionated"—and so I am, I've as much right to my opinion as you have to yours, and as much right to spend it—as little as you think. I wonder what Dr Davie will write about me, he will not have much to say, for you have said about all the mean things that could be said. As this is all the paper I have I will have to close. good bye.

                              A. M. Sheffield.

❧

Ca. 1911
Sheffield to Lanford[54]

*On the occasion of an upcoming visit from her nephew, Sheffield took
the opportunity to remind Lanford of her family's prominence.*

❧ ❧

Dr. Lanford.

You said yesterday morning that you "were going to town to see my
"use-to-be" nephew."[55] I am not anxious that you go to town to see
him—I intended that you see him had he come here. My reason for wanting you to see one of my kin was to convince you the "big" mistake you
made four years ago, that I was of a "low class"—for you thinking that,
and abusing me on account of thinking it, did a good deal for me, sent me
to the violent wards for life—for your abuse to me put me in good shape
and trim for Buck to have no trouble in lying me into 14—so you are indirectly responsible for it all.

You are the only one of the men who have mistaken me for a woman
"reared in an ash bank"—you have long since been convinced of your
mistake—and had you known then, as you do now, there would have been
nothing of it. Yes I intended if my "use to be" nephew had come here to
ask Dr's Searcy and Partlow to *make* you go in the sitting room to see him.
I did not care whether the others saw him or not, but I intended that you
see him—for I wanted you to see what a nice polished gentleman he was.
At twenty years of age he was almost a Chesterfield; dont expect you will
know what I mean by that so will explain—I mean that he was a boy of
polished and elegant manners. You need put yourself to no trouble to go to
town to see him; but should any of my "use-to-be" nephews come here
while you are here you may be assured that I would do all in my power to
force you to the sitting room—I have 15 nephews and only one that I
would be ashamed of. He in Marshall Co, a drunkard and not worth room
in no house. I only wanted *you* to see him, for *you* are the only man who
has ever abused me on account of private patients. But you will not do that
again; you may have me mistreated on account of them, but you will not

---

54. Dated by Sheffield's reference to her having known Lanford for four years. He was at
   the Hospital for only four years, having left in 1911.

55. Probably O. D. Street.

come in my room again abusing me on account of private patients or "pretty girls," for you know me now—that is you know that I am not a "dead head" as you thought four years ago. You have long since been convinced of your "big mistake"—that if I am as Tom Taylor said, the "worst disgraced woman in the state" that I'm not a "dead head," neither was I born and reared in an "ash bank," any more than your pet Mrs Williamson. No you need not put yourself to any trouble to go to town to see him.

A. M. Sheffield.

Chapter 5

''THE LIE ALWAYS GETS *AHEAD* OF THE TRUTH HERE''

1913–1919

By 1913, most faces familiar to Sheffield had gone. Lanford and Buck had left the Hospital. Searcy, the only non-patient of her generation, remained, but he no longer made formal rounds. By the 1910s, the daily operations of the Hospital were in the hands of W. D. Partlow. New ward doctors came and went, seldom staying more than a year or two. Minnie Creagh replaced Mary Buck. Assistant Supervisor Mattie Parr, whom Sheffield loved and who treated the difficult patient as a ''pet,'' also had left. But Sheffield stayed, the drama of her life continuing largely unchanged. A letter to D. M. Collier, her new doctor in 1915, for example, reads much like those to Lanford a few years before. And, according to Sheffield, Creagh's exercises of authority were almost indistinguishable from the hated Buck's.

The rhythm and tone of Sheffield's persona went unchanged as well. Contrary, irrascible, and sarcastic, she never ''came under.'' Her last letter, written in 1919, glimpses the same difficult woman whose family would not keep her nearly thirty years before. A half a lifetime in the Hospital had surely taken its toll, but the essence of Andrew Sheffield, both touching and infuriating, remained.

Ward No. 7

Ca. 1913

SHEFFIELD TO R. C. PARTLOW[1]

---

1. R. C. Partlow was W. D. Partlow's brother. Dated by reference to Sheffield's being on Ward No. 7, which she reentered in 1913. R. C. Partlow began his tenure at the Hospital in 1912.

When Sheffield wrote the following to her ward doctor, her earlier and closest personal contacts—Lanford, Buck, and Parr—had all left the Hospital. But the new head of nurses, Supervisor Minnie Creagh, evidently followed in their footsteps. The characters of the drama, it would seem, had changed by 1913, but not the plot.

ᘓᕲ ᘓᕲ

Dr. R C. Partlow

Now that you have refused me going to walk with the nurses after supper (as many other patients do) I'll promise to ask nothing else of you. Miss Creagh does'nt hesitate giving others permission to go, but if I go the "nurse must get permission from the Dr", and why? because she wants to deprive me the pleasure of going (I am not one of "her crowd" "her pets"[.]) Why she dislikes me I cannot account for unless it is as Miss Young[2] said, "because I like her" (you of course know of Miss Creagh hatred for Miss Young[.]) (I did like Miss Young, she was nice and pleasant with me and seemed to want to do what was right by me, and I was sorry that she had to leave.) I am as far from knowing the cause of Miss Creaghs dislike for me, as you are—but I do know that I have done nothing to give me her ill will—for I did not want it—I've heard her express herself that "if she ever "fell out" with one she never got over it, and always hated them", so no one would want her ill will, as she is in a position to deny and deprive, worry, agrevate and torment, I am sure that I did not want it. I am not even allowed to go to the Chappel, no word is passed to No 7—that "there will be preaching".

Miss Young told me that Miss Creagh claimed that I "disliked her,['] because she "did not pet me as Miss Mattie did"—not true, for I told Miss Creagh that I did not expect her to treat me as Miss Mattie did, and told every one else the same—for because Miss Mattie loved me was no reason why that Miss Creagh should have—because Miss Mattie favored me was no reason why that Miss Creagh should have—and I did not expect it—but I must say that I did not expect her to deprive me of all my privileges—going to walk—to chappel &c.

Miss Creagh had a right to select her *pets*—all prison bosses have their *pets* and *favorites*—and because she did not select me as one of the fortunate ones, I had no right to take any offense, and did not.

---

2.   A former nurse.

Fortunately for me I was a pet of Miss Matties for twenty two years—so it was but right that I ["]slip down and out", and others share Miss Creaghs love and kindness as I did Miss Matties. Miss Creagh had a right to select her pets, and she did—but I thought none the less of her that I was not chosen as "one of them".

Miss Buck and Miss Mattie had there pets, and Miss Creagh has a right to have hers—but I did not, as she says, think less of her because I was not one of the "chosen ones", for I say, that "turn about is fair play" and "every dog should have its day"—and I've had mine so far as Miss Matties love and kindness was concerned—and think none the less of Miss Creagh and her pets—I did not want or expect her or any one else to treat me as kindly as Miss Mattie did and Miss Young heard me tell Miss Creagh so—but must say that I did not want or expect her to deprive me of the few privileges allowed me, walking, going to chappel, on yard and &c. I can stay in doors—it goes hard with me to do so—I need the exercise and fresh air—never feel well when deprived of it. Dr. W. D. Partlow confined me in No 14 for eight months that I was not allowed to put my foot on the ground—so this will not be the first time I've been deprived of going out. The nurses frequently ask me to go to walk with them, and as Miss Creagh would not give me permission to go as she did *"her crowd"*, I thought I'd ask—and I've done so and been refused, so there will be no more of it—for I can stay in doors if it does go hard with me, I can stay in all the time—I can live without going to walk—going to the yard, or to chappel or any where else, and will, rather than give you the pleasure of refusing me again, for I will *never* ask any thing more of you. Miss Creagh could ~~could~~ not have deprived me of these privileges under any Dr, except you and Dr. W. D. Partlow. I don't suppose it will kill me out-right to stay in doors all the time.

Miss Creagh certainly does misrepresent me when she says, (as Miss Young said she did,) that I disliked her because she did not "pet me as Miss Mattie did". Miss Creagh had a right to select her own pets, and to favor as she liked and I thought none the less of her—you all have your pets—and she had a right to hers. But because she did'nt choose me as one of her pets, was no reason why I should have been deprived going to walk, on the yard, or to chappel. As for Miss Creaghs dislike for me, I know nothing except ["]what Miss Young told me", "that she disliked me because I like her["]—and I did like Miss Young, and was sorry she had to leave. I like one who treat me right. I'm of a gratiful and thankful nature if I am "the meanest woman on the Hospital grounds."

A. M. Sheffield.

I hope this letter will be perfectly satisfactory to you and Miss Creagh both—and I can assure you both that I will give neither of you any trouble hereafter, asking for favors, such as going to walk, on yard or to chappel.

Ward No. 7

Ca. 1913

SHEFFIELD TO MINNIE CREAGH[3]

In a letter reminiscent of ones from many years before, Sheffield rehearses her wounded sensibilities—occasioned in this instance by a prospective visit to a fair.

Sunday Eve

Miss Creagh.

Stella Mathews[4] told me last night that you asked her if "she proposed taking me to the Fair, or if I asked her to take me"—and that you said she was "not compelled to go with me unless she wanted to." I'll give you to understand that it was all her own "get up". She said she wanted to go and wanted me to go with her, and asked me to ask to go. I told her that I could not go and come in an evening, that it was too much for me, she then proposed that I ask for a day, I told her that I did not like to do that, for if the Sup't and Dr Partlow left it to *you* that we would certainly not go, and that I did not want to give you the pleasure of refusing me. She insisted that I ask, so I finaly decided to do so, at the same time telling her that it would "fall through." In the first place I did wrong to allow her to influence me, for it was not so much because she wanted to give me pleasure but because she was so anxious to go herself. I feel that she did wrong to insist—she knowing, as all others know, your dislike for me—I suppose she knows it—don't think it is any seacret here.

Miss Young did not hesitate in saying to any and every one that your dislike for me, came from my liking *her*—and *your* dislike for Mary

---

3.   Dated by references to Sheffield's ward assignment.
4.   A nurse.

Buck—I will say that I did learn to like Miss Young very much—whether she liked me or not, she was very nice and pleasant with me—and I could ask no one to treat me any better than she did—and was sorry that things were so very unpleasant and disagreeable that she had to give up her job—at least she told me she had it to do. Yes, I learned to like her. I am sorry that I let Stella influence me, but that is characteristic of my nature—to allow myself influenced by one that I like. Some people are so mean that they want all the pleasures themselves—and some are so mean that they don't enjoy anything themselves and live in dread and fear of doing something to give others pleasure.

You may be assured that it was her own "get up" and she would tell you so in my presence.

A. M. Sheffield.

Ward No. 7

Ca. 1913

SHEFFIELD TO CREAGH[5]

Creagh denied Sheffield's request to attend the fair. In the following, Sheffield states that this denial only confirmed what everyone already knew—that Creagh hated her.

Miss. Creagh.

I feel that it is my duty to inform you of the fact that No 7 has not been turned inside out, no glass broken out, no one killed, no one blessed out, neither am I in a "cross hall," on account of *you* not allowing me to go to the Fair—why I am not even disappointed, I wanted to go, and did as you told me to do sometime ago, "asked the Sup't to let me go," at the same time knowing that Partlow[6] would turn it over to you and that I would not go to the Fair. I know you, and knowing that Partlow allows you to controle, I had not the least hope of going.

---

5. Dated by the letter's content, which follows the preceding one closely.
6. Sheffield refers to W. D. Partlow as "Sup't" here probably because he was the Assistant Superintendent.

Yes, I know you, and only wish that I like Young could "fold my tent and very quietly steal away", get away from under you. Were you the woman that you ought to be in your position, you would have been only too glad to help me off—instead of depriving me—The last time you refused me, I vowed I would never ask any thing else of you, and I *never* will. Hereafter if I have cause to ask any thing of the Sup't, I'll do so, and Partlow can allow you to refuse as he did this time. Of course I know his hatred for me—and of course you have to cater to him, consequently you are afraid to show me any kindness—even if it was your wish to do so.

A. M. Sheffield.

November 20, 1913
O. D. STREET TO SHEFFIELD

This newsy, even sweet, letter from her guardian and nephew back in Guntersville shows that Sheffield had not completely lost contact with her family.

Dear Aunt Dock:—[7]

I do owe you an apology for not having answered your last letter. I have been the busiest this year I believe I have ever been in life. There has scarcely been a week this year that I have not been in court. I do not have any idea what Wilson is going to do with me. Have never had the slightest intimation. If he does not turn me out sooner I will be at Tuscaloosa in Jan'y and will certainly come to see you.[8] All the folks are well[,] had a letter last night from Walter Farwell, he says uncle Jim[9] is some better.

Aunt Mollie[10] had a spell of sickness at Al Farwell's at Bgham two or three weeks ago but she is all right again now. I think she is out at mother's

7. Members of Sheffield's family usually called her "Dock."
8. Street was a Republican appointee as Attorney for the Northern District of Alabama. He is unsure here whether the new Democratic President, Woodrow Wilson, will replace him.
9. Sheffield's brother.
10. Sheffield's sister.

this week. Margarette is also out there. May Julia[11] is again in Nashville at school.

I think of no other news that would interest you so will close with love.

Yours
Oliver.

P. S. I send you a check for 2^{50} to get any little things you might like.

Oliver.

Ward No. 14

Ca. 1914

SHEFFIELD TO SEARCY[12]

In the following, Sheffield summarizes her impression of a quarter century in the Hospital.

After you read this please give it to Lady Creagh and oblige.

Dr. J. T. Searcy

Sir:—

When sent to No 14 Creagh (she calls me Sheffield) *threatened* the nurses with a *discharge* if they give me any "*information*["] as to the *cause* of you having my money taken from me, so as a matter of course they were "*shut mouth*". One of the nurses who very *recently* left here told me all about it. In the first place I want you to *distinctly* understand that I want you to believe *every thing* reported to you by *supervisors, patients* and every one else.

I had rather you would think of me a *rogue* than an *honest* woman; had rather you would think me a *liar* than a *truthful* woman. Any one who told

---

11. Street's daughter.
12. Dated only approximately. Sheffield wrote this letter while on Ward No. 14. From dated letters and her case history, it is known that she was on Ward No. 7 as late as 1913 and that by the first week of 1915 she had been changed from No. 14 to No. 10.

you that *all* my "clothes were made of *house goods*" *lied*, but I want you to believe just what was reported to you.

Ever since I've been here any and *all* the patients, even the *private patients* were allowed to wear any garment issued for the wards that suited them, and allowed to change and alter any garment to suit themselves. I never did wear a *house garment* until the past few years. I altered some that I *liked* and wanted to wear, *and I'll do the same* thing again if I wish to do so. I never wore a pair of *house shoes* until Creagh was made *"mistress"*— Miss Mattie selected my shoes when I did not go to town myself. Have not been to town since Creagh has been *boss*[,] have asked three times to go. Any one who say all my *underwear* was made of *"house goods"* tells a *lie*. Any one who say all my *dresses* were made of *"house goods"* *lie*. Mary Buck could testify to the fact that Miss Mattie selected the goods for my *white dresses* in April before she died. The *outing* garments that Creagh and Lewis made such *an "a-do"* over were made of new garments that *Mrs Cook* tore up in No 7. I gathered up the torn up garments which would have been *wasted* and made them into garments for myself. I have a nice *black cape* that I paid *ten dollars* for the *goods*, and Buck had a nurse to make it,—Creagh says that "it is some private patients cape" that I have "put my name on." Say that all my clothes were made of *"house goods,"* what of it?—Why should a patient not make use of *any thing* in the wards when the nurses, until the past *few years* made their *underwear* of *"house goods"*, but few who did not do it. But few who did not wear house *shoes, stockings,* and *corsets*—but few who did not wear *private patients clothes*—and would take the patients name off and put *theirs* on. Had you seen all that *I've seen* you would not have a patient *punished* for any thing of the kind. Not only *hundreds*, but *thousands* of dollars worth of *States goods* have been taken out of here in *trunks*. For many years the nurses were *open* and *bold* in it, did not try to keep it concealed from the patients, from the fact they knew that Miss Mattie and Miss Buck would not *believe* the patients—and besides the patients were afraid to tell it, for fear of the ill will of the nurses. It made Miss Mattie and Miss Buck *mad* for the patients to tell them any thing of the kind.

I told them of it years ago—they both got *mad*, and as good as *disputed my word*. (I never meddled any more[.]) They took *shoes, stockings, bed spreads, towels, window-curtains, sheets, pillow cases, blankets—corsets*, and garments that suited them—and private patients clothes. No nurse thought of buying a *corset*—they were issued for the back wards where the patients did not were them—so the nurses took them—I have not known but two nurses since *honest Creagh* has been boss—to take or use any thing in the wards. While Miss Oneda Harrison had charge of No 14—she made her *underwear* of *"house goods"*—and the two nurses in the ward Zind and Hinton knew it, but were afraid to tell it, for fear of the *ill will* of all the nurses—Had I told it you would have *denounced* me as a *liar* and had my *punishment increased.* She wore *hall stockings, tennis shoes,* and wore Miss Obears and Mrs Attridges *nice under clothes*—not only that but every time her *father* came to see her she took out to him a *bundle* of *house goods*—one time took two *linen table cloths,* for I saw her rool [*sic*] them up. Nurses and patients said she made *under wear* of *"house goods"* after she went to 13. You need not doubt that this thing *paid her.* Miss Hoycut wore *hall stockings* and also wore *private patients underwear.* Those are the only two nurses I have known to do any thing of the kind since *"honest Creagh"* is in *"behind* them*".* As for my using *house goods* for my fancy work—I give it the *lie,* as a rule the nurses *furnished the goods.* The patients, some of them who did not have the money to buy goods to work with, used *house goods*—for instance Mrs Pelham made several table covers, while in No 7 two years ago of house goods and gave them to Creagh to sell for her. I have never lost any thing through the nurses myself. My losses have been through the *supervisor's.* Miss Buck got in all, *thirty* or *thirty five dollars* of my money. Creagh has gotten *one dollar that I know of,* and Creagh or Lewis took *seven* or *eight* dollars worth of new clothes from me last winter. Creagh says the nurses took them, but I say *she* or *Lewis* took them. I'll never know which one took them, for neither one will ever *owne* to it. I had them, and they did not *"walk* or *fly* away*".* They are both competent to *lie* out of *any thing.* The lie always gets *ahead* of the truth here, and stays *ahead* of it.

You, more than any one else, *denounce* all *patients* as *liars,* and *uphold* all *employes,* and would *swear* any thing in *defense* of the *house* or *employes.* I have never liked you, for you have given me *no cause* to—and while I have as little *policy* as one could have, I have *forced* myself to speak to you *occasionaly*—knowing that my fate was within *your hands,* to *detain* me here, or *send me out.* You have entertained the greatest *hatred* for me all these many years, have *never* shown me the least *kindness*—never *favored* me, except to allow me to handle money, as you allowed *others* to do. I give you *no thanks* for that having allowed me treated as you have in order to get it out of my hands. It was your right and privilege as *"prison boss"* to have my money taken but you should have given me a chance to give it up, it was not necessary to punish me with 14 in order to get it. I would not have given it to Creagh[,] Lewis or any other woman, but would have given it to any one of the *men.* I've suffered too much at hands of *supervisors* to trust them. After all, it all came from Creaghs *wanting* my money out of my hands. So long as I had it she was not *benefitted* by mine. She was not satisfied with getting the money that the *crazy* weomen bring in

here with them—and getting the most of what the patients earn doing *fancy work*—and buying her clothes with private patients money. If she does'nt do it she has been very much *belied*. This thing will pay *Creagh*, as well as it did Miss Buck. She is more *interested* in their doing *fancy work* than in doing house work—and gets after the patients when the money does'nt come in *fast* enough to suit her. I want you to bear in mind that I do not blame you for having my money taken from me, but for the *cruel treatment* you allowed me given. If Mrs Gonzales[13] should *expose* my letters written and *"slipped"* to her while here—no one in Birmingham would *approve* of you allowing even a *hardened criminal* treated as I was. She wrote me that she had been told that my "punishment was terrible" and asked me to write it all to her and I did—patients passed the letters for me. The money matter was *well explained*—and being stripped of my winter clothes middle of Nov and forced to go so thinly clad that I suffered with cold. I wrote it all up. She said in one of her letters to me, that she "intended taking the letters out" with her, "whether she did or not,["] I do not know, neither do I care. It matters not what was *reported*, the *foundation* of all this, was Creaghs *crave* for my *money*, she knew I had it and she *wanted* it, *proof is*, she *stole one dollar*—and would have stolen the seventy five had she found it—and you *know* it. You *know* the *Supervisors steal* the *patients money*, but you don't care so long as *no one* suffer or loose but the *patients*.
Little do you care what the patients loose. The nurses have always claimed that they had as much "right to take as the supervisors have"—and I think so. The supervisors *set the example*. Miss Buck bought *nothing* that she could not get through the house, *neither* will Creagh do so. I am in 14 for *stealing*, nurses *discharged* for *stealing* but *Supervisors* can *steal* in *safety*. If you say they do not steal, you *lie* and you *know* you do.
Creagh, so Miss Manning said, used *"private patients domestic"*—and she will never buy a yard of domestic no more than Buck did.

A. M. Sheffield.

❧

Ward No. 10

January 4, 1915

SHEFFIELD TO SEARCY[14]

---

13. A former patient.
14. Dated by a notation on the letter: "Jan 4th 1915."

Sheffield was changed from Ward No. 14 to No. 10, yet another back ward. Her removal from No. 14 was caused for a second time by her trouble with Roper, the private patient whom she had physically attacked six or seven years before.

ৰ ৰ

Dr Searcy.

It is useless for you to insist on my talking to you, to multiply words with *you* would only make it worse for me, for you "*never* go behind Dr's and supervisors in my case." I fully realize that I have been "*kicked* to the foot of the hill," there to remain, so long as Creagh is allowed to dictate to you all as to where I must go or stay. So long as she is allowed to use her *stubbornness,* and *contrariness,* and spite work with me, just so long will I be on the opposite side.
I was sent out of 14 on Ropers account,[15] she should have come to No 10—but as you all were under the impression that 10 was the worst place—you sent me to 10 instead of her.
I can't account for why it is said that 10 is the filthiest hall here—it is a credit to 14—old Roper will see more filth in 14 in one day than she would have seen in 10 for a month. No 10 is the best kept ward that I have been in for many years. It is far ahead of 14 so far as filth is concerned. Miss Young use to tell me that "Miss Creagh and myself were too much alike to get on"—and there was truth in it.
She hasn't left any thing *undone* that she could have done to worry me, since I went to 14. Had the nurses carried out her orders in *every* thing it would have been worse for me. She has denied and deprived me of what was realy my own—this is a sample, Buck gave me some Outing scraps several years ago to make a quilt for my bed, so I bought silk thread to embroirder the quilt, so when finished she told me to put my name on it, so Creagh or Lewis told 14 nurse not to send me the quilt. "I do not need it["]—but I mention this, to show to you, their spite work with me. Every thing is done to worry me that they can have done. Wilson, Pearson, Betts, Johnson, Farly—Willingham, Snyder[16]—were all nice and good to me and did not carry out all of Supervisors orders. The low ignorant class of nurses mistreated me through Supervisors orders.

---

15.   In 1913 or 1914, Sheffield left Ward No. 7 and went back to No. 14 before being sent
      to No. 10, which was her ward assignment when she wrote this letter.
16.   Nurses.

(Miss Wilson openly stated in 14 the day she took charge of the ward, that "she intended to treat Miss Sheffield right, independent to Miss Creaghs orders—that she would be discharged rather than mistreat a patient in order to carry out Miss Creaghs spite.—") I did nothing to bring all this on, for had I been asked for the money I would have given it up to any one of the men.

It all came about from Partlows hatred for me, and Creaghs crave for money. She takes advantage of his hatred for the patients. Buck did not, for had she I would have been *worried, harrassed,* and punished all these many years as have been the past three. No indeed No 10 is not the filthy wards that No 7 and 14 are. You never have treated me right and never will—now for one thing, not a *dime* of my money have I been allowed to spend. Get one box of snuff a week, (as a rule I've had it,) and would not be surprised for Creagh to have you to cut that out, No I will not talk to you for *nothing* that I could say would add to my good or pleasure. All I ask of you is to let me alone.

Please give this to Creagh as she says I "write lies["] to you all.

A. M. Sheffield.

Ward No. 10

January 4, 1915

SHEFFIELD TO DR. D. M. COLLIER[17]

This letter to her new physician is reminiscent of many that Sheffield wrote several years earlier to John Lanford. She was bitter about having been moved off of Ward No. 14 on account of the private patient Roper.

Please read and give to Creagh.

Dr Collier.

As you are *new* here I thought I'd let you know that *this* is not the first time that I've been "torn up" and sent out of a ward on account of a

---

17. Dated by a notation at the top of the letter: "Jan 4th 1915." D. M. Collier was an assistant physician from 1914 to 1917.

"*boarder.*"[18] This, is the third time. Mrs Roper has been begging to leave No 21 ever since she was sent there, but did not succeed until she worked herself into your "good graces." I was sent out of 14 on her account.[19] She wanted out of 21—and as she was a "*boarder*",[20] she of course was too good to go to *dismal,* gloomy, no 10—(but the "hardened criminal" was not too good.) If she conducted herself in a way "that she had to be changed, she should have been sent to No 10['']—for I had given no trouble in 14. I had rather been sent out on account of any patient than Mrs Roper—I don't say that she is a prostitute or criminal, but I do say that she is a *meaner* woman than I am. It certainly does seem hard to me, (but not to any of you) that after struggling a whole year trying to get a *clean bed* that I had to give it up just a few days after I got a clean mattress, through one of the nurses. All last year I lay on a *filthy mattress* that no doubt a number of *consumptives* and *pellagra*[21] patients have *died* on, could not get a clean, new *one* until a few days before I gave it up—seems hard, but God has said, "If ye are not chastened ye are none of mine". Mrs Roper did not want to go in a ward with me, for she, as well as yourselves knew that I would not allow her to boss me, as she does all others. This was yours and Creaghs "get up," of course Partlow *sanctioned* it. I understand it, can see through it all. She was "too good to come to 10.[''] She stands in with you and Creagh, and you both *cater* to her, so she was sent to 14 and me to 10. I see through it all. She is a "*boarder,*" so could not send her to No 10--to "dismal and gloomy." I'll admit that this is the hardest trial I've ever had, to set in for a *year,* or *years,* in gloomy 10—but I'll make the best of it that I can. Creagh has the "wire shutters"[22] locked day and night—because she knows it looks more gloomy and desolate, but I'll get through some way. Had I had any notion of going to 21 or 22 I would not have gone after Creagh talked as she did. As good as said I *had* to go. When any message is to be sent to me, it would be best to send Lewis, she does'nt like me, but she does'nt have that authoratative, commanding tone that Creagh has. Creagh will go on one with her head thrown back, making

---

18. A reference to her recent move from Ward No. 14 to No. 10, on account of fellow patient Roper.
19. Evidently Roper was moved from Ward No. 21 to No. 14, and because of their past difficulties, Sheffield was then moved off No. 14 to No. 10.
20. The use of the term "boarder" denotes that Roper was a private patient.
21. Pellagra, a diet deficiency disease, would not have caused any risk to Sheffield. But its etiology was not understood until the 1930s. Many eminent physicians in 1915 considered the disease to be infectious. Consumption, or pulmonary tuberculosis, of course, was a well understood and clearly infectious disease.
22. Restraints placed on the windows for security.

her gestures and in that domineering comanding tone, and it makes me mad. I hated to force the nurses to strain their nerves and muscles in bringing me to No 10, but I had frequently said that I'd never *walk* out of 14—so made my word good. Yes, I see through it all, it was all because Roper stood in with you and Creagh and Partlow—I do not. I can make allowances for you, for you are young, and of course, are easily *taken in* by these *deceitful*, oily *tongued* weomen.

If 21 and 22 are such *nice good* places why did Roper not want to stay there? Why does Dr Searcy not send Lamar, Oswell, Northam, Darby, Davie, and others of his pets down there? Yes, I can make allowances for you, a *flattering* tongue will take in any young boy.

Had you sent Roper to the north end of 10—no *heat*, no *light* at night you would have heard from her—she is not Miss Sheffield to go quietly on and make but *few*, if any complaints. Private patients are entitled to better *fare* (and better than they get,) and more *privileges*, but you will never beat it into my head that it is *right* to *mistreat* an *indigent* on account of a *private patient*, as I have been. Roper stands in with Creagh, and she would discharge a nurse if they mistreated Roper—while she gives orders for my *mistreatment*. But few of the nurses mistreated me in 14—for only a few carried out Creaghs orders. The low class of nurses treated me, just as Curry told them to. Miss Pearson, Betts, Snyder, Johnson, Farley and some others treated me right—more especialy did Miss Wilson fail to carry out Creaghs order and openly stated in the *ward* that she "intended to treat me right, regardless of Creaghs orders, that she would be discharged rather than carry out her orders with me." If Creagh does'nt like a patient she tries to make the nurses *mistreat* them, carry out her *spite* through the *nurses*—some nurses are realy *afraid* to speak to me since Creagh has fallen out with me. Buck was different, with all her faults, she did not allow, much less encourage, a nurse in mistreating a patient because she was mad with them. Creagh and Lewis gave the nurses many orders in 14 for my mistreatment that you all knew nothing about, and that you would not believe. Lewis does'nt like me, but she speaks to me occasionaly, and if I speak to her she gives me a pleasant answer, and it would be better to send her with messages to me for better *results* would come from it. Had I ever had any notion of going to 21 or 22 I would be farther from it now than ever, that Roper had you to change me, and any one of you who say that I was not changed on account of *her, lie, maliciously, knowingly,* and willfully. As soon as I saw her going into 14—I knew I was changed on account of her. You did not want me out of 14 except to go to 21 or 22, but she was too good for 10—She is a meaner woman than I, and has always been mean hearted, and will always be—

and it is not all insanity, but downright meanness. Yes, she is a meaner woman than I. (I knocked her once on inspection[)][23] but when we were thrown together last winter in 14 she asked me if I "would speak to her and be pleasant with her", I told her I would, and was. But she did not want to go into 14 to stay any length of time with me, for she knows she could not make a "*foot* mat" of me, so she asked you all to change me. I take *abuse* from the patients, yes I do—but I could not take any from Roper and she knows it—I'd pull her hair, and slap her jaws just as I did years ago—and she knows it and had me changed. But I say it was not right to have me torn up on account of her, if she is a "boarder." Please give this to Creagh.

A. M. Sheffield.

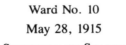

Ward No. 10

May 28, 1915

SHEFFIELD TO SEARCY

Searcy asked Sheffield to talk to him about her longstanding troubles with Creagh. The feud was evidently disrupting institutional harmony.

(Please read this at your leisure—and give it to "Lady Creagh.["])

Dr. J. T. Searcy.

As many times as I have written you, that I'd never speak to you again, you come insisting that I "talk to you". The best woman on earth would not want to speak to you under the *circumstances*. Only taking in my treatment for the past eighteen months,[24] no woman to have *suffered* as I have would want to speak to you. Who should I *blame? You.* Who do I *blame? You.* You are responsible for my treatment, situation, and surroundings.

I *know,* that you do not know a *third* of what I've had to contend with since I exposed Creagh. (the money.) (As Miss Young use to say, "she will do

---

23.   The physicians' daily rounds. Sheffield attacked Roper in W. D. Partlow's presence.

24.   It was probably eighteen months before that Creagh became the Supervisor. It may also be the length of time since Sheffield had "exposed" Creagh.

her *meanness* east of the *front door*, and go out to yours and Partlows *office*[25] and with her *oily, palavering* tongue put all the *blame* off on *others* and leave you both under the impression that *she* is *innocent*, and every one else in *fault*."

Think about my having been confined in doors for *eighteen months*, all on account of Creaghs *ill will*, who is *blame*? You. After I'd been confined in doors for *seven* months, I asked you to let me go on the yard—the first time Lewis saw me out, she told the nurse to "keep me *in*"—the nurse *persuaded* me to ask again—and when Creagh saw me out she had me kept in. When I complained to you, your answer *was* that "you would not go behind Dr's and *supervisors*.["] So I could do nothing but stay in, and I have'nt spoken to you since. I was never stopped from going to *yard*, *walk*, *dances* or *chappel* I went to 14, and I was under the impression, for a *year*, that *you* and *Partlow* had *authorized* Creagh to give the order. You have no idea the *fear* and *dread* that *nurses* live under on *my account*, for *fear* of doing me some *little kindness* that Creagh would *charge* or *discharge* them for. The nurses know her, and know how bitter she is toward *me*—and *I* fear also that she may get up "spite"—for some of them on my account. I do not ask any thing of the nurses, for I do not want them to *favor* or *befriend* me in any way to give her any "clue" on them. She repeats her orders concerning myself every two or three weeks—and with *threats* to the nurses.

One thing that seems to bother her more than anything else, is, that the nurses will favor me in my *eating* give me some thing from "*their table*"[26]—has given the order in No 10 several times that she "would *charge* any nurse who give me anything to eat besides *hall food*." They give me nothing but "*hall food*" sick or well, neither do I ask them for any thing else. (I asked Dr Collier this morning if the nurse could go to No 3 and get me a cup of *soup* as I was *sick*—she was *afraid* to go unless he said so[.]) I eat at the table with the *filthy patients*—eat *hall food*, without *knife* or *fork*—and make no complaints—for I am not *Miss Will* that my complaints be given *attention*. [C]omplaints from me account to *nothing*. It worries me to know that she keeps the nurses in *dread* and *fear* of being *found fault* with—*charged* and *discharged* on account of her *hatred* for *me*. She would *discharge* them, and they know it—for she *discharged* two on account of her *hatred* for Miss Young—Miss Manning was one of them. She tells you all, (so I've been told) that she *speaks* to me, but that

---

25. The women's wards were all to the east of the central administrative hall, where Searcy's and the Partlows' offices were located.

26. Nurses ate in the dining rooms with patients, but at different tables. Their food was usually better than that given the patients. Private patients also got a better diet than the indigent patients.

"I will not *speak* to her," she *lies* she has not spoken to me since I exposed
her—<but *once*> [27] and that was the night I came to *No 10.* As for her not
speaking to me, that is all *right*—I've heard her say that when she once
"*fell out* with one she *always hated* them and *never spoke* to them any
more." The nurses *know* her, and *know* that she *charges* and *discharges* for
little or *nothing*—So they live in "*mortal dread* and *fear* of her.['] I do not
want any of them to suffer on account of *me*, so I try to *help* them out,
instead of wanting them to favor me, giving her a chance to "*score*" it to
them.

She gave the nurses orders some time ago that they "must not speak to me
except to say, yes or no." She gives her orders in Dr Partlows name, when
I've no idea he knows of half of them. *This*[28] is the *trouble* with her, she
knows her *guilt*—she knows that she was *exposed*, and that not *every one*
will give her the "*benefit* of a *doubt* ['']— and she knows that I'll stick to
the *truth*, let come what may, and she has no way of getting *satisfaction*,
but to worry and agrevate *me*, as she *thinks* she is doing. The trouble is she
is *worrying* the nurses *more* than she is *me.*

Miss Smally is an *exception* of a nurse—the most *industrious* woman I
ever knew, keeps the *nicest, cleanest,* and *best hall* I've ever stayed in—
earns her *wages*, and not an *unpleasant* word has passed between *she* and
I, at the *same time*, she is *scared* to even look at me so much afraid that
she will be *found fault* with on account of *me*, as so many *orders* have been
given her—so of course it makes me feel bad to know that she labors under
so much dread and fear on my account. To tell the *truth* I do not feel that
I would be *justifiable* complaining of Creaghs treatment, from the fact I
exposed her with my eyes *wide* open, for I knew her, knew her *spiteful* and
revengeful nature, and that she would say and do *any thing*, resort to *any
thing* in order to "*carry her point*"—besides I had Miss Betts[29] (an extra
good woman) to advise me. She beged me not to "*expose* her," that if I
did she would [*"]make it *hot* for me the balance of my life," that I'd better
"say nothing about it, or talk it in frightened whispers, as others talked of
their losses—and that if you bosses *believed* her *guilty*—that an exposure
would increase your *dislike* for me." So you see I did not lack for advice.
But, it was not me to do that, I knew her *guilt*—*she* knew it, and she knew
that *I* knew it—so at a cannons mouth I would have openly told the truth
on her. As for the loss of the one dollar I *care* nothing for it—but the trouble is she cares that she was *caught*—by the "old nervous wreck"—little

---

27.   The enclosed words are interlineated.

28.   Sheffield underlined the word "This" twice.

29.   A nurse.

thinking at the time she took it that I would ever know it. Had she not been *guilty*,—she would not have gotten so mad—"*guilt* and *anger* go hand in hand together". It may be very well that it happened for it may be the means of the patients getting the *benifit* of more of their money hereafter. I could and would drop the money muss but for her keeping the nurses in "*hot water*," and giving her "long string" of *useless* orders every few days. Yes, I knew her when I *exposed* her, and knew what it would do for *me*—she had been here long enough for us all to know her. I ask no favors of the *nurses*, and in safety to *them* I do not want them to show me the *least kindness*, for I do not want them to have to *suffer* on account of *me*. Miss Creagh has a very bad *reputation* about not getting on with the people *outside* the Hospital, I've been told that she never did get on with any of the employes in sick *Hospitals*,[30] and was ["]*sent away* from several." I heard Miss Young say that she "could not get a position in a Montgomery Hospital"—so how do you expect nurses and patients to please her? No indeed I'll never speak to you under the circumstances—for no one is to blame in all of this but you. To go back to the first—you should have had me asked for my money, given me a *chance* to have given it up, instead of allowing Creagh to *stuff* you with the belief that "my money would have to be taken by *force*," you should not have allowed Partlow to go "*sneaking*" to my room. His *nature* is, to sneak, and do *low, mean*, things but you could have prevented it all—neither should you have allowed Partlow, Collier, and Creagh to send me to *No 10* to *punish* me for what *Roper had done*. I don't blame them for not wanting Ropers *ill will*, her *tongue* turned loose against them—but *she* should have *suffered* instead of *me*. I ask no favors of nurses and have "*settled down*" to spend my few years in No 10 or some other *filthy* place—and to "take what comes", except a ["]*lick, or abuse* or *tongue clash*." If Creagh could come on *me* and abuse and "*tongue clash*" me as she does the *nurses* and some of the *patients* she would not be so *mad* at me. Under the circumstances I do not feel that it would be *right* for me to speak to you. If you wanted to do so, you could not put a stop to any of Creaghs *meanness*, she would not care for *your orders*—she will do as she *pleases*, and *lie* out of all her meanness.

No I cannot and will not speak to you under the *circumstances*. You not having me *asked* for my money, giving me a *chance* to give it up, caused all my *punishment*.

Creagh did not want me asked for it, she wanted to go to the trunk herself—but the old trunk was "true to her *trust*." I was expecting for my

---

30. Hospitals designed for the treatment of physical ailments rather than insanity.

money to be taken from me—from the fact Creagh had been *mad* and *not speaking* to me for a year before I went to No 14—(ever since I first went to see Mary Buck.) As I've been treated as have been on account of the *money,* I'd give, (if I had it) a *thousand dollars* had the money been under *ground* where I had it six months.

Will you please give this to "Lady Creagh"—she has a good deal to say about my "writing *lies*"—I want her to know that I write no *lies* on her.

A. M. Sheffield.

May 28—1915.

June 23, 1915

SHEFFIELD TO SEARCY

With this brief, seemingly trivial note—written almost exactly twenty-five years after she came to the Hospital—the aging Sheffield shows that she remained full of anger and resolve.

Dr. J. T. Searcy.

I am wanting my *hair* trimmed, short, and if you do not give orders for it to be *cut,* I intend to get a piece of *glass* and cut it off the best I can. It is right that I have *short hair* if I prefer it—and I intend to have it, if I can't get it the right way by asking for it I'll cut it off with a piece of glass.

A. M. Sheffield.

June 23—1915.

Guntersville

April 5, 1918

O. D. STREET TO SEARCY

The following letter from Sheffield's nephew reveals how tenuous her contact with her family had become. He asks Searcy here about a policy

regarding patients' clothing that had been a familiar house rule through-
out Sheffield's tenure in the institution.

April 5, 1918.

Dr. James T. Searcy,
Tuscaloosa, Ala.

Dear Doctor:

I am in receipt of a long letter from Miss A. M. Sheffield, an inmate
of the hospital. Of course I know not what weight to attach to what she
says, ~~not~~ knowing her mental condition. She says patients have been asked
to write their relatives to send them clothing. In her letter, she asks me not
to do so in the event I am requested by the hospital authorities. She is, as
you may know, a half-aunt of mine, and I am her only near relative that
she has to whom she could look for any financial assistance. Up to three
or four years ago, I frequently sent her money, but was finally advised that
the hospital authorities had forbidden this, because it led to some patients
having more than others; and it was stated to me that all patients were
sufficiently provided for. If Miss Sheffield is in need of anything which the
state cannot furnish, I would thank you to advise me, and I will see that
she gets it. I infer from her letter and from the address on the envelope that
possibly you read the letter before she sent it out. I would thank you for an
early reply.

Yours truly,
O. D. Street

Tuscaloosa
April 8, 1918
R. C. PARTLOW TO STREET[31]

---

31.   This is a carbon copy of the letter sent to Street.

Responding to Street's letter, Sheffield's ward doctor gives a statement of her condition which is remarkably consistent with those provided over the previous twenty years.

ε᷎᷾ ε᷎᷾

April 8th 1918.

Mr. O. D. Street.
    Guntersville, Ala.

Dear Sir:—

We have received your letter concerning Miss A. M. Sheffield and in reply we wish to state that her mental condition continues very much as it has been all during her stay in the Hospital; she is bright, apparently intelligent and takes great interest in her surroundings, but she continues to have delusions, thinks she is being mistreated and of course is usually rather unpleasant and very stubborn. She, for the last two or three years has shown slight symptoms of pellagra,[32] having red sore mouth part of the time and much of the time having diarrhoea. She continues well nourished, however, and eats well; she is of course up constantly and very seldom complains, except of her mouth being a little sore at times.

Concerning the clothing, &c, you inquire about;—we wish to state that the patient's relatives are supposed to furnish clothing needed, but she has clothing of her own and also sixty-eight ($68.59) dollars and fifty-nine cents to her credit here, which could be spent for that purpose if needed. I have talked with her about getting clothing from home, but she says if she receives anything from home she will destroy it, so we do not think it advisable for you to send her anything at present, but sometime later she may accept something. Patients are not allowed to keep money in their possession on the ward, but we keep any funds that they may have to their credit in the Steward's office.

---

32. Pellagra usually results from a monotonous, chronically poor diet lacking in nicotinic acid. Doctors in 1918 did not understand this, however. If they had, W. D. Partlow almost certainly would not have reported to a patient's relative that his aunt was ill with a disease that indicated an inadequate diet. He certainly would not have added, as he does in the next sentence, the absurdity that Sheffield was "well nourished."

We appreciate the interest you show and assure you we are glad to co-operate in any way we can to keep her as comfortable as we can.

Yours truly,
THE BRYCE HOSPITAL.
By R. C. Partlow M. D.
Ass't Physician.

Ca. 1918/19
SHEFFIELD TO SEARCY[33]

Sheffield is angry in the following that nearly seventy dollars of her money was being withheld from her.

❧ ❧

Dr. J. T. Searcy.

  Sir:—

As you are soon to abdicate your throne in favor of W. D. Partlow I have a request to make of you. I am no minor in law, therefore have the right at the disposition of my *little affairs, monetary,* or otherwise. I have as you know some money in the office (or should have) I've never been allowed to spend any of it except a nickle a week for a box of snuff. What I wish to do before you resign is to ask you to give the small amount of money to some worthy charity.

I made one or two orders two years ago, asking for such as lemons, sugar—apples and oranges, but did not hear from the orders—did not get any thing (Creagh threw my orders in the waste basket or W. D. failed to *OK* them[).]

If I should say please to Lord William—I think he would allow me to spend my dimes as he allows others to spend theirs—but *that* I *cannot* do. I cannot say *please,* never have said it in all my life—I'll *never, never,* say *please,* please, please.

---

33.   Dated by Sheffield's reference to Searcy's impending retirement, which occurred in 1919.

It is said there is a divinity that doth hedge about a King, but in this case I can't see it—or else being so far ahead of common stock myself I'm not a good subject. I'd like that this little money matter be adjusted before you go into retirement I'll never be allowed to spend any of it unless I do say *please*, I'm sure I'll never do that, so had rather give it to some charity—The Orphans homes are all begging—and I'm sure $70.00[34] would be a snug little sum for one of the houses. The poor patients beg and plead with Partlow pitifully and he of course thinks I should do likewise. I can't, and never could eat *humble* pie—and more, if I could eat it, I could not digest it.

Please attend to this little matter.

And oblige.
A. M. Sheffield

February 29, 1920
FAULK TO STREET

In the following, the Hospital informs Street that his aunt's condition is quite serious.

February 29, 1920—

Hon. O. D. Street,
Guntersville, Alabama.

Dear Sir:

Miss A. M. Sheffield, a patient in this Hospital, developed Influenza night-before-last, and has been real sick since that time. Her temperature is about 103, and she is partially delirious at times. So far she has not developed Pneumonia or any other serious complication though Influenza often proves fatal in elderly people, and this fact makes us uneasy about her.

---

34. According to a letter in Sheffield's file from R. C. Partlow to O. D. Street, April 8, 1918, Sheffield had $68.59 on account in the Steward's office at the Hospital. This letter also explains that she did not have access to the money.

We will give her every attention, and in the event she grows worse we will notify you.

Yours very truly,
W. D. Partlow[35]
BY W. M. Faulk M. D. Ass't Supt.

Guntersville

March 2, 1920

STREET TO W. D. PARTLOW

Street responds here to the news that his aunt is near death.

March 2, 1920.

Dr. W. D. Partlow,
Bryce Hospital,
Tuscaloosa, Ala.

My dear Sir:

I acknowledge receipt of your letter of February 29 and thank you for the information relative to the condition of Miss A. M. Sheffield. Please keep me advised and should death ensue, notify me by telegram. I know that she will have the best attention under your care.

Very truly yours,
O. D. Street

Birmingham

March 5, 1920

STREET TO W. D. PARTLOW

Street discusses the disposition of Andrew's remains.

---

35.   This letter is actually signed by Dr. W. M. Faulk, the Assistant Superintendent.

ả ả

March 5, 1920

Dr. W. D. Partlow
  Tuscaloosa Ala

Dear Doctor:—

Your telegram was forwarded to me at Birmingham. I wired to bury Miss Sheffield there—None of her people are buried at Guntersville. Her father is buried at Montgomery, her mother at another place and each of her sisters and brothers at other places. Her only living sister says bury at the Hospital as this sister does not know where she herself will be buried. If there are any little articles belonging to Miss Sheffield you can send them to Mrs. Mollie Taylor, Guntersville Ala.

Very truly yours,
O. D. Street

Epilogue

Andrew Sheffield was not alone among nineteenth-century women who struggled to escape the confinement of asylums. Most, of course, left no record and hence no pathways for the historian on a journey of discovery. Several prominent women, all Northern, however, did leave important published records of their commitment and care in mental hospitals that offer useful parallels to Sheffield's experience in Alabama. Unlike Sheffield, these women all won their release and wrote their accounts self-consciously for public consumption. More than Sheffield, they appropriated the personae of public reformers.

Most famous among this group was Elizabeth Packard, whose case was noted in the introduction to these letters. Despite some differences, she and Sheffield told stories that shared important similarities. Like Sheffield, Packard skirted the edges of respectability. During the 1850s, she angered and perhaps worried her husband, a Presbyterian minister, by her profession of unorthodox ideas. She embraced spiritualism, flirted with Swedenborgianism, and came to view the dark doctrines of Calvinism (and hence the views of her husband) as essentially unchristian. In 1859 she defended John Brown's raid on Harper's Ferry, Virginia, and reportedly outraged her Illinois neighbors. At last, in 1860, the Rev. Theophilus Packard committed her to the Illinois State Hospital in Jacksonville.[1]

Like Sheffield, Packard reacted defiantly to her forced confinement. For example, she could never bring herself to call the asylum a "hospital"; to her, it was a "prison." Dr. Andrew McFarland, Superintendent of the Illinois asylum, diagnosed her as "morally insane," much as Searcy would describe Sheffield more than three decades later. In language that

---

1. The best treatment of Packard's case is Barbara Sapinsley, *The Private War of Mrs. Packard* (New York: Paragon House, 1991). See also Myra S. Himelhoch and Arthur H. Shaffer, "Elizabeth Packard: Nineteenth-Century Crusader for the Rights of Mental Patients," *Journal of American Studies* 13 (December 1979): 343–76.

foreshadowed Dr. Searcy's characterization of Sheffield, McFarland described Packard as a woman of "extraordinary mental capacity and power."[2] Packard likewise experienced the demotion from the front wards to the back, where the noise, filth, odors, and confusion constantly plagued her. Like Sheffield, too, she interpreted this move as punishment. For Packard, there was the threat of the "screen room," a seclusion room virtually the same as the Alabama hospital's "cross hall." She also learned how to smuggle out letters, how to get on the nurses' good side, and how it felt to be denied access to the outdoors for long periods.[3]

Packard won release from her husband's custody in January 1864, after a friend set in motion a hearing before a judge on a writ of habeas corpus. The exasperated Dr. McFarland and the hospital's trustees had released her as unrecovered the year before. Packard soon became famous in northern and eastern states as a sort of antithesis of the antebellum reformer Dorothea Dix. Over the next decade, she wrote several sensational books that attempted to expose McFarland, her husband, and the hospital that held her. In the course of her crusade, she traveled widely and succeeded in lobbying several state legislatures to pass laws protecting patients' rights. In particular, she urged unannounced visits by boards of asylum inspectors that included both men and women. She lobbied for "jury bills" that would require a jury to find a person insane prior to commitment. She also advocated "mail-box" bills that would place U. S. Postal boxes in asylums where patients could be assured of posting letters without the surveillance of hospital officials. Finally, she championed married women's parental and property rights so as to make wives more independent of their husbands.[4]

Packard's example held a special significance as a defining case for late nineteenth-century asylum superintendents. They were intimately familiar with her story and viewed it as a realization of their worst fears. Superintendent McFarland in particular felt the brunt of her anger. In 1868 he summarized the problem that Packard posed for his profession: "My

---

2. Quoted in Sapinsley, *The Private War of Mrs. Packard*, 97. See Searcy's remarks in Searcy to Gov. William C. Oates, January 1, 1896.

3. See Sapinsley, *The Private War of Mrs. Packard*, chapter 5, "Skirmishes."

4. For the best description of Packard's career as a lobbyist and reformer, see Sapinsley, 171–94. For some of Packard's books, see *Great Disclosures of Spiritual Wickedness!! In High Places. With an Appeal to the Government to Protect the Inalienable Rights of Married Women* (Boston, 1864); *Modern Persecution, Or Insane Asylums Unveiled, as Demonstrated by the Report of the Investigating Committee of the Legislature of Illinois*, 2 vols. (Hartford, Conn.: Case, Lockwood & Brainard, 1891); and *Mrs. Packard's Reproof of Dr. McFarland, for His Abuse of His Patients* (Chicago: Times Steam Printing House, 1864).

greatest fears have been (and still are) that Mrs. Packard—who is a sort of Joan D'Arc in the matter of stirring up the popular prejudices—may carry her crusade against institutions in other states."[5] Fellow insanity specialists shared McFarland's anxiety. At the annual meeting of the Association of Medical Superintendents of American Institutions for the Insane (today known as the American Psychiatric Association) in 1867, McFarland had presented a short paper on his "recent troubles." According to the published report of the proceedings, "a good deal of sympathy was expressed by many members for Dr. McFarland in his trying circumstances which . . . are equally liable to befall any one who is engaged in our thankless profession, and honestly tries to do his duty in it."[6]

The superintendents had reason to worry. Packard's crusade did spread throughout much of the nation and met with some success in a number of states. Moreover, the memory of Packard's case, which was widely discussed in the professional journals, may have operated subtly to make superintendents cautious about releasing such determined and articulate women. Sheffield's supposed madness, like Packard's, was seldom visible at first meetings. Intelligence and lucidity more often marked such initial contacts. Admittedly, it is difficult to imagine Andrew Sheffield as a *fin de siècle* Joan of Arc, but it is possible to see her raising serious doubts among lay persons about the processes of diagnosis and confinement. The reactions of those governors she succeeded in reaching suggested as much—and not only to modern readers, but to Superintendent Searcy as well.

A largely unknown and considerably less colorful contemporary of Packard's was Adriana P. Brincklé of Pennsylvania. Committed to the State Hospital in Harrisburg in 1857, she spent twenty-eight years as a patient, nearly as long as Sheffield remained confined in Tuscaloosa. Single and thirty-two years old with a "gay temperament and inclined to extravagance," she ran up debts that her family was unable to pay. According to her own testimony, her embarrassed father committed her in order to preserve "family honor" by shielding her actions in the cloak of derangement. In 1885 Brincklé won her release by appeal to Pennsylvania's new Committee on Lunacy of the State Board of Charities, which examined her case and found her sane.[7]

---

5. Quoted in Himelhoch and Shaffer, "Elizabeth Packard," 365.
6. "The Association and the Chronic Insane," *American Journal of Insanity* 24 (January 1868): 295.
7. Brincklé, "Life Among the Insane," *North American Review* 144 (February 1887): 190–99.

Brincklé's memories of life in the Pennsylvania asylum sound much like Sheffield's account of Bryce Hospital. She considered many of the nurses to be less rational than the patients, calling the majority of them "ex-laundry-women or factory girls." (Sheffield, the Southerner, described her nurses as "country girls.") Like Sheffield, she complained that the attendants showed little solemnity or respect when they disposed of the dead. Brincklé too believed that the only way to stay on the good side of the all-important nurses was to work for them in order to please them. She also explained how she would slip out her letters by means of the night watch, who passed her door several times each evening. More than Sheffield, however, Brincklé compared the doctors favorably with the nurses, describing them as courteous and helpful.

More sensational but less informative about asylum routine is an account of the commitment of two sisters, Rose and Barbara Trautman, of Sauk City, Wisconsin, in 1888. Both were school teachers and single. They evidently enjoyed a reputation for some eccentricity. In particular, they were ardent champions of the rights of workers in a period when organized labor was struggling for respectability following the negative publicity of the Haymarket affair. Taken against their will to the state hospital in Mendota, Wisconsin, the Trautman sisters accused both nurses and doctors of excessive force in the handling of patients. Rose, for example, remembered that she first entered a back ward where she was drugged in order to make her compliant. In stories far worse than any Sheffield ever told, the Trautmans complained of physical abuse, especially at the hands of physicians. Like Elizabeth Packard, the sisters won their freedom in 1890 on writs of habeas corpus.[8]

Except for Packard's several volumes, the most detailed remembrance of a contemporary female patient is that of Clarissa Caldwell Lathrop, who was confined at the New York Lunatic Asylum in Utica between 1880 and 1882. Like the Trautmans, she was a single school teacher, and like Sheffield, her troubles were rooted in a failed romance about a decade before her commitment. Her book, *A Secret Institution,* was published in 1890, the year that Sheffield entered Bryce Hospital. It includes vivid descriptions of the internal workings of what was a leading American mental hospital. Much less sensational than the Trautmans' remembrance, *A Secret Institution* offers a more balanced perspective on asylum life. Lathrop remembered good attendants as well as bad, insane patients as well as

---

8. Trautman and Trautman, *Wisconsin's Shame. Insane Asylums or the American Bastile! The Narrative of the Kidnapping of the Misses Trautman, of Sauk City, Wis., on a Sunday Afternoon, and Running Them into an Insane Asylum* (Chicago: Guiding Star, 1892).

sane. Always a patient on a front ward, she nonetheless feared the back wards and considered them, as Sheffield did, to be places of punishment for the more rational patients like herself.[9]

Lathrop's recollections also impart a wealth of detail that is remarkably similar to what Sheffield's letters provide. The distinctions between "pay" patients and those supported by the state, for example, receive close attention. She writes as well of the daily walks on the grounds and the various amusements. Repulsion to the wretchedness of the food never left her. She also recounts in detail the vagaries of her attempts to slip out letters undetected by the authorities. Lathrop hints too at the emotional strategies of mental patients. For example, she tried never to cry or to show emotion in front of nurses or doctors, affecting instead a calm presence. So, like Sheffield, who had a harder time seeming calm, Lathrop tried (more successfully, it would seem) to manage and select the measure of emotion she presented publicly, usually confining the full range of her feelings to herself or to words on the page. In their crowded institutions, then, both of these women saw loneliness as a means of self-defense.

Lathrop also rails against being labeled as delusional. Quoting the English novelist Charles Reade, she concludes, "Delusion is a big word, particularly in a mad house."[10] As with Sheffield, doctors could identify no specific delusion, but found in Lathrop's remonstrance against the diagnosis a proof of derangement. But for Lathrop, the matter was not finally left to the doctors. She was given the opportunity to disprove her delusions. Like Packard and the Trautmans, Lathrop won her release on a writ of habeas corpus about two years after her commitment.

Only one patient in the nineteenth century published an exposé of the Alabama asylum which held Sheffield. In 1882 the Rev. Joseph Camp, a self-educated Methodist preacher, published *An Insight into an Insane Asylum,* which provides great detail about Bryce Hospital (then called the Alabama Insane Hospital) as it functioned on the men's side a decade before Sheffield was admitted. Like those in Sheffield's account, the particulars of Camp's story prove accurate whenever they can be corroborated. He remembered names and dates quite well and provides rich detail of daily routines (work, "punishment," the cross halls, recreation, and access to tobacco, for example) that suggest a bureaucratic operation much like the one Sheffield's letters reveal. Camp's sanity was also arguable, his

---

9. *A Secret Institution* (New York: Bryant, 1890).
10. *A Secret Institution,* p. 123.

persona seeming alternatively rational and peculiar.[11] Both in its recollection of detail and its quality of emotion, Camp's *Insight* supports the spirit of Sheffield's letters.

The recollections of other women who were contemporaries of Sheffield also provide a measure of corroboration. Mrs. M. F. Crenshaw, a patient at Bryce in 1903 and 1904, told the legislature's Investigative Commission in 1907 that the nurses rather than the doctors actually controlled the conditions of life for patients. Like Sheffield, she claimed to have been sent to the back wards by Supervisor Mary Buck as punishment. "Miss Buck," she testified in language reminiscent of Sheffield's, "is an old maid who never had her heart expanded, and is cruel to all of the feminine sex." Superintendent Searcy, Crenshaw claimed, was fully aware of the conditions under Buck, but chose to support her authority.[12]

More striking than the testimony of ex-patients such as Crenshaw who sought publicly to discredit the Hospital are views from the unpublished letters of other patients. One patient in particular, Ruth Smalley,[13] had a career that overlapped with Sheffield's almost exactly. Admitted two months after Sheffield in 1890, she died in the Hospital in December 1918, just over a year before Sheffield's death. Smalley too was well educated (a music teacher), articulate, and by all accounts extremely difficult to live with. Married twice, she was deserted by both of her husbands. Members of her family also could tolerate her only for short periods. Smalley's first case note from 1890 explains that her confinement had become necessary because it was "impossible for her friends to control her."[14] Like Sheffield, she had no known delusions, but had become extremely troublesome to her own family. Unlike Sheffield, however, she sometimes threatened suicide.[15]

---

11. ([Memphis], 1882). A copy of Camp's book is in the Alabama Collection, Gorgas Library, University of Alabama, Tuscaloosa.

12. Montgomery *Advertiser*, August 22, 1907, p. 8, col. 1. Crenshaw also complained that she never had enough to eat, that her Bible was taken from her, and that the nurses routinely used profanity.

13. This is my pseudonym for patient #3966. Unlike Sheffield's, this patient's name never became a part of the public record. Therefore the pseudonym is used to protect her confidentiality. This patient had also been admitted to Bryce once before, for about ten months in 1886 and 1887. At that time her patient number was 2633.

14. *Case History Book #6*, p. 240.

15. This fact was reported by a sister of patient #3966 in a letter to Bryce, January 28, 1891. Bryce evidently had written to the family to explain that the patient was doing well and to suggest that she might return home. The sister's letter is a long explanation of the patient's precommitment history and a plea that she not be allowed to leave the Hospital.

There is no evidence that Smalley and Sheffield ever resided on the same ward at the same time, but it is certain that they knew one another. In particular, they shared Dr. John Lanford as their ward physician in the years following the legislative investigation. Smalley's interaction with the young doctor was remarkably similar to Sheffield's. Writing to Lanford to complain of the nurses' "willful threats and snaps," for example, she told him that he had treated her worse than her earlier doctors, especially Bryce, Bondurant, and Somerville. Indeed, she claimed, Lanford had made "a back hall dog of me."[16] Beginning at the close of 1907, it will be recalled, Sheffield was saying something remarkably similar.

During Lanford's tenure, Smalley resided on Ward No. 19 ("'19 hell as I call it," she told him),[17] which was next to Sheffield's ward, No. 14, at the back of the Hospital. Her nurses, she said, would "threaten" to send her to Ward No. 14 when she made them angry, thereby offering some corroboration of Sheffield's insistence that her ward was the worst available. Smalley's pet phrase for describing life on these back wards was being "buried alive."[18] In a letter to her former lawyer (which, incidentally, the staff intercepted and never mailed), she complains bitterly of the back wards, much as Sheffield did during the same period—and with the same tone of class and race consciousness: "I had a great deal rather be in the Poor house of Jefferson or Tuscaloosa Countys any time than stay locked up and kept back here another day amongst all grades and classes of insanity. . . . Some [patients] are beneath a good decent honest white womans notice, that is my reputation, I have to endure uselessly and inexcusably a good deal of such willful impositions, am not used to any such out of here, never was. . . . "[19] Smalley, like Sheffield, never won her freedom. For five months in 1899 and 1900, she was "furloughed" to her family in Birmingham. But furlough was not an outright release. Patients returned to their families in this way were released only on trial (and technically kept on the Hospital's books) and were liable to be sent back at any time without a new commitment order, indeed without any formal procedure. And this is precisely what happened to Smalley. As ten years before,

16. Patient #3966 to Lanford, undated, in file of patient. Smalley wrote the letter between 1907 and 1911, the years that Lanford worked in the Hospital.
17. Undated letter to Lanford.
18. For uses of this phrase, see patient #3966 to Judge L. E. Greene of Birmingham, August 12, 1907, and February 18, 1908, and patient #3966 to Bud Bailey of Tuscaloosa, February 12, 1909.
19. Patient #3966 to Judge L. E. Greene, August 12, 1907.

her family found her too troublesome to keep and returned her to Searcy's care in Tuscaloosa. And there she stayed until her death in 1918.[20]

Having outlived Smalley, and several generations of doctors and nurses, Andrew Sheffield died shortly after dawn March 5, 1920. A combination of factors accounted for her passing. Old age and the complications of pellagra, a deficiency disease common among persons with monotonous diets, combined with influenza to end her life. The death certificate, which remains in her file, interestingly enough makes no mention of mental illness, though it does label her a "criminal." Shortly after recording on the certificate that Sheffield had resided at the Hospital for "29 yrs. 7 mos. 23 ds.," Dr. William Faulk, the Assistant Superintendent, lists her occupation quite simply and apparently without irony as "at home."[21]

Just as there had ceased to be a home for Andrew Sheffield in Marshall County in 1890, neither was there a resting place for her there in 1920. As the last letter in the collection shows, on learning of her death, her nephew and guardian, O. D. Street, informed the Hospital to bury her with the other unfortunates who no longer had a place outside the institution. Later he arranged for a headstone to mark her grave. No family member, however, attended the interment or the erection of the stone.[22]

Sometime on March 6, 1920, a local mortician placed Sheffield's body in the ground of the asylum which had been her home for nearly thirty years. It was there, she told Dr. Lanford in 1910, that she wanted to be buried: "I would like to know that the fragments of my body would be put in the Hospital grave yard, why do I? because in *looks,* it corresponds with my feelings—is the most desolate, gloomy, lonely, neglected, uncared for and forsaken looking place that I've ever seen—no one visit there—no one go there except the negroes. . . . "

---

20. *Case History Book #4,* p. 117.
21. Sheffield's Certificate of Death makes no mention of pellagra, a disease caused by a deficiency of the B vitamin niacin. Evidence of this condition comes from her case history. See entry for October 8, 1918, for example, for evidence that she was pellagrinous.
22. See Street to W. D. Partlow, March 5, 1920; and Street to Faulk, March 13, 1920.

Bibliography

PRIMARY SOURCES

Articles and Books

The Alabama Insane Hospitals: Notice to Persons Applying for Positions as Nurses. . . . Tuscaloosa: Hospital Print, 1902.

Annual Report of the Officers of the Alabama Insane Hospital, at Tuskaloosa for the Year 1870. To His Excellency W. H. Smith, the Governor. Montgomery: John G. Stokes, State Printers, 1870.

"The Association [of Medical Superintendents for American Institutions for the Insane] and the Chronic Insane." *American Journal of Insanity* 24 (January 1868): 288–336.

Bell, Clark. "Mechanical Restraint in the Care of the Insane." *Medico-Legal Journal* 10 (1891): 203–48, 384–99.

Biennial Report of the Alabama Insane Hospital at Tuscaloosa. For the Years Ending 30th September, 1889 and 1890. Montgomery: Brown Printing, State Printers and Book Binders, 1890.

Biennial Report of the Alabama Bryce Insane Hospital at Tuscaloosa. For the Years Ending 30th September, 1895 and 1896. Montgomery: Roemer Printing, State Printers and Binders, 1896.

Beers, Clifford. *A Mind That Found Itself.* Garden City, N.Y.: Doubleday, 1923.

Brincklé, Adriana P. "Life Among the Insane." *North American Review* 144 (February 1887): 190–99.

By-Laws, Alabama Insane Hospital, 1861. Tuscaloosa: "Observer" Book and Job Office, 1861.

By-Laws, Rules, and Regulations of the Alabama Insane Hospital, at Tuscaloosa, Alabama. Tuscaloosa: Montgomery I. Burton, 1890.

Fourteenth Annual Report of the Alabama Insane Hospital. October, 1874. Montgomery: W. W. Screws, State Printers, 1875.

Camp, Joseph. *An Insight into an Insane Asylum.* [Memphis], 1882.

Crothers, T. D. *The Drug Habits and Their Treatment: A Clinical Summary of Some of the General Facts Recorded in Practice.* Chicago: G. P. Engelhard, 1902.

Flexner, Abraham. *Medical Education in the United States.* New York: Carnegie Foundation, 1910.

Kirkbride, Thomas S. *On the Construction, Organization, and General Arrangements of Hospitals for the Insane. With Some Remarks on Insanity and Its Treatment.* Philadelphia: J. B. Lippincott, 1880.

Lathrop, Clarissa Caldwell. *A Secret Institution.* New York: Bryant, 1890.

Owen, Thomas M. *History of Alabama and Dictionary of Alabama Biography.* 4 vols. Chicago: S. J. Clarke, 1921.

———. *Alabama Official and Statistical Register, 1907.* Montgomery: Brown Printing, 1907.

Packard, Elizabeth P. W. *Great Disclosures of Spiritual Wickedness!! In High Places. With an Appeal to the Government to Protect the Inalienable Rights of Married Women.* Boston, 1864.

———. *Marital Power Exemplified in Mrs. Packard's Trial, and Self-Defence from the Charge of Insanity: or, Three Years Imprisonment for Religious Belief, by the Arbitrary Will of a Husband, with an Appeal to the Government to So Change the Laws as to Afford Legal Protection to Married Women.* Hartford, Conn.: Case, Lockwood, 1866.

———. *Modern Persecution, Or Insane Asylums Unveiled, as Demonstrated by the Report of the Investigating Committee of the Legislature of Illinois.* 12th ed. Hartford, Conn.: Case, Lockwood & Brainard, 1891.

———. *Mrs. Packard's Reproof of Dr. McFarland, for His Abuses of His Patients.* Chicago: Times Steam Printing House, 1864.

———. *The Mystic Key: or, The Asylum Secret Unlocked.* Hartford, Conn.: Case, Lockwood & Brainard, 1886.

Percute Iterum [pseud.]. "The History and Present Position of the Doctrine of Moral Insanity." *Medico-Legal Journal* 10 (1891): 249–64, 356–83.

[Ray, Isaac.] "Legislation for the Insane." *Medical Times* (Philadelphia) 4 (March 14, 1874): 378.

Reports on the Legislative Investigation of the Alabama Insane Hospitals in 1907. Tuscaloosa: Hospital Print, 1907.

Richardson, A. B. "Nurses in Hospitals for the Insane." *Proceedings of the American Medico-Psychological Association, 1902.* Baltimore: American Medico-Psychological Association, 1902.

[Searcy, James T.] *Book of Rules and Service Manual of the Alabama Bryce Insane Hospital, Adopted by the Trustees, November 1895.* Tuscaloosa: Burton & Weatherford, 1895.

———. "For What Classes Should the State Make Provision?" *Proceedings of the National Conference of Charities and Correction, 1903.* Boston: George H. Ellis, 1904.

———. *The Service Manual for the Instruction and Guidance of Employes of the Alabama Insane Hospitals, The Bryce Hospital, Tuscaloosa, opened in 1861. The Mt. Vernon Hospital, Mt. Vernon. Opened in 1901.* Tuscaloosa: Hospital Print, 1901.

Trautman, Barbara, and Rose Trautman. *Wisconsin's Shame. Insane Asylums or the American Bastile! The Narrative of the Kidnapping of the Misses Trautman. Of Sauk City, Wis., on a Sunday Afternoon, and Running Them into an Insane Asylum.* Chicago: Guiding Star, 1892.

Manuscript Collections

Alabama Collection. Gorgas Library, University of Alabama, Tuscaloosa, Alabama.

Historical Collection. Staff Library, Bryce Hospital, Tuscaloosa, Alabama.

Manuscript Census Rolls, Marshall County, 1850, 1860, 1870, 1880; Tuscaloosa County, 1880, 1900, 1910.

Medical Records Office. Bryce Hospital.

State Hospitals Collection. Alabama Department of Archives and History, Montgomery, Alabama. [Cited as ADAH.]

Newspapers

Birmingham Daily News
Guntersville Democrat
Montgomery *Advertiser*
Tuscaloosa Gazette

SECONDARY SOURCES

Berg, Barbara J. *The Remembered Gate: Origins of American Feminism: The Woman and the City, 1800–1860*. New York: Oxford University Press, 1978.

Bleser, Carol. *In Joy and in Sorrow: Women, Family, and Marriage in the Victorian South, 1830–1900*. New York: Oxford University Press, 1991.

Boles, John B., and Evelyn T. Nolen, eds. *Interpreting Southern History: Historiographical Essays in Honor of Sanford W. Higginbotham*. Baton Rouge: Louisiana State University Press, 1987.

Cahow, Clark R. "The History of the North Carolina Mental Hospitals, 1848–1960." Ph.D. diss., Duke University, 1967.

Cherry, Charles L. *A Quiet Haven: Quakers, Moral Treatment, and Asylum Reform*. Rutherford, N. J.: Fairleigh Dickinson University Press, 1989.

Clinton, M. W. *Dr. Peter Bryce and the Alabama Insane Hospital*. Tuscaloosa: Tuscaloosa Central Labor and Industrial Council, 1961.

Cott, Nancy. *The Bonds of Womanhood: "Women's Sphere" in New England, 1780–1835*. New Haven: Yale University Press, 1977.

Courtwright, David T. *Dark Paradise: Opiate Addiction in America Before 1940*. Cambridge, Mass.: Harvard University Press, 1982.

———. "The Female Opiate Addict in Nineteenth-Century America." *Essays in Arts and Science* 10 (1982): 161–71.

———. "The Hidden Epidemic: Opiate Addiction and Cocaine Use in the South, 1860–1920." *Journal of Southern History* 49 (February 1983): 57–72.

Dain, Norman. *Clifford W. Beers: Advocate for the Insane*. Pittsburgh: University of Pittsburgh Press, 1980.

———. *Concepts of Insanity in the United States, 1789–1865*. New Brunswick, N.J.: Rutgers University Press, 1964.

———. *Disordered Minds: The First Century of Eastern State Hospital in Williamsburg, Virginia 1766–1866*. Williamsburg: Colonial Williamsburg Foundation, 1971.

Deutsch, Albert. *The Mentally Ill in America: A History of Their Care and Treatment from Colonial Times.* Garden City, N.Y.: Doubleday, 1937.

Digby, Anne. *Madness, Morality, and Medicine: A Study of the York Retreat, 1796–1914.* Cambridge: Cambridge University Press, 1985.

Dubos, René. *Mirage of Health: Utopias, Progress, and Biological Change.* New Brunswick, N.J.: Rutgers University Press, 1987 [1959].

Duncan, Katherine M., and Larry Joe Smith. *The History of Marshall County, Alabama. Vol. I; Prehistory to 1939.* Albertville, Ala.: Thompson Printing, 1969.

Dwyer, Ellen. "A Historical Perspective." In Cathy S. Wilson, ed., *Sex Roles and Psychopathology.* New York: Plenum, 1984. 19–48.

——— . *Homes for the Mad: Life Inside Two Nineteenth-Century Asylums.* New Brunswick, N.J.: Rutgers University Press, 1987.

Etheridge, Elizabeth W. *The Butterfly Caste: A Social History of Pellagra in the South.* Westport, Conn.: Greenwood Publishing, 1972.

Foucault, Michel. *Madness and Civilization: A History of Insanity in an Age of Reason.* New York: Random House, 1965.

Fox-Genovese, Elizabeth. *Within the Plantation House: Black and White Women in the Old South.* Chapel Hill: University of North Carolina Press, 1988.

Friedman, Jean E. *The Enclosed Garden: Women and Community in the Evangelical South, 1830–1900.* Chapel Hill: University of North Carolina Press, 1985.

Goffman, Erving. *Asylums: Essays on the Social Situation of Mental Patients and Other Inmates.* Garden City, N.Y.: Doubleday, 1961.

Grob, Gerald N. *The Inner World of American Psychiatry, 1890–1940: Selected Correspondence.* New Brunswick, N.J.: Rutgers University Press, 1985.

——— . *Mental Illness and American Society, 1875–1940.* Princeton: Princeton University Press, 1983.

——— . *Mental Institutions in America: Social Policy to 1875.* New York: Free Press, 1973.

——— . "Rediscovering Asylums: The Unhistorical History of the Mental Hospital." *Hastings Center Report* 7 (August 1977): 33–41.

——— . *The State and the Mentally Ill: A History of the Worcester State Hospital in Massachusetts, 1830–1920.* Chapel Hill: University of North Carolina Press, 1966.

Hawks, Joanne V., and Sheila L. Skemp, eds. *Sex, Race, and the Role of Women in the South.* Jackson: University of Mississippi Press, 1983.

Himelhoch, Myra S., and Arthur H. Shaffer. "Elizabeth Packard: Nineteenth-Century Crusader for the Rights of Mental Patients." *Journal of American Studies* 13 (1979): 343–76.

Horwitz, Allan V. *The Social Control of Mental Illness.* New York: Academic, 1982.

Hughes, John S. "Alabama's Families and Involuntary Commitment of the Insane, 1861–1900: New Solutions to Old Problems." *Working Papers* (Institute for Legal Studies, University of Wisconsin–Madison) 2d ser. (May 1987).

———— . "Commitment Law, Family Stress, and Legal Culture: The Case of Victorian Alabama." In Donald G. Nieman, ed., *The Constitution, Law, and American Society: Critical Aspects of the Nineteenth-Century Experience.* Athens, Georgia: University of Georgia Press, 1992. 133–61.

———— . *In the Law's Darkness: Isaac Ray and the Medical Jurisprudence of Insanity in Nineteenth-Century America.* New York: Oceana Press, 1986.

———— . "The Madness of Separate Spheres: Insanity and Masculinity in Victorian Alabama." In Mark Carnes and Clyde Griffen, eds., *Meanings for Manhood: Constructions of Masculinity in Victorian America.* Chicago: University of Chicago Press, 1990. 67–78.

Ignatieff, Michael. *The Needs of Strangers.* New York: Viking, 1984.

Laing, R. D. *The Politics of Experience.* New York: Pantheon, 1967.

———— . *Sanity, Madness and the Family.* London: Tavistock, 1964.

Lasch, Christopher. *Haven in a Heartless World: The Family Besieged.* New York: Basic Books, 1977.

Lebsock, Suzanne. *The Free Women of Petersburg: Status and Culture in a Southern Town, 1784–1860.* New York: Norton, 1984.

McCandless, Peter. " 'A House of Cure': The Antebellum South Carolina Lunatic Asylum." *Bulletin of the History of Medicine* 64 (Summer 1990): 220–42.

———— . "Liberty and Lunacy: The Victorians and Wrongful Confinement." *Journal of Social History* 11 (Spring 1978): 366–86.

McGovern, Constance M. "The Myths of Social Control and Custodial Oppression: Patterns of Psychiatric Medicine in Late Nineteenth-Century Institutions." *Journal of Social History* 20 (Fall 1986): 3–24.

Mellown, Robert O. *Bryce Hospital Historic Structures Report.* Tuscaloosa: Heritage Commission of Tuscaloosa County, 1990.

———— . "The Construction of the Alabama Insane Hospital, 1852–1861." *Alabama Review* 38 (April 1985): 83–104.

Peterson, Dale, ed. *A Mad People's History of Madness.* Pittsburgh: University of Pittsburgh Press, 1982.

Porter, Roy. *A Social History of Madness: The World Through the Eyes of the Insane.* New York: Weidenfeld & Nicholson, 1987.

Rosen, Ruth. *The Lost Sisterhood: Prostitution in America 1900–1918.* Baltimore: Johns Hopkins University Press, 1982.

Rosenberg, Charles. *Trial of the Assassin Guiteau: Law and Psychiatry in the Gilded Age.* Chicago: University of Chicago Press, 1968.

Rothman, David J. *The Discovery of the Asylum: Social Order and Disorder in the New Republic.* Boston: Little, Brown, 1971.

———— . "Social Control: The Uses and Abuses of the Concept in the History of Incarceration." *Rice University Studies* 67 (Winter 1981): 9–20.

Santos, Elvin, and Edward Stainbrook. "A History of Psychiatric Nursing in the Nineteenth Century." *Journal of the History of Medicine and Allied Sciences* 4 (1949): 48–74.

Sapinsley, Barbara. *The Private War of Mrs. Packard.* New York: Paragon House, 1991.

Scheff, Thomas J. *Being Mentally Ill: A Sociological Theory.* Chicago: Aldine, 1966.

———. "Control Over Policy by Attendants in a Mental Hospital." *Journal of Health and Human Behavior* 2 (Summer 1961): 93–105.

———, ed. *Labelling Madness.* Englewood Cliffs, N.J.: Prentice-Hall, 1975.

———. "The Labelling Theory of Mental Illness." *American Sociological Review* 39 (June 1974): 444–52.

Scott, Anne Firor. "Historians Construct the Southern Woman." In Joanne V. Hawks and Sheila L. Skemp, eds., *Sex, Race, and the Role of Women in the South.* Jackson: University of Mississippi Press, 1983. 95–110.

———. *The Southern Lady from Pedestal to Politics, 1830–1930.* Chicago: University of Chicago Press, 1970.

Scull, Andrew, ed. "Humanitarianism or Control? Some Observations on the Historiography of Anglo-American Psychiatry." *Rice University Studies* 67 (Winter 1981): 21–41.

———. *Madhouses, Mad-Doctors, and Madmen.* Philadelphia: University of Pennsylvania Press, 1981.

Shortt, S. E. D. *Victorian Lunacy: Richard M. Bucke and the Practice of Late Nineteenth-Century Psychiatry.* Cambridge: Cambridge University Press, 1986.

Showalter, Elaine. *The Female Malady: Woman, Madness, and English Culture, 1830–1980.* New York: Pantheon, 1985.

———. "Victorian Women and Insanity." *Victorian Studies* 23 (Winter 1980): 157–81.

Smith-Rosenberg, Carol, and Charles Rosenberg. "The Female Animal: Medical and Biological Views of Woman and Her Role in Nineteenth-Century America." *Journal of American History* 60 (1973): 332–56.

———. "The Hysterical Woman: Sex Roles and Role Conflict in 19th-Century America." *Social Research* 39 (Winter 1972): 653–78.

———. "Puberty to Menopause: The Cycle of Femininity in Nineteenth-Century America." In Mary S. Hartman and Lois Banner, eds., *Clio's Consciousness Raised: New Perspectives on the History of Women.* New York: Harper & Row, 1974. 23–37.

Szasz, Thomas. *Law, Liberty and Psychiatry: An Inquiry into the Social Uses of Mental Health Practices.* New York: Colliers, 1968.

———. *The Manufacture of Madness: A Comparative Study of the Inquisition and the Mental Health Movement.* New York: Harper & Row, 1970.

———. *The Myth of Mental Illness: Foundations of a Theory of Personal Conduct.* Rev. ed. New York: Harper & Row, 1974 [1960].

Thielman, Samuel B. "Madness and Medicine: Medical Therapeutics for Insanity in Antebellum America, with Special Reference to the Eastern Lunatic Asylum of Virginia and the South Carolina Lunatic Asylum." Ph.D. diss., Duke University, 1986.

———. "Madness and Medicine: Trends in American Medical Therapeutics for Insanity, 1820–1860." *Bulletin of the History of Medicine* 61 (1987): 35.

————— . "Southern Madness: The Shape of Mental Health Care in the Old
South." In Ronald L. Numbers and Todd L. Savitt, eds., *Science and Medicine in the Old South.* Baton Rouge: Louisiana State University Press, 1989.
256–75.

Tomes, Nancy. *A Generous Confidence: Thomas Story Kirkbride and the Art of
Asylum-Keeping, 1840–1883.* New York: Cambridge University Press, 1984.

Vickery, Katherine. *A History of Mental Health in Alabama.* Montgomery: Alabama Dept. of Mental Health, 1971.

Index

Alabama Insane Hospital. *See* Bryce Hospital
alcohol, 17, 117, 133. *See also* drug abuse
Anderson, Richard, 55
architecture of asylums, 7
arson, charge of, 1, 17, 20, 26, 43, 57, 61, 64, 88, 96, 97
assistant physicians. *See* medical staff

back wards, 23, 30, 39, 49, 60, 62–63, 68, 70–72, 76, 79–81, 83, 114–15, 126,
   147–49, 165–66, 177–79, 186, 194–96, 243
Barnwell, Mrs. (patient), 135, 136, 140, 145, 150–51, 155, 159, 160, 166, 169,
   179, 181, 186
Beers, Clifford, 3, 10, 11
Berg, Barbara, 13
black nurses, 100, 100 n. 12, 121, 160
black patients, 32, 32 n. 83
Bleser, Carol, 14
Bondurant, Dr. Eugene D. (assistant superintendent), 28, 42, 47, 81, 159; alleged
   diagnosis of Sheffield by, 57–58, 66, 70, 98, 105–6, 147; biographical information regarding, 47 n. 2; departure of, from the Hospital, 74–75, 78,
   80, 89–90; relations of, with Sheffield, 68, 71–72, 74–75, 78, 81, 88, 89–
   90, 141, 160, 165, 190–91
Brincklé, Adriana P., 239–40
Bryce Hospital, 1, 5, 7, 8, 9, 10, 20, 25, 29–30, 31, 126, 133, 161, 168, 240, 241
Bryce, Dr. Peter (superintendent), 1 n. 1, 25, 53, 57, 70 n. 47, 98, 105
Buck, Mary (supervisor), 75, 78, 114, 114 n. 43, 118, 120–21, 123, 125, 131–32,
   140, 155, 167, 172, 175, 179, 185, 193, 194, 197, 206, 212, 214, 215–16,
   219, 222, 223, 230, 242; alleged drinking of, 116–17, 119, 133–34, 150,
   166, 169, 182, 183, 186, 191; alleged favor of private patients by, 124, 143,
   151, 152, 168, 184; control of Sheffield's money by, 80–81, 108–9, 179–
   80, 220–21; influence over Sheffield's ward assignments, 78–79, 123–25,
   185–86, 191, 197–98, 201–5; letters to, 203, 205; relationship of, with
   nurses and doctors, 36, 38, 159–60, 169–71, 174, 183–84, 197–98, 205,